October 2015

Dear Patrick,

I hope you are as excited as I am about joining Fresenius.

I feel that we've joined a great company that is improving lives and innovating care models across the globe today - in much the same way that this company got started in the U.S. - as this book describes.

You have already proven yourself as providing insight and expertise to our business and we are very pleased to have you join us as a colleague. I look forward to working with you for many years.

Best,

Karen Hochhill

THE PRICE OF ACCESS

The Story of Life and Death and Money
and the First National Health Care Program
and the Three Doctors Who Changed
Medicine in America Forever

by
Tim McFeeley

Copyright © 2001
MDL Press
61 Spit Brook Road, Suite 400A
Nashua, New Hampshire 03063
603.897.0890
www.thepriceofaccess.com

ISBN 0-9716058-0-7

Printed in the United States of America

Table of Contents

Foreword

I began working on this book in the fall of 1996 after returning from a gathering of past and present employees and friends of National Medical Care on the occasion of Dr. Hampers' departure from the company that he co-founded with Dr. Hager and Dr. Schupak. I was an employee of NMC for fifteen years (1974 to 1989) and had served as Corporate Counsel during that time, reporting directly to Dr. Hampers. With Hampers' resignation, an important story was coming to an end, and I wanted to bring the many pieces of that story together in one body of work. This book is the saga of a unique American corporation as well as a history of the Medicare End-Stage Renal Disease Program and the story of three physician/entrepreneurs who created a new way of delivering life saving healthcare to thousands of patients worldwide.

My intent is to inform and entertain, but mostly to inspire others with this true tale of courage, skill and innovation. Whether in the world of business, medicine, law, government or any other human endeavor, we often find ourselves repeating the same procedures and realizing the same results. My hope is that *The Price of Access* motivates all of us to find new solutions and not be deterred by those who have invested in the traditional. Let me be clear about my biases. I have enormous respect and admiration for Drs. Hampers, Hager and Schupak. In my view they are heroes of our times. Nonetheless, I have tried to present an objective recounting of the NMC story. Since its implementation in 1973, the ESRD Program has been criticized incessantly and is often used as the prime example of why we cannot have a national healthcare program in the United States and also why for-profit medicine is bad for America. This book is my dissent to that majority view.

I want to acknowledge and thank the many individuals who helped me compose this history. First and foremost, I am grateful to Constantine ("Gus") L. Hampers, M.D., his wife, Joyce Hampers, and their family and friends who adopted this project and provided information and inspiration in its construction. I also received enormous help and advice from the physician/heroes of this tale: Edward Hager, M.D., Eugene Schupak, M.D., Edmund G. Lowrie, M.D., Alan Hull, M.D., Joseph Murray, M.D., George Thorn, M.D., Larry Siegel, M.D., Michael Lazarus, M.D., William Cirksena, M.D. I also appreciate the recollections of a long list of contributors: Paul Brountas, Patrick Grace, Paul Paganucci, Ernestine M. Lowrie, Pauline D'Angelo, Jane Hager, Bob Armstrong, Carol Wildeman, A. Miles Nogelo, Sam Scialabba, Marcelle Levine, Betty Simpkins, Laura Baker, Terry Daniels, Chris Ford, Rick Faber, Sue Faber, Ruth Reisman, Arnold Relman, M.D., Peter Phildius, David Lubrano, Ed Berger, Gordon Humphrey, Virginia Kamsky, and Bob Macauley.

This book is about medical institutions, a large government program, doctors, nurses and business people. However, the heart of the story is the courage of renal patients and their families.

This book is dedicated to the memory of
Ernestine M. Lowrie, R.N.

1

Taking Risks For Life

There was a time in the recent past when people with irreversible kidney disease prepared to die. Less than fifty years ago doctors delivered the fateful diagnosis of end-stage renal failure to their patients with a helpless resolve to simply ameliorate the unpleasant but inevitable consequences of uremic poisoning. In the 1950's kidney failure was listed as the eighth leading cause of death in the United States. In fact, vital statistics likely under-reported fatalities from uremia, as well as the incidence and prevalence of kidney disease, since its significance in causing heart attacks and strokes was often overlooked. Renal failure played an undetected role as a sinister and necessary accomplice in many premature deaths from cardiovascular disease. Back then no one really knew how many individuals died from kidney failure. Since no cure existed, there was a natural aversion to look for cases. Quantifying failure is not a gratifying exercise.

Suddenly, within the span of less than a decade, medicine provided some dramatic solutions - "new" kidneys, either artificial or transplants from healthy individuals- that were inconceivable only a few years before. Instead of trying to heal the diseased kidneys and reverse their deterioration, physicians looked to replicate failed kidneys with a man made prosthetic version, composed of tubes, membranes, pumps, chemical baths and monitors, or, better yet, replace them entirely with a kidney from another human being. Today, this course change would be labeled a "paradigm shift" in thinking about a problem. In the 1960's it was called "breaking the mold." Critics howled, of course, that keeping patients alive on an artificial kidney or suppressing their immune systems and implanting another human kidney was "going too far."

Innovative thinking, braced with bold risk taking, extended the lives of thousands of patients with end-stage renal disease. Science, without the courage to apply it to save lives, was inconsequential.

The "miracle cure" for kidney disease created a new problem: ironically, more people were classified as dying from renal failure after the onset of dialysis and transplantation than before these new therapies had been perfected. What had been previously ignored, became significant. Doctors had a reason and incentive to identify uremic patients once therapies had been developed, resulting in a demand that could not be met. Patients expired waiting for hospitals to deliver these new therapies. For a few years doctors, administrators, and government experts tried to solve this new problem by fixing the hospital. It took another paradigm shift to give up on repairing the unresponsive hospitals and replace them with a new institution. Just as the dialysis machine replaced the diseased kidney, the model created by the founders of National Medical Care replaced dysfunctional hospitals in delivering care to thousands of patients who would have died waiting for the hospital system to respond. The healthcare system was not functioning any better than the damaged kidneys of these patients. Again, critics, some of whom were the same naysayers who denounced dialysis and kidney transplantation therapies, argued that, despite its high quality and low cost, the National Medical Care model was "going too far."

Ted Hager, Gus Hampers, and Gene Schupak were drawn to the Peter Bent Brigham Hospital to study kidney disease and the revolutionary therapies of dialysis and transplantation that transformed nephrologists from the ushers of death into the extenders of life. In Boston these young, energetic doctors studied with the pioneers in kidney dialysis and transplantation, contributed fresh research to the neglected field of nephrology, and perfected the application of dialysis to an ever expanding population of patients with an ever widening array of medical complications. They didn't come to the Harvard Medical School and the Peter Bent Brigham Hospital to study healthcare economics or to develop new ways to deliver complicated therapies more efficiently than the charitable hospitals where they had received their training. But the atmosphere of adventure, innovation and risk taking that sparked the Brigham environment led Hager, Hampers and Schupak to break the mold, shift the paradigm, and shake the system of healthcare delivery. The genesis of NMC lay in the intellect and character of its founders as these were shaped and sharpened by their encounters at the Peter Bent Brigham Hospital, where they had developed an appreciation of risk taking for life.

The Peter Bent Brigham Hospital was still a relatively young and small hospital in the 1960's, compared to the great teaching hospitals in the United States, like its Boston neighbor, the venerable Massachusetts General Hospital, founded during the Revolutionary War and located on the banks of the Charles River. In his will Boston financier Peter Bent Brigham bequeathed his fortune to "the indigent of Suffolk County," and in 1906 the hospital bearing his name opened in the Longwood area of Boston, adjacent to and encompassed by the "new" campus of the Harvard Medical School, which had simultaneously relocated from its former site in Copley Square in Boston's Back Bay. Plans to build the new medical school near the rest of Harvard University in Cambridge were set aside, since Cambridge lay in Middlesex County and Brigham's will was explicit about serving the people of Suffolk County. In those pre-World War I years the Longwood section of Roxbury, southwest of the Fenway and closer to the town of Brookline than the heart of Boston's downtown, was largely devoted to farmland. Cows still grazed on pastures near the medical school and its newly minted affiliated hospital. Because of strong objections from Mass General, the new hospital was not named "University Hospital," as might have been expected, and became, instead, the Peter Bent Brigham Hospital, or more popularly, just "The Brigham." (Today, after a series of mergers and consolidations the hospital is officially the Brigham and Women's Hospital, but "The Brigham" remains its popular moniker.)

The relocation of the medical school campus and the Brigham bequest that provided the means to construct an affiliated, adjacent teaching hospital were accompanied by the appointment of Harvey Cushing as the head of the Harvard Medical School, and as the first chief of staff of the new Peter Bent Brigham Hospital. A Harvard graduate himself, Doctor Cushing was recruited by the

Brigham/Harvard trustees away from the faculty of the prestigious Johns Hopkins University Medical School in Baltimore. Doctor Cushing, a world renowned pioneer in neurosurgery, brought several other skilled physicians and surgeons with him from Hopkins and transplanted the "Hopkins system" to Harvard and the Brigham. In fact, the first four chiefs at the Brigham - medicine, surgery, radiology, and pathology - were all recruited from the Hopkins' faculty.

The Johns Hopkins system created a fulltime faculty, which divided its time among research endeavors in the laboratory and the clinics, teaching duties in the classrooms and the wards, and direct patient care. Cushing insisted on the establishment of a research laboratory and a fulltime faculty at the medical school. This was a major and controversial change from the practice of Harvard since its founding in the eighteenth century. Before Cushing introduced the Hopkins system, Harvard had followed the traditional practice of inviting practicing physicians and surgeons to serve as adjunct professors. Research was not part of the required regimen, teaching was secondary, and the faculty was simply a loose confederation of independent doctors without institutional discipline or direction. Cushing began a system a paying doctors a salary to join the Harvard faculty and to concentrate more of their energy on teaching medical students and on clinical and laboratory research. The Brigham was a critical and necessary element in these changes, primarily because of its proximity to the school, and because Cushing and later his successors controlled appointments to both the faculty of the medical school and to the staff of the hospital.

In 1942 George W. Thorn was appointed to the post originated by Doctor Cushing less than thirty years before, becoming the "Hersey Professor of the Theory and Practice of Physick" at the Harvard Medical School and physician-in-chief at the Peter Bent Brigham Hospital. Thorn would retain these positions for thirty years, longer than anyone in Harvard's history. In this dual capacity Doctor Thorn attracted the brightest and best physicians and surgeons to the Harvard faculty and consequently to the clinical practice of medicine at the Brigham. He also presided over a period of enormous and unprecedented growth in research conducted at these facilities. As a result of World War II, the federal government became an ever increasing funder and therefore, director, of medical research at teaching hospitals and medical schools all over the United States. Medical schools and research hospitals had to have the leadership and the staff to compete for these research grants that quickly dwarfed the traditional, and largely eleemosynary, sources of funding for the education of medical students, nurses and the care of the indigent. By the time Doctor Thorn assumed emeritus status in 1972 and became the founding chairman of the Howard Hughes Medical Institute, the Harvard Medical School and The Brigham had become virtually unrecognizable from the institutions as they existed right after Pearl Harbor when Thorn came to Boston from Johns Hopkins at the urging of Dr. Eliot Cutler, then the chief of surgery at the Brigham.

Thorn was only 36 years old when he became physician-in-chief at the Brigham, but he had already won the recognition of his peers in research, patient care and teaching while at Johns Hopkins, and before that, at the University of Buffalo. In the field of endocrinology Thorn was at that time without peer, having discovered and developed a critical diagnostic test for Addison's disease, a fatal affliction that destroyed the adrenal glands (two small glands located next to the kidneys, thus "adrenal") and therefore the body's ability to regulate salt and sugar, metabolic imbalances that would lead to certain death. Before Thorn's discoveries and applications, patients with Addison's disease had a life expectancy of twelve to eighteen months. In the early 1930's, working with Frank Hartman, a professor of physiology at the University of Buffalo, where Thorn was a member of the adjunct, volunteer and unpaid faculty, Dr. Thorn discovered that cats whose adrenal glands had been removed could survive with the administration of cortin, a compound extracted from the adrenal glands of slaughtered animals. Thorn recalled:

I took those cats all the way from Buffalo to New Orleans and demonstrated the experiment at an American Medical Association conference, and we won the Gold Medal at the AMA in 1932.

Thorn was the first physician to administer Hartman's cortin to a human patient suffering from Addison's disease. As a result of this early research, conducted as a "volunteer" during time taken from his regular practice of medicine in Buffalo, Thorn accepted a three-year research fellowship from the Rockefeller Foundation. He gave up his medical practice in Buffalo and moved to Boston in order to spend the first year at Harvard, and subsequently to Baltimore and Johns Hopkins where he remained until 1942. During that time Doctor Thorn developed the technique of implanting under the skin of patients with adrenal dysfunction a tablet of a crystalline form of a compound ("desoxycorticosterone") that replicated the adrenal hormone and had been synthesized by a Swiss biochemist (Reichstein), whom Thorn had visited in the thirties. It was not surprising that despite his youth, George Thorn was Harvard's top choice to fill the Hersey professorship in early March 1942 just as he was prepared to receive his war time commission as a major in the Johns Hopkins hospital unit. "I'd already been issued my uniform," Thorn recalled, when Doctor Cutler, the Brigham's chief of surgery and a brilliant early pioneer in cardiac surgery, persuaded Thorn to come to Boston.

George Thorn's benign personality and polite demeanor disguised the courage and determination he brought to his duties at the Brigham. Thorn, who later received the Public Welfare Medal, the most prestigious award from the National Academy of Science, was first and foremost a clinician, and despite his phenomenal success as a researcher, his focus remained on patient care and patient outcomes. Thorn was willing to take risks and this spirit of innovation, where a patient's condition offered little or no alternatives, was infused by Thorn into the institutions he led and developed. Years later Doctor Joseph E. Murray, a close friend and colleague of Thorn, and the recipient of the Nobel prize for his role in the world's first kidney transplant operation at the Brigham, commented, "Because it was small, the Brigham always had a more innovative view of research, and George Thorn had the vision."

An incident that occurred early in Doctor Thorn's career revealed that spirit of compassionate risk taking. While still a student in his third year of medical school, Thorn took a summer job as the medical assistant at Camp Wyonna, a YMCA summer camp on the shores of Lake Erie about thirty miles from Buffalo. One evening he received a call from Doctor Kendall, a prominent physician at the Mayo Clinic in Minnesota, who was vacationing with his family at their summer home not too far from Camp Wyonna. Kendall and his wife were very ill and they asked for Thorn's help. Kendall thought that he and his wife had symptoms of typhoid fever, but Thorn, concluding that it was not likely that two patients would develop symptoms from typhoid at precisely the same hour, given that disease's long incubation period, looked for a more immediate cause. He found an old, rancid salad in the refrigerator and asked Kendall whether he and his wife had eaten any of it. They had. Moreover, the Kendall children, who were not sick, had not had any of the salad. Thorn, with just two years of medical school under his belt, diagnosed food poisoning and prescribed castor oil, knowing that if he was wrong, castor oil would probably kill a typhoid patient. "I gave them the castor oil and I went home and didn't sleep that night," Thorn recalled. The patients recovered. Many years later Kendall, who went on to be the first to synthesize a cortisone-like compound, remembered Thorn's help by giving Thorn a supply of the chemical, against the wishes of the Mayo Clinic. Thorn, who was then at Johns Hopkins, administered Kendall's hormone to a patient who had collapsed at his clinic. She was the first patient in the world to be treated with the drug. Thorn's decisiveness, courage and focus on patient care continued throughout his tenure at Harvard and the Brigham and had an obvious influence on the students, interns and fellows who trained with Doctor Thorn, described later by Doctor Schupak, one of those students, as an "absolute genius."

George Thorn's unpretentious and congenial nature allowed other research scientists and physicians to suspend their competitive instincts and to trust him. His capacity to seek and accept help from other prominent scientists and clinicians was critical in his own accomplishments, as illustrated by his application of Hartman's cortin extract, Reichstein's synthesized desoxycorticosterone and Kendall's synthesized hormone to treat adrenal disease. His openness and cordiality toward the inventor of the artificial kidney allowed the Brigham to become the world's first and most prominent kidney transplant center in the world.

Wilhelm ("Pim") Kolff, a Dutch physician and inventor, who had created an artificial kidney, or "dialyzer," during his years of confinement by the Germans during World War II, was invited by George Thorn to come to Harvard and the Brigham to demonstrate his prosthetic kidney to the Boston medical community right after the end of the war. Thorn had read about Kolff's invention and envisioned some dramatic and profound applications. He formulated an application of the device for patients with acute, episodic renal shutdown, similar to that experienced by victims of the German bombing in London, who died from renal failure as a result of so called "crush syndrome." These patients would survive major injuries received in the bombing only to die three weeks later from uremia caused by a shut down of the kidneys. Thorn had personally observed a similar instance of crush syndrome in a patient who had hemorrhaged during childbirth and was referred to the Brigham from Boston's Lying-in Hospital. If patients could have their blood dialyzed using the Kolff kidney, Thorn reasoned, it would give them time for their own kidneys to recover from the trauma and acute failure.

Of course, the necessity of stabilizing very sick patients with renal failure through the use of the artificial kidney became a precondition to successful kidney transplantation, but according to Thorn, "No one thought about kidney transplantation back then," referring to the immediate post war period when Kolff first came to the United States to visit Thorn and the Brigham staff. Kolff not only came to the Brigham and delivered grand rounds, but he left one of the four existing machines that he had developed with Doctor Thorn at the Brigham. Thorn made sure it was used. At Thorn's urging, Carl Walter, a Brigham surgeon and inventor, improved the Kolff machine, correcting flaws in Kolff's original design. Walter's improvements were later patented and sold to Baxter, now the world's leading supplier of artificial kidney products. At the same time, Thorn assigned the fledgling dialysis program and the application of the "Kolff-Brigham" artificial kidney machine to a young, aggressive Brigham resident who had just returned from military service. His name was John P. Merrill, and he was to become very quickly, in the words of Ted Hager, one of

National Medical Care's founders, "the potentate of kidneys."

Initially, however, Doctor Merrill was not pleased with his new assignment from physician-in-chief Thorn. As relayed by a Merrill contemporary to Joe Murray, Merrill was "mad as hell" that George Thorn "has assigned me the chore" of running the dialysis program. Merrill, like Thorn, was a medical doctor, not a surgeon. His specialty was internal medicine and cardiology. The future implications of Thorn's decision to assign the dialysis program and the application of the artificial kidney to the medical staff, rather than as a surgical adjunct, were major, but largely unforeseen at that time. In later years many transplant surgeons chafed under the control that the medical side of the hospital had over dialysis programs, not just at the Brigham, but all over the country. It's not a stretch to say that in assigning dialysis to Merrill, Doctor Thorn created the subspecialty of nephrology and ordained Merrill as the world's first nephrologist.

John Merrill turned his anger into action and created the world's first comprehensive kidney dialysis and transplantation program at the Brigham. He was able to secure, and tightly control, government grants, foundation funding and private charitable contributions to support his growing research and clinical practice. As a result, Merrill and the Brigham were able to attract the finest residents and fellows to pursue training and research in nephrology. And in turn, as the reputation of Merrill and the Brigham spread from the publication of their research findings, physicians were sending their patients with renal disease to the Brigham from all over the world for life saving care.

By the early 1950's, as a result of advances made during World War II, the stage was set for the first attempt at a kidney transplant. During his war time confinement Kolff had developed the artificial kidney, a necessary first step in any effort to transplant a kidney from a living, related donor to a sick patient who had lost kidney function. Second, dialysis was impossible until the advent of heparin, a drug that prevents blood from coagulating when it is removed from the human body, and heparin was also a byproduct of the medical advances made during the second world war. A third, necessary advance came in the surgical field in treating the wounds of severely injured soldiers with skin grafts. Skilled plastic surgeons like Joseph E. Murray, a Harvard graduate and Brigham surgeon, who served in the Army medical corp from 1942 until 1947, working with experts in the field of immunology, devised methods and procedures to prevent the body from attacking the transplanted skin, which under relentless assault from the body's immune system would literally dissolve after grafting. They had learned, largely through trial and error, that the donors and recipients could be classified by tissue type and that the success of transplants was directly related to the degree of similarity in tissue typing characteristics between the donor and the recipient.

When Doctor Murray returned to Boston and the Brigham, his interest in transplantation had intensified, but he found that his contemporary, David Hume, was leading the effort at the hospital. A brilliant research surgeon, Hume had served in the Navy during the war and had been discharged immediately following hostilities in 1945, and therefore had resumed his practice and research at the Brigham two years ahead of Murray, who was retained by the U.S. Army until 1947. Murray, a self-effacing and extraordinarily generous man, happily discovered that his friend Hume was eager to make a place for Murray on the Brigham's transplant team. When Hume was recalled into the Navy during the Korean conflict, Joe Murray took over the leadership of the transplant project at the Brigham, and in 1954 performed the world's first successful kidney transplant on identical twins, an extraordinary surgical breakthrough that justly, if somewhat belatedly, brought Doctor Murray a Nobel prize in medicine in 1990.

It's difficult over forty years later to understand the excitement - and, in fact, the fear - that the 1954 Brigham kidney transplant generated in the medical community as well as with the public. Aside from skin grafts and corneal implants, body parts had never before been taken from one individual and integrated into another human being. The procedure invited speculation and fantasy and stimulated religious, ethical and political debates never before then considered. If the surgical skills and medical mastery were noteworthy, the collective courage of the Brigham team in attempting the procedure and initiating an adventure that had never been undertaken was cosmic.

The team consisted not only of surgeons, internists, urologists and anesthesiologists, but also, bold administrators, trustees, and even lawyers, who were willing to challenge status quo thinking and take risks. As later recalled by Doctor Thorn, "nobody had done anything like that before," but as physician-in-chief, he not only permitted the procedure, but supported and encouraged the effort in every way possible, not for the greater glory of the Brigham - although that was the result - but because, in his words, "there was no other way to keep the patient alive." Lawyers for the hospital were dispatched to secure court approval to "attack" the healthy twin, remove one of his kidneys, and implant it in his brother, even though both twins had clearly given their informed consent. And mindful of the sensibilities of Irish Catholic Boston, and in an attempt to cover his political as well as religious bases, Merrill sought the approval of the Cardinal Archbishop of Boston.

Surgeons as skillful as Joe Murray certainly were practicing at other, older, larger and more prestigious medical centers around the country. And there were surely other cardio-renal specialists with more experience than John Merrill in 1954, and even a few urologists as impressive as Hartwell Harrison at other institutions. However, it would be wrong to suggest that the Brigham was simply "lucky" to be the first to draw the perfectly compatible identical twins and therefore initiate the era of homotransplantation. More than luck, the Brigham had developed a sense of cooperative teamwork and a spirit of innovation that supported a risky endeavor in order to save the lives of its patients.

The operation was performed at the Brigham on December 23, 1954. Begun at 8:15 a.m., it took no more than three and a half hours to remove the left kidney from a healthy, 24-year old donor and implant it in the lower abdominal cavity (iliac fossa) of his uremic twin brother. Urine flowed from the transplanted kidney almost immediately, and the twins survived, each with one, healthy, properly functioning kidney for many years.

In their report on the operation published in The Journal of the American Medical Association, Doctors Merrill, Murray and their colleagues cited several observations that led them to go ahead with the procedure, despite the fact that, "[t]he transplantation of functioning tissue from one individual to another of the same species has, with few exceptions, not been successfully accomplished to date." First, it was known that skin grafts between identical twins had been successful. There was also strong evidence that the immune system's response to a transplanted kidney would replicate its response to a skin graft from the same donor. Thus, as a preliminary step, the Brigham team grafted skin from the donor-twin to the recipient-twin, and, after a month without an adverse immune response, concluded that the recipient's immune system would "probably" accept the new kidney from the same source. There was other evidence that the twins were identical, or "monozygotic" (developed from the same, single fertilized egg and therefore, genetically similar), including identical eye color, blood test results, hospital records that noted the twins shared a common placenta at birth, and the fact that both twins had the rare "Darwin's tubercle" (a slight, presumably vestigial, projection) on their ears. In addition, in earlier experiments on dogs, Doctor Murray had demonstrated that kidney transplants (in those cases, autografts, or the removal and replacement of the same kidney at a different location in the body) would function indefinitely.

But the clincher was the undeniable, clinical fact that the donor could survive with one healthy kidney, and without a transplant the sick twin brother, whose uremia had resulted in congestive heart failure, high blood pressure, edema and psychosis, would surely die. "Doctor Merrill made a critical decision in December, 1954 to take a kidney out of a living donor and put it into somebody that was going to die anyway. In the tenor of the times that was a huge, risky decision," NMC co-founder, Ted Hager, later reflected.

The operation caused a sensation. If kidneys could be transplanted, why not hearts, livers or other organs? If humans could easily survive with one functioning kidney, nearly everyone had an "extra" kidney to donate to people whose kidneys had failed. The combination of dialysis with the Kolff artificial kidney and transplantation following the Brigham procedure could end the scourge of kidney disease. Not everyone viewed the breakthrough positively, and commentators editorialized against scientists assuming "god-like" roles. The Brigham phenomenon even revitalized the Frankenstein genre of science fiction, capturing the popular imagination with books and films about transplanted faces, hands and brains.

For the vast majority of kidney patients who did not have an identical twin, however, the practical consequences were still a few years away. As the Merrill-Murray team put it in 1956: "Tissue transplantation including that of a functioning kidney appears to be a feasible procedure in identical twins, but to date successful permanently functioning homografts appear to be limited to such individuals." Nonetheless, the trail had been blazed, and within a decade, during the early sixties when Gus Hampers, Ted Hager and Gene Schupak were engaged in advanced training under the tutelage of John Merrill, therapies that used steroids and other drugs to suppress the recipient's immune response to the "foreign" kidney transplant allowed the procedure to become theoretically available to all uremic patients. Advances in transplantation, immune suppression, tissue typing, vascular access surgery, and dialysis that started at the Brigham with the "World War II generation" of doctors like Thorn, Merrill, Murray, Hume and Harrison converted renal failure from a fatal diagnosis to a manageable, chronic condition by the mid-60's. It would take the succeeding generation of nephrologists and surgeons to make these breakthroughs accessible and commonplace, so that they had real practical value to kidney patients outside the handful lucky enough to receive care in the major university affiliated medical centers like Harvard, Georgetown and U.C.L.A.

In 1984 Thomas E. Starzl, M.D. wrote a commentary in The Journal of the American Medical Association that analyzed the significance of the Brigham effort, and concluded: "If gold medals and prizes were awarded to institutions instead of individuals, the Peter Bent Brigham Hospital of 30 years ago would have qualified. The ruling board and administrative structure of that hospital did not falter in their support of the quixotic objective of treating end-stage renal disease despite the long list of tragic failures that resulted from these early efforts, leavened only by occasional encouraging notations such as those in the identical twin case. Those who were there at the time have credited Dr. George Thorn, chairman of medicine, and Dr. Francis D. Moore, chairman of surgery, with the qualities of leadership, creativity, courage and unselfishness that made the Peter Bent Brigham Hospital a unique world resource for that moment of history." In 1990 Doctor Murray received the Nobel Prize for his work in transplantation and he not only quoted Starzl's encomium in his effort to share the award with his colleagues, but donated the entire Nobel prize money to the Harvard Medical School.

2

Clinical Dimensions

By 1964 the world had changed for physicians specializing in studying and treating diseases of the kidneys and for patients with renal disease. The center of these changes was the Brigham in Boston, and the centripetal force pulling young doctors like Hampers, Schupak and Hager to the Brigham, was John P. Merrill. Initially unhappy with Doctor Thorn's assignment to "run the dialysis machine," Merrill turned the proverbial sow's ear into a silk purse. Merrill was perfectly cast for the role of a distinguished professor of medicine. "He looked 'Harvard,'" said Gene Schupak, who trained with Merrill from July 1962 to June 1964, recalling that the "potentate of kidneys" was "good looking, polished, and enormously articulate. He would have made a wonderful politician." John Merrill is also remembered as vain, temperamental and insecure. "He had two lab coats he'd wear," Schupak remembered about his silver-haired mentor. "If he was wearing the tan lab coat, he was 'doing research' and did not want to be bothered by the residents and fellows assigned to him. A white lab coat meant he was seeing patients and would discuss clinical matters."

Doctor Merrill was a consummate politician and was very skillful in securing money for his program whether from the university itself, the federal government, or private philanthropic sources, and he controlled these grants closely, leveraging them into more published research, books, visiting lectures, publicity and attracting the world's foremost kidney specialists to the Brigham. In turn, each of these activities strengthened his position and elevated his profile, so he was able to secure even more funding to expand his empire in the next academic cycle. Security and survival in the environment of academic medicine consisted then and now in one's ability to attract and retain research funding. Being a great physician attracted sick patients, and these were largely viewed as an expensive drain on the institution's resources. However, being a successful researcher and fundraiser provided a net gain for the institution.

Merrill was reluctant to share the fame or fortune with his fellows, who labored extraordinarily long hours at the hospital and in the lab to please him, while "JPM" was giving grand rounds at the world's most renowned medical schools and coaxing money from politicians and foundation trustees. Schupak recalled a time when Merrill was out of Boston on one of his lecture tours and a junior staff member admitted a patient and attended to his care for several days during Merrill's absence. The course of care was successful, and upon his return Merrill saw the patient for the first time as he was about to be discharged. The patient told Merrill how impressed and grateful he was for all that Merrill's assistant had done for him. After several minutes of listening to the patient praise the junior staff doctor, Merrill turned to the patient and said, "What about me?" Ted Hager described various "megaconferences where John Merrill would stand up in front as the idol." If anyone suggested an innovation or a new approach, Merrill would always respond, "Yes, we've been looking at that in our lab." The amazing thing was that everyone believed him.

Among the cadre of residents and fellows who worked for John Merrill, learned from him and grew to tolerate his foibles and demands were the three founders of National Medical Care. In many respects, sharing the common experience of virtual indentured servitude under Merrill was a "boot camp, bonding" type of experience that formed the basis of the Hager-Hampers-Schupak partnership and friendship that endured for decades thereafter. Ted Hager arrived at the Brigham as an intern in 1955, only a few short months after the identical twin kidney transplantation. Edward Birge Hager earned his M.D. degree from Washington University School of Medicine in his hometown of St. Louis in 1955, having previously graduated from Amherst College. Tall, handsome and witty, Ted exuded charm and goodwill - the kind of man who could and would liven up any gathering. Ted's spontaneity and passion were rare and welcomed, especially in the dour and dusty atmosphere of Harvard. As Doctor Hampers later recalled, "Ted would come up with a hundred new ideas everyday, and even when 99 of them were 'off-the-wall,' that didn't stop him from pushing another hundred just as enthusiastically the next day."

Hager, who left the Brigham in 1956 to fulfill his military obligation in the U.S. Army, returned to Harvard and its affiliated hospital as a renal research fellow in 1960. His interest in research, empathy with patients, and irrepressible enthusiasm endeared him to physician-in-chief, George Thorn, but much less so to John Merrill, who found it hard to control Hager. Ted wisely established his independence from Merrill by seeking and receiving his own research grants – generally from the Army – that provided him a base income and supported his work in the field of transplantation. As a protege of Doctor Thorn, he also provided back-up for his mentor at the Brigham and circumvented Merrill by securing his own admitting privileges at the Brigham and at other Boston hospitals, and thereby establishing his own private medical practice. This infuriated Merrill. Doctor Schupak recalled Merrill "blowing up" when he discovered that a junior staff urologist had referred a patient to Doctor Hager. Schupak reported that Merrill said, "I am the Brigham's nephrologist," indicating that every renal patient at the Brigham belonged to Merrill.

Ted Hager acknowledged Merrill's role as "potentate of kidneys," learned as much as he could from John Merrill, but never became subservient. And in a pinch, George Thorn could protect him from Merrill. Nonetheless, Ted learned a lot from Merrill ("Merrill was the Chief, and I was the Indian," Hager often said) and pioneered the expansion of the dialysis service at the Brigham. In the early years, a dialysis session became a major procedure and required the active participation of at least one physician and a trained nurse. Merrill needed doctors to do the grunt work of preparing the machine itself, essentially recreating an artificial kidney for every dialysis procedure, and Hager gleefully remembered the task: "We bought cellophane from Oscar Meyer - the same stuff they wrapped around sausages - and we'd boil it for forty-five minutes. Then it took two of us to wrap the membrane around the drum. We even mixed the chemicals in the dialysis bath by hand."

Having literally "learned the hard way," Hager, and subsequently his colleagues, Schupak and Hampers, were always trying to think of ways to make it easier, cheaper and consequently, accessible to a population beyond the walls of academic medicine. Even after Wilhelm Kolff had developed a disposable coil dialyzer that Baxter, a medical products supplier, manufactured, Merrill retained a "strange attachment to the old Kolff-Brigham dialyzer," according to Schupak, and required his fellows to laboriously prepare the machine. Today, a technician with a high school education and some basic, technical training, can set up a dialysis machine with its disposable, sterile artificial kidney within a matter of minutes, and nephrologists of the 1990's view Hager's "war stories" about dialysis in the 1950's as a jet pilot would view the saga of the Wright brothers.

Ted Hager would not be satisfied with the practice of nephrology in the 1990's, with his need to be a frontiersman - a man on the edge of innovations, and also a renaissance man, who, unlike many of his colleagues, harbored a skill and desire to contextualize and prioritize. He viewed medicine like any other human activity, full of pretension, superstition, outdated practices and over-inflated egos. Bureaucracies and hierarchies became Ted's favorite targets, and tradition was always suspect. He was fond of saying, "Until a few years ago, patients rarely survived an encounter with a hospital," a criticism which did not ingratiate Hager with the medical establishment at Harvard. In an earlier age Ted Hager would have been smashing icons, defending Galileo or nailing protests on the cathedral doors. He directed his sharpest barbs at himself, and his self-deprecating humor was too often endorsed by other, less insightful, colleagues. To his credit, Gus Hampers ignored Hager's self-deprecations and overextended rhetoric, always mining Hager's prolific, if somewhat unfocused, output for the flashes of brilliance that were there for those with the patience and intelligence to find.

Just as he was too iconoclastic to scale the hierarchy of academic medicine, Ted Hager was similarly unimpressed with self-important business leaders and the moguls of capitalism. At a stockholders meeting in National Medical Care's early years, Hager shocked the assembled investment advisers and financial reporters when, in responding to a question about how the country could encourage a higher rate of kidney transplantation, Hager replied, "By lobbying the government to allow people to ride motorcycles without helmets, so we can harvest more viable kidneys." Only after seeing Hampers and Schupak double over with laughter did the grey suited analysts understand Hager's joke.

The second of the NMC founding trio to work with John Merrill was Eugene Schupak, a native New Yorker, who had graduated from Seton Hall University and the University of Chicago Medical School. It was during a residency at Chicago's Cook County Hospital that Gene Schupak first met Gus Hampers and began a life long friendship that included introducing Gus to his future wife, Joyce. Like Ted Hager, Doctor Schupak was gregarious and magnetic, making friends easily, never shy, and unbelievably inquisitive. Unlike Hager, whose mind ranged widely and simultaneously encompassed medicine, history, literature and philosophy in a ricocheting trajectory, Gene Schupak was intensely focused on solving problems, determined and undeterable. Practical and resourceful, Doctor Schupak, who had worked briefly with Pim Kolff at the Cleveland Clinic in 1961, spent two years with John Merrill at the Brigham and Harvard Medical School in the 1962-1964 academic years, during which he contributed enormously to Merrill's program.

From the start, Merrill exploited Schupak's talents and got from his fellow more than he gave in return. "Merrill was not very generous to his fellows, either while they were there at the Brigham, or later in helping them with their careers," Schupak stated. Still, Schupak was grateful for the experience. "Merrill was enormously creative - a visionary man." Merrill was penurious, not just with credit and advice, but monetarily. Schupak and others recall that he would have parties at his home but required the residents and junior staff physicians, most of whom could barely pay the rent, to bring the beer and the food. Schupak caught on quickly. At a medical conference at New York's Academy of Science, a visiting foreign doctor became ill and Merrill summoned Gene to fetch some antibiotics from a nearby drug store. "I'll never forget it - it was a Sunday and most of the drugstores were closed," Schupak laughed. "Merrill dug deep in his pocket and gave me two dollars. I know he expected me to buy a standard prescription that would have cost over ten dollars, but I got just what he asked for - two dollars worth of antibiotics!"

Merrill was fiercely competitive and the attention that his rival, Doctor Belding Scribner, was receiving from his work in Seattle released Merrill's combative hormones. In 1960 Scribner introduced and developed the concept of chronic hemodialysis, creating a thrice weekly treatment regimen for patients with end-stage renal disease. Scribner's first chronic dialysis patient was Clyde Shields and he survived on this "maintenance" dialysis for eleven years, succumbing to a heart attack in 1971. In 1962 Scribner opened the Seattle Artificial Kidney Center at Swedish Hospital, and its success in caring for patients, who were not immediate candidates for kidney transplants, was widely reported by the popular press, culminating in the November 9, 1962 Life Magazine article on the so called "death committee" instituted by Scribner in Seattle, entitled "They Decide Who Lives." Before Scribner's application of the dialysis procedure as a long term therapy and not one that was merely an adjunct to the kidney transplantation procedure, most end-stage renal disease patients still faced a terminal diagnosis. Very few were lucky enough to receive a transplant. Chronic dialysis, while not desirable, provided a "viable" option. It also created a demand that could not be met. Hence, the need for a committee to "play god" and decide how to ration the scarce dialysis resources then available. Scribner's solution was to empower a committee of doctors, priests, ethicists and philosophers to ration care. A few years later Merrill's "progeny" would create a different solution.

In 1962, however, there was no chronic program at the Brigham and Merrill was jealous of Scribner's fame. He also foresaw that research dollars would be attracted to this form of therapy. Merrill wanted chronic dialysis for the Brigham, but he was not the kind of man who could go to Scribner and ask for his help. Doctor Schupak, who had just arrived at the Brigham, was the perfect emissary, and so Merrill sent Schupak to Seattle to find out all he could about operating a chronic hemodialysis service. Since Schupak was young, inquisitive, and aggressive, he went to Seattle and asked all the right questions. A large, imposing man with a smile that transformed his entire face and could brighten the darkest room, Gene Schupak's charm and feigned naivete and awe created trust that was in fact always returned and never forgotten. As a result, Merrill and the Brigham started their own chronic dialysis program.

Also, in the brief time that he was in Boston, Doctor Schupak introduced home dialysis as a treatment option. In 1964 one of the Brigham's first chronic dialysis patients was a neighbor of Schupak, and Gene shared a ride with the patient to the Brigham twice a week. Schupak saw no reason why the patient and his wife, both intelligent and highly motivated individuals, could not be trained to set up a machine and administer the dialysis in their home. This was a truly bold idea, but John Merrill, who already saw that chronic dialysis could demand and overwhelm the resources of the hospital, considered this a reasonable suggestion and decided to put it to a vote of the Brigham physicians, fellows and residents on his renal team. They met on a Saturday morning in Merrill's renal lab, and Doctor Merrill let Schupak present his suggestion, which was promptly challenged and ridiculed by the more senior physicians. Merrill put it to a vote and the result, with Merrill not voting, was eleven to one. Gene Schupak was alone, and reluctantly accepted the negative verdict. Then, as Doctor Schupak remembers, "Merrill said he hadn't voted yet, and as the chief, he had twelve votes. He voted in my favor, and that's how we began home dialysis." During his final months at the Brigham in 1964, Schupak developed the home dialysis program and suggested to Merrill that they write up the experience for publication. Merrill told him it was premature. As Gene later recalled, "As soon as I left, Merrill published the data."

The experiences in creating a chronic dialysis service and starting home dialysis for patients who were not going to be able to benefit from a transplant and who would otherwise expire, despite the fact that there was a procedure that could keep them alive, made an important impression on Gene Schupak. He realized that no matter how awesome the advances that academic medicine produced, they were useless, unless and until accessible to the patients who needed them. There was a disdain among academic physicians, who were often at the top of their class, to look down on doctors who spent their time taking care of patients.

Patients were generally a financial drain on the hospital and taking care of routine cases was a waste of the valuable time of professors of medicine who needed to focus their clinical energies on the unusual, more challenging cases. Research, publication and clinical investigation were the requisites of status among the smartest physicians and surgeons then and largely still today. Caring for patients implied a lesser status, and the faculty title "clinical professor" was a step or two lower on the academic ladder. Schupak left Harvard in the spring of 1964 and started a chronic dialysis and home care program at Brooklyn Hospital and its affiliate, the Downstate Medical Center, where Schupak also had teaching duties. Still "inculcated" with the values and prejudices of academic medicine, Schupak nevertheless returned to his native Brooklyn with a passion to bring these revolutionary dialysis services to a grossly underserviced urban population.

Before he left Boston, however, Schupak had persuaded Gus Hampers to follow his path and accept a fellowship with Merrill at the Brigham, and as part of Hampers' orientation, Gene instructed Hampers on the operation of the kidney dialysis machine - Hampers' first introduction to the device. Gus remembered the instruction vividly: "I came to Boston over the Christmas break in 1963, and Gene gave me a crash course in running the machine." Schupak's memory was hazier: "If I taught Gus how to do dialysis, it probably took less than an hour. It wouldn't have taken Gus that long to grasp everything I knew. In all honesty, Gus Hampers is the smartest man I ever met in my life."

Dr. Schupak's late-1963 tutorial for Hampers on operating the artificial kidney was not Hampers' first encounter with the device, however. In the summer of 1959, having completed his internship, Dr. Hampers was ordered to active duty in the United States Navy. Just as he was embarking from San Francisco to his posting in Okinawa, his father was diagnosed with a ruptured lumbar disk and underwent back surgery in Pittsburgh. A few days later, upon his arrival in the Far East, Hampers learned from the Red Cross that his dad was in critical condition. The hospital blood bank made a serious error and mismatched Hampers' fathers' blood, giving him type A instead of type O blood. As a result, the elder Hampers experienced massive hemolysis, releasing free hemoglobin into his blood stream and subsequently plugging his kidneys, a condition known as "acute tubular necrosis." Hampers rushed back to Pittsburgh and not a moment too soon, as his father was uremic and gravely ill. There was only one artificial kidney in Pittsburgh at the time and Hampers assisted Dr. Mateer in administering dialysis to his father with this primitive device, which required a new surgical cut to gain access to the artery and vein for each treatment. The elder Hampers endured three treatments and eventually recovered, but the incident seared in Hampers' mind both the potential and the limitations of the prosthetic kidney. Gaining access was critical.

Five years later Constantine L. ("Gus") Hampers left Philadelphia General Hospital and took Schupak's spot on Doctor Merrill's team at the Brigham. Hampers and his wife, Joyce, had been married only weeks before arriving in Boston, renting what Joyce described as a "dismal" apartment on Commonwealth Court, near the medical school. "As I walked in the door at the Brigham, I saw the back of Gene Schupak's head on the way out," Hampers recalled figuratively. If Gus' first view at the Brigham was the back of Schupak's head, the second was looking at the front of Ted Hager's face. Doctor Merrill had instructed Hampers to work with Doctor Hager in the renal laboratory, as well as take over the operation of the chronic dialysis program that Schupak had started two years before. Ted and Gus became a team from the start. Their skills and temperaments were different but complementary. Shorter, quieter and more cerebral and introspective than Hager, Doctor Hampers admired Hager's wit and gregarious nature. For his part, like Schupak and thousands of others, Hager was impressed with Doctor Hampers' intellectual brilliance, extraordinary energy for hard work, and modesty. Theirs was one of those rare, productive and intellectually symbiotic relationships where the whole is greater than the two individual halves. The best qualities of these two young doctors were sharpened by the interplay between them. They energized, amused, taught and motivated each other.

Gus Hampers made an immediate difference in the chronic dialysis program at the Brigham. John Merrill, ever the show horse, needed a work horse, and he found the best in Gus

Hampers. Merrill's long time colleague, transplant surgeon, Joe Murray, remembered Gus Hampers in those years at Harvard and at the Brigham as "one of our best." "John Merrill started dialysis at the Brigham, but Gus Hampers perfected it - he made it work efficiently," Murray recollects. What impressed Doctor Murray and others most about Gus Hampers, was his overriding commitment to his patients. "I came to rely on his judgment," Murray continued. "If Hampers made a diagnosis, I could count on it," he said. Gus' secretary, Betty Simpkins, who also functioned as a volunteer, informal friend and counselor to Hampers' many patients and their family members over the years, recalled how much these patients trusted and adored Hampers. "They knew he'd do anything for them, and they felt the same about him. It was a sad day for patients and for the hospital when Gus left the fulltime practice of medicine," Simpkins said.

Hampers' relationship with John Merrill was complex. Along with his future partner, Doctor Schupak, Gus Hampers saw through Merrill's vanity and showmanship and knew from first hand experience that Merrill took advantage of the fellows and residents. "Merrill was smart, but lazy," Gus recalls. "If you could get him to focus for five minutes on a case, he was the best clinician in the field, but it was hard to find him or pin him down for five minutes." The hospital staff knew that if they wanted help they shouldn't waste precious time trying to find Merrill, but call his young assistant right away. Gus Hampers also shared Ted Hager's disdain for Merrill's "Harvard induced" pretensions, but did not try to circumvent the chief, as Hager did. For one thing, Gus' income and future were directly dependent during that time on Merrill, but more importantly, Hampers knew that he could learn more from Merrill about nephrology than anyone else in the world, and that with small effort he could make Merrill dependent on him. Hampers' studies with Merrill transcended medicine and delved into areas of hospital politics, the use of power, and building networks of skillful, independently minded, but nonetheless, dependent, colleagues. Feeling he lacked the natural political talents of a leader like Merrill, Hampers set out to become a leader by understanding and adopting Merrill's more attractive attributes and discarding the negative features. By handling the 2 a.m.

emergencies, filling in on Merrill's teaching assignments, conceiving and implementing brilliant research on Merrill's behalf, and lending a sympathetic ear to patients, nurses, and other doctors, Gus Hampers became indispensable to Merrill and the Brigham. Hampers identified Merrill's critical weakness - his penchant to avoid hard work - and by "helping" Merrill with his work load, created a dependency that balanced the scales in Hampers' favor. These were skills that Gus Hampers could use later in building National Medical Care and becoming a leader in the world of business as well.

In the spring of 1965, after nearly a year as Doctor Merrill's fellow at the Brigham, Gus Hampers, whose wife Joyce was in law school and was pregnant with their first of three sons, had to find a way to support his family, and the $6,000 annual stipend that John Merrill had paid him from his renal program coffers, even when supplemented by Joyce's salary as an assistant in a law firm, fell somewhere in the range between subsistence and inadequate. Joyce Hampers recalled that when they were married, Gus told her that they'd never be rich. "He explained that he loved academic medicine and that we'd never be wealthy from that," Joyce remembered. So when Gus returned from a visit with Pim Kolff, who wanted Gus to join him at The Cleveland Clinic, and told Joyce that Doctor Kolff had offered him a salary of $19,000 a year, "I had our bags packed and I was ready to leave," she recalled.

The move never occurred, however, and Hampers stayed at the Brigham, after Merrill increased the annual stipend to $7,000 and Ted Hager assured Gus another $7,000 if he would stay. "Ted cobbled together some money from his research grants and his private practice income so I could stay at Harvard, and even though it was still $5,000 less than I would get from Kolff, Joyce and I stayed in Boston," Hampers reflected. Hampers was not motivated by money but by the prestige of Harvard and the challenge of matching wits and talent with the best medical minds at the Brigham. The lure that attracted Gus Hampers was the company and friendly competition among the coterie of truly brilliant doctors that practiced at the Brigham and staffed the Harvard faculty. His own natural proclivity toward taking risks - he was reputed to be a skilled poker player among the residents and junior staff - resonated within the environment George Thorn and John Merrill had created at the Brigham. Money would prove to be a poor substitute marker of excellence.

Merrill got his money's worth from Gus Hampers. Hampers became the director of the dialysis operation, taught at the medical school, continued to help Merrill and Hager in the lab and supervised a growing corps of young renal fellows who wanted to train with Merrill at the Brigham, many of whom later became key medical directors in the dialysis clinics that National Medical Care would establish throughout the country. In addition, Hampers covered Merrill's hospital practice, generating thousands of dollars in medical service fees for Merrill, all of which went into a pot controlled by the cardio-renal chief. Hampers was also largely responsible for the endowment of a professor's chair at Harvard Medical School and the Brigham which, of course, became Merrill's sinecure. The endowment was a gift from Peter Stuyvesant, a young, wealthy kidney patient who came under the care of Doctor Hampers. Stuyvesant, the namesake and descendant of the Dutch colonist from New York, was living in Paris when he developed end-stage renal failure and his lawyer contacted John Merrill. Merrill assigned his care to Hampers who became not only Peter's physician, but a very close friend. Merrill didn't miss the opportunity and persuaded Gus Hampers to suggest that Peter endow a professor's chair at the medical school that Merrill would fill.

Indirectly Peter Stuyvesant brought Gus Hampers more than a gift for the medical school. Because he could afford a private duty nurse and the best equipment and supplies then available, Stuyvesant was dialyzed at his home. Under Doctor Hampers' supervision the nurse would set up the machine, prime the artificial kidney, regulate the dialysis bath, or "dialysate," insert the venous and arterial needles, and perform the dialysis treatment, watching the patient's vital signs and correcting or addressing any problems that might arise during the procedure. In those days, the artificial kidney coils would leak from time to time, and any number of other complications could occur within the four hours during which the patient's blood was circulating out of his artery into plastic tubing, through a thin membrane which was itself immersed in a bath of dialysate, and then back into the patient's vein.

Water and toxic matter would pass through the semi-permeable membrane from the blood on one side of the membrane and into the bath on the other through osmosis, thereby "dialyzing," or separating, certain elements out of the blood through a process of simple diffusion. Dialysis in the home setting in the nineteen sixties required a nurse with dexterity, who could think and respond to emergencies coolly and quickly and understood the essential variables and adjusted the treatment accordingly. She'd cover the patient with a blanket to relieve the chills he'd encounter as his blood returned from the machine and reentered his body a degree or two cooler than normal body temperature. She'd massage his calves and elevate his legs as the inevitable cramps squeezed his muscles into hard knots of pain. Mostly, however, the time was spent one-on-one with the patient, talking, listening, offering advice, and just being a companion during a stressful and tedious process.

In 1964 Ernestine ("Ernie") Lowrie accepted a special duty assignment at the Brigham where she ran into a nursing school classmate who told her about a private duty opportunity of administering dialysis at home to Peter Stuyvesant. Her classmate taught Ernie, who fit the private duty assignment into her busy life as a full time registered nurse at the Baptist Hospital in Boston and as a homemaker and mother, how to administer the procedure, and Ernie began taking care of Peter while Gus Hampers was away on vacation. A couple weeks later Ernie met Doctor Hampers for the first time at Peter's apartment. "I was scared to death," Ernie remembers, and, as Dr. Hampers watched her attach his favorite patient to the machine, Peter said "She's very good at this stuff." Hampers agreed. They were both right. Ernie was so good at "this dialysis stuff" that she later became Hampers' second-in-command of hundreds of kidney centers all over the world, providing millions of dialysis treatments to end-stage renal disease patients every year. It all started in 1964 in Peter Stuyvesant's basement apartment in Brookline, Massachusetts.

Even with dialysis, patients with end-stage renal failure like Peter Stuyvesant face an uncomfortable and stressful life. So do their families. Their ability to adapt and readjust their lives and the lives of their spouses and other family members is a testament to the human spirit and the unquenchable thirst for life. The normal human kidney is a multipurpose organ, about the size of a fist and weighing approximately four ounces. It consists of blood vessels and tiny tubular tissues called "nephrons" that remove impurities (excess water and chemicals and the waste products of normal human metabolism) from the blood. Eighteen gallons of blood pass through the kidneys every hour. In addition to continuously filtering the blood, the kidneys act as a dynamic laboratory, testing the content of the blood and responding appropriately in order to keep the body's chemical environment in balance. Virtually all human beings have two kidneys, although it's not clear why. People's health and longevity don't appear to depend on having two kidneys - they live just as long and just as well with only one. Moreover, human kidneys have an enormous reserve capacity, so much so that individuals with only 25% of normal kidney function remain essentially asymptomatic. Usually by the time signs of renal disease appear, the kidneys are more than 90% impaired.

The kidneys are susceptible to a variety of diseases as well as injury that can lead to renal failure. The current estimate is that approximately 315 individuals per million contract some form of kidney disease every year, or in a country of 275 million people like the United States, about 88,000 annually (this incidence statistic has risen dramatically in the past two decades). That statistic represents the "incidence" of kidney failure, or the new cases each year that are added to the population of existing, surviving patients. Before the nineteen sixties, they all died.

Trauma or severe injury like an automobile accident or a drug overdose, can quickly destroy the kidneys, but most renal failure is progressive, and because the kidneys are so resilient, it often remains undetected until the kidneys are largely useless. Infections ("glomerulonephritis" and other forms), hypertension, cancer and diabetes are all causes of progressive and irreversible renal failure. Whatever the cause of renal failure, the result is uremia, which is a syndrome of diverse dysfunctions in the body, several of which can be fatal. Generally, when the kidneys fail, the body can't rid itself of metabolic waste products, including excess water and urea, and as toxins build up in the body, death will result from heart attacks, strokes and other proximate causes.

An individual with renal failure who has developed uremia, experiences a broad range of unpleasant symptoms. His skin takes on a grayish-yellow pallor from the build up of pigments and insufficient oxygen in the blood. The skin is usually dry, and he suffers from itching that can be maddening. His hair becomes dry and brittle, and his nails, thin. He may develop purple discoloration on the skin as capillaries close to the surface rupture and bleed. The buildup of excess water causes his ankles and legs to swell with edema, and as his lungs fill with water, shortness of breath. The urea in his saliva makes his breath smell of ammonia. He may experience a burning in the soles of his feet, footdrop, impotence and involuntary muscular twitches from an impaired nervous system. Patients are fatigued, sleepless, headachy, listless and often nauseated and anorectic.

Internally, uremia and the resulting chemical imbalances in the blood wreak havoc with the body's organs and functions - nothing "works" as it should, once the levels of sodium, potassium, calcium, phosphates (so called "electrolytes") and other chemicals become abnormal. The patient often develops ulcers and inflammation in the gastrointestinal tract. His red blood cell count decreases, resulting in anemia. Children with renal disease fail to grow, and women cease ovulation. The most life threatening symptoms involve the patient's cardiovascular system, as the buildup of proteins leads to arteriosclerosis, excess sodium increases the blood pressure, and "potassium intoxication" results in cardiac arrest.

The healthy kidney is an amazingly efficient organ. For example, if the kidney detects a lack of oxygen in the blood ("hypoxia"), it will automatically produce and release a chemical called erythropoietin which stimulates the bone marrow to produce more oxygen carrying red blood cells. Similarly, when the kidneys are insufficiently suffused with blood ("ischemia"), they create and excrete a chemical known as renin, which actually increase the blood pressure. Thus, badly damaged kidneys pose a double threat in terms of blood pressure, since they not only fail to remove excess salt, but they release ever increasing amounts of renin, which itself elevates the blood pressure. That's why "dead" kidneys are often surgically removed from the patient's body.

Before the post-World War II breakthroughs in kidney transplantation and dialysis, doctors attempted to treat the symptoms, but could do nothing to reverse the inevitable decline from uremia that would result in premature death. The physician's job was to extend life as much as possible, soften the harsh effects and make the patient comfortable - tasks not unlike those confronting oncologists today for their patients with malignant, untreatable cancers, or those facing physicians caring for patients with AIDS. By the 1960's, however, science and medicine could replace failed kidney functions, at least to the degree necessary to prolong life, with transplants or dialysis. Nonetheless, thousands and thousands of end-stage renal disease patients continued to die unnecessarily after 1960, because the "healthcare system," i.e., hospitals, doctors, insurance companies, and government bureaucracies, could not, or would not, adapt quickly to provide these new and expensive therapies to kidney patients.

Patients like Peter Stuyvesant, who had financial resources, could alter the neglectful procedures and behaviors of individuals, charitable corporations, and government agencies. They could buy machines and supplies from companies like Baxter, and they could get the attention of experts like John Merrill and his Brigham colleagues by endowing an academic chair. Stuyvesant had two kidney transplants, the first unsuccessful, the second, from his sister, successful, although he died prematurely from cancer four years later. But for every patient like Peter Stuyvesant, there were thousands who in the 1960's faced the same end as their pre-World War II counterparts with end-stage renal disease. Medicine had changed but their healthcare had not.

It became increasingly difficult, perplexing and upsetting for nephrologists like Hampers, Hager and Schupak, to see patients die even though they knew there were therapies that could extend their lives. Before 1960 doctors attending end-stage renal disease patients could offer no hope because there were no substitutes for damaged kidneys. The 1954 Brigham transplant was experimental, and until the development of immune suppressing drugs, was of no practical value. Use of the 15-year old Kolff artificial kidney was restricted to acute treatments, because it was very difficult to access a patient's circulatory system more than a few times. By 1965, however, the arterial venous shunt (and later the fistula implant) allowed nephrologists to keep patients alive on chronic hemodialysis, and transplantation began to proliferate as doctors learned how to control the body's rejection mechanism. Still, thousands died because there were not enough dialysis machines or transplantable kidneys. Doctors continued to send their patients home to die, but not because there was no alternative, but because there was no "available" alternative.

For solutions, young, skilled doctors, like Gene Schupak in New York, Ted Hager and Gus Hampers in Boston, Alan Hull in Dallas, Larry Siegel in Washington, and Dick Glassock in Los Angeles, were spending less time in the renal laboratories and medical schools and spending more time in the offices and conference rooms of hospital administrators, government rehabilitation agencies and insurance carriers, trying to secure financial support for their patients. "We started spending more time trying to get funding for patients than we did providing dialysis," Ted Hager recalled. And Ed Lowrie, one of Doctor Hampers' earliest Brigham fellows, and in later years, a National Medical Care executive, put it, "If the doctor was concerned about the total patient, he had to find money so the patient could survive." A conscientious nephrologist had to become as expert about public health grantsmanship, rehabilitation funding regulations, and private insurance "caps" and coinsurance provisions, as he or she was about clotting times, dialysate formulations, or the effects of hyperlipoproteinemia.

Doctor Hampers began to have doubts about the utility and value of the career path he had chosen and for which he had trained for over a decade. Joyce Hampers recalled his discouragement and depression as more and more of his patients expired. In the mid-sixties, the Brigham was the only treatment center for end-stage renal disease patients in New England. Nobel prize recipient Joe Murray remembered, "People were coming to the Brigham from all over the world, and Gus was the man in the trenches." Years later in a 1980 interview with the magazine

Science, Hampers said, "We used to sit around and decide who would go on dialysis. I felt terrible about making those decisions and tended to blot them out of my mind."

At the same time, as more patients took advantage of chronic dialysis as a long term, maintenance therapy, the relationships between the attending physician and his patients whom he would see three times a week, became close and complex. When these patients died, the doctors paid an emotional price. "We were attending a lot of funerals and it was devastating," Joyce Hampers recalled. One of those funerals that devastated Joyce and Gus Hampers was that of Peter Stuyvesant, who was one of Hampers' first home maintenance patients after arriving at the Brigham in 1964. Peter was like a member of the Hampers' family and he and Joyce rode an emotional rollercoaster through Peter's first unsuccessful cadaver transplant in 1966, and his subsequent, successful kidney transplant from his sister a year later. "Peter would never let anyone but Gus take care of him," Ernie Lowrie, Peter's nurse, remembered. "And he would never leave Boston because he would not leave Gus."

After his successful, living-related-donor transplant, Peter Stuyvesant happily planned an extended trip around the world. In Cypress, the second stop on his voyage, Peter became very ill and called Doctor Hampers. He had developed cancer and symptoms of internal bleeding had manifested. Cancer was extinguishing his young life very quickly. He ignored Hampers advice to return to Boston, and on his next stop in Hong Kong, he collapsed. With the help of Peter's lawyer, a doctor in Hong Kong and a former renal fellow who was then in Hawaii, they got Peter to Honolulu where Gus met him and accompanied him back to Boston. He died in Boston a few days later. "It really affected Gus," Ernie Lowrie remembered. "Through my own tears I watched him cry like you would for a close relative."

Gus Hampers loved the intellectual challenge of academic medicine and he was extraordinarily gifted as a teacher and clinical investigator. During his years at the Brigham, Hampers was prolific and frequently published in the leading medical journals on topics ranging from "insulin glucose relationships in uremia" to "major surgery in patients on hemodialysis." In 1967 Hampers and Schupak coauthored Long-Term Hemodialysis: The Management of the Patient with Chronic Renal Failure, which became the standard reference for chronic dialysis for a generation of clinical nephrologists worldwide. However, he lacked the detachment of an academician and the distance of a professor. Along with colleagues like Schupak, Hager, George Bailey, Hampers first renal fellow at the Brigham, and others, Hampers wanted to use his time and talents to prolong the lives and improve the health of his patients. His head was at home in the "ivory towers" of Harvard, but his heart was with the patients in the clinics. Hampers and Hager and their colleagues became impatient and disdainful of the academic view that chronic maintenance dialysis was wasteful, extending lives linked to a kidney machine that lacked "quality" and "value." This view of long term dialysis is still prevalent today among academicians, who have little contact with patients, and in some countries, like Great Britain, that view has been translated into public policy: elderly kidney patients are not offered transplantation or chronic hemodialysis in England, for example.

On the other hand, Gus Hampers and scores of practicing nephrologists saw the lives of many kidney patients take on a heightened value and quality precisely because their struggle to avoid death permitted them to appreciate life even more than healthy individuals. Doctor Lowrie cites the example of Mr. Grossman, a successful elderly man in Boston, who expressed his appreciation for the extension of his life through dialysis in telling Lowrie that "Dialysis has allowed me to see my grandsons bar mitzvah'd."

For Ruth Reisman, an energetic, elderly, but not retiring, businesswoman in Toronto, there's no question about the value of chronic dialysis and transplantation. Her husband, George Reisman, lived for 28 years after developing end-stage renal failure in 1965 at the age of 41, long enough to see his six children mature and to receive several Canadian social security pension payments. "My husband never would have lived without Gus and Ted," Mrs. Reisman said in a recent interview. After finding no help from doctors in Toronto in 1965 and being told that George's symptoms were "psychological," Ruth told her husband's brother that she had read about the extraordinary breakthroughs that had been made in Boston at the Brigham. The brother, Al Reisman, picked up the telephone, called the Brigham and told the first person he talked to that he was arriving the next day with his sick brother, George. The receptionist told him that he'd have to have a staff doctor admit his brother to the hospital, so Al Reisman asked her, "Who's the top guy there at the Brigham?" "Doctor George Thorn is the chief of medicine," came the reply. Reisman insisted on being connected to Doctor Thorn, and when Thorn answered, Al Reisman feigned familiarity with the "top guy" whom he had never met in his life. "Hi, George, this is Al Reisman in Toronto." Ever the diplomat, Doctor Thorn was embarrassed to admit he'd never heard of Al Reisman, and two days later admitted Reisman's brother, George, to the Brigham and assigned his care to Ted Hager and Gus Hampers.

Ruth accompanied her husband to Boston, rented an apartment, and spent 18 hours a day at the Brigham, so much time, in fact, that Doctor Thorn would jokingly ask her to "tell me what goes on here when I'm at home!" During his course of care, George Reisman's aged father travelled from Canada to Boston to visit his ailing son at the Brigham. Thorn told Ruth to call him as soon as the old man arrived, which she did. Doctor Thorn told Reisman's father that "anything that can be done, we will try for your son." When Thorn left, the elder Reisman turned to his son and daughter-in-law and said, "I think I just talked to God." In Ruth Reisman's eyes at least, Doctor Thorn, the Brigham, Gus Hampers and Ted Hager were the best - "they were two unique doctors," Ruth said of Hampers and Hager. After an initial kidney transplant failed, George Reisman went on chronic hemodialysis, and Ruth was one of the first spouses to be trained to provide the dialysis care at home. For six and a half years, Ruth Reisman dialyzed her husband, not just at their Toronto home, but wherever they travelled or vacationed, including on board a cruise ship. In 1972, George Reisman received a successful transplant at the Brigham and survived, continuing to work, supporting his family and enjoying life until 1993.

Of necessity, home care became the only option available for many patients in the late nineteen sixties, not because home care was good for them, but because the healthcare system failed to meet their needs. The Brigham was the only resource in New England at that time, and the hospital had only six dialysis machines for chronic hemodialysis. If these six machines, or "stations," were operated at maximum efficiency, each station could support six patients - three on Mondays, Wednesdays and Fridays and three other patients on Tuesdays, Thursdays, and Saturdays - for a total of thirty-six chronic dialysis patients. With the need to clean and maintain the equipment, recalibrate the machine with each use, and prepare individual patients for their treatments, supporting these thirty-six patients required staffing in the dialysis clinic from six in the morning until midnight.

The costs for the hospital were consequently very large, and the Brigham was charging $360 for each treatment, or approximately $4,700 per month to keep each patient alive, and this did not include the physician's fee. Very few patients had health insurance that would cover these costs for very long, and there were no comprehensive government programs, although Medicare for patients over 65 and Medicaid for the indigent had begun in 1965. Patients weren't turned away from the Brigham for lack of financing, but each charity case increased the burden and financial loss on the institution and made it unlikely that the hospital would add more dialysis stations, since resources were limited and dialysis was beginning to consume a disproportionate share of scarce capital.

In addition to the administrative and financial disincentives, the medical leadership of the hospital did not push for expansion. The culture and design of teaching hospitals like the Brigham are geared to meet the needs of its faculty, and these academic and scientific needs didn't include chronic care for patients with "routine" diagnoses and therapies. Science and clinical investigation worthy of publication demanded the exceptional, non-routine, challenging cases. Medical knowledge advances largely through the discovery, analysis and treatment of the "exceptions," which then result in a more complex exposition of the general rule. Thus, from the viewpoint of the professor of medicine, investing in facilities to increase the hospital's capacity to treat more chronic hemodialysis patients, all of whom presented the same conditions and required similar therapies, didn't add value to the institution.

It's noteworthy that in the years following the efficiencies introduced by National Medical Care and the universal funding for kidney dialysis provided by the federal Medicare system starting in mid-1973, commentators, mostly from the ranks of academic medicine, criticized NMC and its imitators for "skimming" the routine, easy and therefore, less costly, cases and leaving the non-routine, more challenging cases for the hospitals to treat. While the charge was largely unsubstantiated in the aggregate, to the extent that the case loads were different, the hospitals, not National Medical Care or the other clinic operators, were responsible.

Since expanding dialysis capacity made no sense to the administrative officers and was redundant for the medical officers, attending doctors like the founders of National Medical Care, who were seeing more and more patients, had to find alternatives outside the hospital in order to keep their patients alive. Thus, home care became the necessary, but by no means, preferred, option. Doctor Schupak, who originated home care as an option, and his Brigham colleagues who followed and expanded his model, knew that successful administration of hemodialysis in the home required the confluence of several factors, some medical, but most, social and economic.

Home care required the intense involvement of a partner, usually the patient's husband or wife, but sometimes a parent, sibling or child. Complex psychological forces are unleashed when a loved one becomes utterly dependent on the caregiver. The entire rhythm of family life is adapted to accommodate the four to five hour dialysis sessions, three times a week, the need to receive and store crates of medical supplies, the visits of doctors, nurse trainers and equipment technicians into the home. The home itself must be physically changed to reserve space for the machine and supplies. Sometimes plumbing and electrical alterations are required. The family members, even those who are not caregivers, become witnesses to the sight, smells and sounds of hemodialysis - the blood spills, large fistula needles, the hums and beeps of the machine, the moans of the patient suffering painful cramps, the odors of strong disinfectants. In effect, the home becomes a medical center, effecting behavior changes in all the family members. The wife of one patient recalled that their children never invited friends over to the home in order to avoid their playmates' questions, and as they grew older, they spent more and more time away from their own home. One patient complained, "I always felt guilty that my wife had to give up her own career in order to be there for me."

Obviously, home care demanded a great deal of courage on the part of the patient and his or her partner, not to mention an unusually high level of trust between them. Even in the most stable families, dialysis came to dominate the domicile. In addition, home dialysis required physical conditions that were often lacking, particularly for poor patients, both in urban housing projects and in inaccessible rural settings. The therapy was useful for stable, middle-class, well-educated, highly-motivated, married patients - the kind that Schupak and Hampers originally selected for the program. Successful home dialysis for patients who lacked these socioeconomic advantages required enormous motivation and sacrifice. As demand increased and supply failed to expand, Schupak, Hampers, Hager and other nephrologists around the country were sending more and more patients home, even though they knew the conditions were not conducive for successful care. Faced with a choice of home hemodialysis or death, families accepted home care, but in an increasing number of cases, knowing this modality of care would be dangerous for the patient and disruptive for his family.

Even where home care was appropriate, as in the case of Peter Stuyvesant who could afford to hire a well trained registered nurse, or in the case of George Reisman, whose wife, Ruth, dedicated herself to her husband's care, dialysis was (and remains) difficult. Samuel Chyatte was a diabetic, kidney patient and himself a doctor, who chose home dialysis in order to maintain a normal professional schedule. Just before he died in 1978 he wrote a book, On Borrowed Time: Living With Hemodialysis, in which he describes the experience:

I leave work early... the earlier I begin, the sooner it's over... I think about my intestinal tract... Once I was caught on the machine with diarrhea that I had to hold for four hours. I've never forgotten... [A]s soon as I enter the house, I go to the refrigerator...[O]n nights when I dialyze... I revisit gastronomic delights such as corned beef, salami, ice cream, tuna fish and the like...One reason I do this is that without salt I cramp on dialysis so badly that I have to reduce the transmembrane pressure and then I don't take off enough fluid... The machine hums... I'm on the lounge... It's smooth naugahyde finish is cool now, but in a couple hours it will make my shirt stick to my sweaty back...It has the feel of an operating room... Helen cleans the fistula site on my left arm with betadine... The alcohol feels cold and wet as Helen washes off the yellow betadine... I feel the tourniquet tighten... Most of the time the huge bore needle slides in and there is no pain. But sometimes the pain is overwhelming, not just as the needle pierces the skin... but as it pierces the vessel there is a deep aching that lasts for 10 or 15 minutes. It can happens, though it's rare, that the needle goes through the vessel and out the other side. Then, as blood pours into the surrounding tissue, the pain builds... Now the deep crimson rises in the arterial bloodline, and soon stains the dialyzer. The redness slowly fills the kidney and then enters the venous line... Now a chill comes over me as the blood returns to my body a few degrees colder. Helen covers me with a blanket... Every once in a while, the machine blinks warning lights and screeches alarms. Blood leak, arterial pressure, conductivity gauge... If the arterial needle is up against the wall of the fistula vessel, I can feel it sucking against the fistula, stinging and burning. Helen adjusts it, and I close my eyes... Two hours to go. I feel light-headed, a little woozy... a headache begins to pound... I can feel my skin shrink as the fluid is sucked away... My back itches... I've begun to perspire... a cramp begins in my left leg...I feel a little nauseated... Helen stretches my foot and the cramp eases. She lowers the transmembrane pressure, and the cramps ease off... I feel faint. My head hurts, my gut begins to churn... Cramps squeeze my legs and arms. Helen can't grab all of them, so she calls for help. Sometimes it takes one son, sometimes two to stretch my limbs... Helen tilts the lounge so that my legs are above the level of my head... Now it's time to come off...Helen ties to remove the fistula needle... the needle is out and I'm pressing on the cotton pad to stop the bleeding... the cramp eases... Now the last of the blood in the machine returns to my body... My dizziness lessens, my headache eases. I hold both the arterial and venous puncture sites, while Helen cleans the machine... I want to sleep more than anything else... My head swims, and I lose my balance as I approach my bed. The headache is back, but it's dulled by drowsiness.

Even under the best circumstances, home care was risky and burdensome. Every month more and more patients, who were unsuitable for home care, were being referred to major hospitals like the Brigham as primary care doctors became more aware of uremia and tried to refer their patients to these centers of advanced care. Unnecessarily, thousands of these patients were dying. With in hospital chronic dialysis so limited and so expensive and with home care so difficult and dangerous, physicians all over America were desperate to find alternative ways to deliver this life saving service to their patients.

As long as the healthcare system failed to make maintenance dialysis available and affordable, the hope of hemodialysis remained a hoax for thousands of end-stage renal disease patients and their families. The patients bore all the risks. Hampers, Hager and Schupak decided to find some way for the healthcare system, the government and the larger community to accept some level of risk and responsibility for providing care for these patients. In doing so, they started a life changing journey for themselves and millions of patients with kidney disease around the world.

3

Finding Investors

In 1966 Sam Saitz, an accountant who serviced many health-care professionals and facilities, began to recruit his personal physician, Ted Hager, to become medical director of an extended care facility owned by one of Sam's clients in Melrose, a working-class suburb about seven miles north of Boston. Only a few months earlier Dr. Hager had encouraged Gus Hampers to reject an offer to join Dr. Kolff, the inventor of the artificial kidney, at the Cleveland Clinic, and to stay in Boston and the Harvard Medical School/Brigham Hospital campus. Hager shared the proposal with Hampers, and together they approached the owner of the extended care facility, the Normandy House.

Offering less expensive care than hospitals, ECF's provided a halfway stop between the acute care of a medical center and the patient's home or a residential facility. Services provided by ECF's for elderly patients were, unlike the custodial care of traditional nursing homes, covered under Medicare. Enacted in 1965, Medicare was then brand new and was already reconfiguring the way medical services would be delivered to its disabled and aged beneficiaries. In order to qualify for favorable Medicare coverage, a facility like the Normandy House had to engage a physician to serve as its medical director. Prompted by Sam Saitz, who was exceptionally impressed with Hager and Hampers, the Normandy House owner was very eager to have doctors of their calibre for his facility. That kind of affiliation with members of the Harvard faculty was very valuable in the competitive world of Boston medicine, but not so valuable that he could offer the comedical directors any sort of salary. They would simply be compensated from medical fees they could charge Normandy House patients and their healthcare insurers.

Dr. Hampers was not enthusiastic about becoming medical director of an extended care facility. For their part, Hampers and Hager, weren't underemployed or looking for more things to do. They were both working an average of seventy hours a week in operating the dialysis clinic at the Brigham, teaching at Harvard, conducting research, and taking care of an expanding private medical practice. For the first time, physicians specializing in renal care were not simply sending their patients home to die, but were responsible for the on going care of chronically ill patients whose conditions demanded a lot of the nephrologist's time. However, for all their "busyness" they were not earning medical fees or salaries commensurate with the effort. Hampers liked to say, "We were the busiest men in the poor house." The last thing they needed was to work more hours for no or little income.

This was not unusual for academically based, junior, hospital staff physicians at the time. Drawn to prestigious medical schools like Harvard and their affiliated teaching hospitals like the Brigham, the best and the brightest specialists in cutting edge disciplines like nephrology did not come expecting to earn, but to learn from the most prominent experts in their fields. They were motivated by the opportunity to contribute to the expansion of medical science through clinical and laboratory research, to be challenged by the most complicated and difficult cases that were referred to these tertiary care centers, and most importantly, to associate with other like minded, brilliant, dedicated physicians, who had graduated at the top of their medical school class. The downside was that it was very difficult to earn a living and support a family. These idealistic young doctors worked under the tutelage and tight control of the senior staff physicians who hired them and paid them out of their own research grants and physician fees. Only these "chiefs" could collect fees. Technically all the patients on a particular service in teaching hospitals were the chief's patients, and he (rarely, she) alone collected the fees. The fellows and junior staff doctors provided the clinical care under the chief's direction and were paid just a fraction of the fees they earned for the chief. Similarly, the service chiefs controlled the research money. Once they could no longer accept these minimal earnings in light of their obligations to their families and, sometimes, the bankers who had lent them money for medical school, these overworked and underpaid doctors departed to establish their own medical practices, simply to be replaced by the next crop of idealistic, young doctors.

Although Ted Hager, unlike Hampers, had established his own practice outside the halls of Harvard, and had an office on Beacon Street near the Brigham Hospital, he too was struggling to support a family in those years. Because of his fondness and respect for Hampers, Hager began to share this practice with Hampers, so cutting him in on the opportunity at the Normandy House was not unusual. Moreover, Hager, who had a penchant for "thinking outside the box," and creating new opportunities, saw the potential at the Normandy House to solve the problem of unmet dialysis demand from an ever increasing population of end-stage renal disease patients.

By 1966 the shortage of dialysis machines had become severe. The Brigham operated its stations at full capacity. Despite ever-lengthening waiting times for kidney transplants, doctors from throughout New England and beyond kept referring their patients to the Peter Bent Brigham Hospital. There wasn't a doctor in the country that wasn't aware of the Brigham's historic and continuing contributions to kidney transplantation and dialysis. Once at the Brigham, these desperately ill patients became the responsibility of Hampers and his colleagues, and increasingly all the doctors could offer the patients was self-care at home. More and more patients were simply unable or unwilling to undergo dialysis in their homes three times a week. Home care required high standards of hygiene, discipline and courage, not just from the patient, but from his or her spouse or other family member as well. Many patients simply could not handle the stress and the details - everything from creating a space in their homes to house the machine and boxes of supplies, to reacting calmly and competently to blood leaks caused by the rupture of coil dialyzers - not a rare occurrence in the sixties. Ted Hager, Gus Hampers and the other Brigham renal fellows like George Bailey, Mike Lazarus and Ed Lowrie, were at their wit's end, trying to find a way to provide maintenance dialysis for their patients.

They went to the Massachusetts Department of Public Health,

where officials advised them to set up a "death committee," like the one created by Dr. Belding Scribner in Seattle to ration care and decide who would live and who would die. Expanding capacity was not an option that the DPH could facilitate. Asking Harvard and the Brigham to expand dialysis at the hospital was ineffectual. The research and pedagogic missions of Harvard/Brigham were being met with their existing stations, and investing scarce capital resources to expand the chronic dialysis capacity wouldn't add any significant value. It was not the Brigham's mission to become a large outpatient chronic care facility serving all of New England. Other Boston area hospitals were also unmoved to invest in dialysis. Suddenly, with the Normandy House opportunity, Hampers, Hager and their colleagues had a solution. As Ted Hager remarked, "After five years of being turned down by government, academia and the hospitals, we got what we wanted from the private sector in just three weeks." It was a revelation for Hager and Hampers that a private investor, looking for a return on invested capital, would solve their problem virtually overnight by increasing supply to meet the demand, while government advised rationing care, and the medical establishment walked away.

The owner of the Normandy House was a businessman and naturally wanted to know how much it would cost to set up the stations at his extended care facility, how these would be licensed, how much he could charge for the treatments, whether the patients' insurers would cover the procedure, and who would be liable if something went wrong. Hager and Hampers had no answers, but with the help of their friends and colleagues, they found out enough to secure the owner's permission, and the project was off the ground. Today, each of these concerns would at best require three months of research by teams of lawyers and bureaucrats, and at worse, create impenetrable barriers. In the mid-sixties, the chance to apply life saving, high tech medicine to save lives trumped legal, liability and reimbursement issues.

With the help of Sam Saitz, who was not just a skillful accountant, but was also a tough, tight fisted businessman, who never spent a dollar that he didn't have to, the doctors presented a conservative estimate of how much it would cost to equip a room at the Normandy House for the dialysis stations. Fearing that a high price tag would squelch the deal, they cut their needs to the bone. The exercise in low ball budgeting was exactly opposite from the kind of budgeting they had experienced in preparing grant requests for scientific research, where creative padding was the hallmark of the gifted grantsman - padding that would then be available to subsidize unrelated overhead, research assistants, travel, perks and other projects on the periphery of the research. Funders of research - usually the government - were looking for innovative ideas, not bargains, especially since they weren't spending their own money. If the research was meaningful, neither the grant seeker nor the grant maker had any incentive to cut costs. However, there would be no room for markups, perks or margins of error in requesting the Normandy House investors to risk their own money on the dialysis service.

Hager and Hampers also received welcomed and uncompromising support from their seniors at the Brigham, and some unexpected, and sobering, advice from the head of the Massachusetts Department of Public Health. Dr. Alfred Frechette was then the head of the Department of Public Health and the Public Health Commission, which were responsible for enforcing licensure and other regulations and statutes that governed the provision of medical care in the Commonwealth of Massachusetts. As a practicing physician, unaccustomed and unimpressed with the ways of bureaucrats, Dr. Frechette analyzed licensure issues from the point of view of the patient and his physician. Dr. Hampers met with Commissioner Frechette and Dr. Harry Phillips, a South African physician who would later operate a dialysis facility for the state run Lemuel Shattuck Hospital, and explained the problem of unmet dialysis demand, the dilemma that he and other kidney specialists were facing, and the proposed solution of putting some stations at the Normandy House. As a doctor, Frechette was impressed with the plan proposed by Hampers and Hager to expand resources by tapping into the private sector, having been turned down by the government and non-profit institutions. As a government official, Frechette had to advise Hampers that there was no room for error, and he told Hampers that if anything went wrong, "We'll take your medical license away."

The risk would have deterred many doctors, but Hampers had already faced and accepted a similar risk with home dialysis. He was responsible for any mishaps that might occur during home care, and viewed in that light, the risk at the Normandy House would be reduced, since Hampers, Hager and their colleagues would be in a better position to control and monitor the procedures. The Commonwealth had no laws or regulations governing the provision of outpatient hemodialysis at the time, and Dr. Frechette opined that the six station unit at the Normandy House would have to be regulated as if it were a satellite and an extension of the Peter Bent Brigham Hospital. Billing for dialysis services would have to be run through the Brigham and the hospital's administration would be responsible for ensuring quality care.

Next, they had to secure permission from the Brigham. Hampers' chief, Dr. Merrill, was enthusiastic about the idea, especially since it would relieve pressure on him to pay Hampers more out of Merrill's fees. In addition, it meant that Merrill and the Brigham would be able to hold onto more chronic patients until compatible kidneys were harvested for the Brigham's transplant program, and with more patients, "the potentate of kidneys" could hire more renal fellows and extend his reach and his clout at Harvard. However, Merrill couldn't act without the permission of his superior, Dr. Thorn. For his part, Thorn saw no alternative. He had no resources with which to expand the Brigham's dialysis service, and he was confident of Hampers' and Hager's medical competence. Just as he had years earlier embraced the risks attendant to performing the world's first kidney transplant at the Brigham, Thorn supported Merrill and Hampers with the hospital administration and board of trustees, and for the same reason: because it was best for the patients. What was best for the hospital was secondary for Thorn. Although a bit more cautious, the administrative side of the Brigham also supported the Hager-Hampers plan to run a "satellite" dialysis program at the Normandy House. The hospital administrator at the time, Bill Hassan, didn't ignore the risks involved, and he cautioned Hampers that any malpractice liability would be the doctors' problem, not the Brigham's. Nonetheless, Hassan gave the necessary approval.

With the necessary state and hospital approvals in hand, and with an investor ready to finance the renovations, fixtures and equipment, Hager and Hampers had to decide how much to charge for the dialysis service. They turned to Sam Saitz, telling him that all they knew was that the Brigham charged $360 for each dialysis treatment. Saitz kept asking them what was missing. Sam was sure that the doctors had overlooked some important costs. What else did they need - personnel, supplies, equipment? Finally, assured that everything was included, Saitz and the doctors agreed on charging a fee of $160 per treatment, less than half the fee charged by the Brigham. By charging so much less than they could have, Hampers and Hager were hoping that patients with less generous insurance plans would be covered at the Normandy House and that for patients who had insurance with annual or lifetime caps, the lower fee would extend coverage over a longer period of time, hopefully until these patients could benefit from transplants and get off dialysis. In setting the charge at the lowest level that was still adequate to compensate the Normandy House owner for his investment and pay their expenses, Hampers and Hager adopted a policy of providing high quality care at a low price, a policy that would facilitate enormous demand for similar clinics and the future growth of National Medical Care. It also set a mark that other outpatient dialysis providers would have to meet, to the benefit several years later of the Medicare renal program. Without the precedent of the $160 Normandy House and subsequent NMC charge, the Medicare kidney disease program might never have been enacted, and once implemented in 1973, would have cost the taxpayers far more.

Gaining access for the largest number of patients was the mission, not securing a handsome return for the Normandy House or additional income for the doctors, and to achieve that mission, Hager and Hampers established the lowest price possible.

The notion of a federal government program that would pay for dialysis for virtually all Americans was far fetched when Hampers and Hager began dialyzing their first patients at the Normandy House in 1966. They and their colleagues - George Bailey, Ed Lowrie, Mike Lazarus, Frank McDonald and others - worked long hours, but always with a sense of enthusiasm and excitement that was infectious. They had broken out of a box. Over the course of a few weeks they had been able to create treatment capacity for 24 additional patients. Many patients would still have to dialyze at home with the help of a family member, but now there were options for patients for whom home care was not possible. Not everyone saw these expanded options as an advance. Critics emerged to challenge the very idea that keeping end-stage renal disease patients alive was wasteful, especially if those patients were unlikely transplant candidates or were old or were suffering from other serious diseases and conditions. It didn't take long for cynics to imply that chronic maintenance dialysis, especially when practiced by for-profit centers, was a scheme to make money from the near dead. These critics didn't bother to meet any kidney patients.

Rick Faber lived through those years at the Brigham, and the Normandy House before undergoing dialysis at home. For the past thirty years Rick Faber has lived on dialysis, and during that time he has raised a family with his wife, Sue, pursued a successful career as a professor of mathematics at Boston College, and witnessed and participated in the joys and sorrows, the thrills and boredom of a full, rich life, just like everyone else in his suburban Boston neighborhood. In 1962 Faber witnessed his mother's premature death from uremia as a result of kidney failure brought on by Alford's disease, and in 1965, after receiving his Ph. D. in mathematics from Brandeis University, Rick and Sue Faber set out for San Diego, where Rick had secured a teaching position at the University of California. Their expectations of a happy life on the west coast, however, were tempered by the knowledge that Rick, too, at the age of ten had been diagnosed with Alford's disease.

In 1967 Faber developed symptoms of irreversible kidney failure, and in 1968, less than three years after leaving Boston, Rick and Sue Faber returned. Rick's kidneys no longer functioned and without dialysis or a kidney transplant, he would be dead within a few months. The Fabers returned to Boston primarily because of the kidney program at the Brigham. George Bailey, Dr. Hampers' first renal fellow, a brilliant, gregarious Louisianan, who loved and was loved in return by his patients, became Rick's doctor. Faber underwent dialysis at the Brigham for the first time on June 12,

1968. Shortly thereafter he became a patient at the Normandy House where Dr. Bailey continued to take care of him. Still later, Rick and Sue took on the responsibility of home care. Today, after an unsuccessful attempt at a transplant, Faber continues to receive dialysis treatments in an NMC center near his home in Newton, Massachusetts.

Within a few months of opening the small unit at the Normandy House, the patient demand for maintenance dialysis exceeded the unit's capacity. Moreover, the suburban location of the Normandy House made it inaccessible to many inner city patients who needed incenter dialysis most. The fledgling, out-of-hospital dialysis center at the Normandy House had been successful in several, significant ways. First and foremost, it provided an option for patients who were unable to dialyze at home while they were waiting for a transplant operation. Second, it relieved pressure on the Brigham and other Boston area hospitals to invest in expanding dialysis capacity. Third, it provided income and training for kidney specialists and renal fellows outside the hospital setting. Fourth, it was less expensive for the patients who could pay, the third-party insurers for patients with health coverage, and for the government programs - such as Medicare, Medicaid, and various rehabilitation projects - that paid for the healthcare delivered to their patient-beneficiaries. Moreover, the quality of care was excellent. By early 1968 it was clear that the model was a success and needed to be extended.

Replication demanded more capital and neither the Normandy House owners or the doctors had the resources to expand. The success of the Normandy House operation came to the attention of Ed DeLorey and Dave McNeish, officers of Breck, McNeish & Nagle, Inc., a small Boston investment firm, that specialized in high risk, venture capital deals, i.e., finding opportunities for their wealthy clients to invest in risky, startup companies with the expectation that some of these would eventually expand, go public, or be acquired, thus yielding handsome rewards for the initial investors. McNeish was impressed with a presentation he had attended in late 1967 about the investment opportunities in the ECF field that was starting to attract the attention of major chain hotel operators like Holiday Inns and Marriott. McNeish wanted to put together a group of his investors to start a set of extended care facilities at about the time he met Hampers and Hager through Ed DeLorey. Although dialysis was not part of McNeish's original concept, it fit nicely with the package and distinguished it from the standard ECF idea. Moreover, the dialysis unit at the Normandy House was making money. As McNeish later recalled, "Dialysis took up about five percent of the space and was bringing in 40% of the profits. It didn't take a genius to want to include dialysis in the mix."

McNeish and his partners decided to see whether they could raise a million dollars in seed money and invest it in an ECF that was being constructed in Brighton by a group of Boston businessmen headed by Frank Ventre, whom he had met through a mutual acquaintance, John Davies. The concept that McNeish sold to potential investors and the Ventre group was to enlist Hampers and Hager in the project by making them medical directors and installing a dialysis unit in the new ECF, which would become a prototype for similar centers throughout the country. Raising the million dollars was easier than McNeish expected. Combining the Harvard doctors and the businessmen, whose experience was mainly in the construction and shipping business, was a different story. There were problems from the beginning, and at a show down directors meeting attended by McNeish and DeLorey, along with their lawyer, Paul Brountas of Hale and Dorr, and Drs. Hampers and Hager and Frank Ventre and his colleagues in an office on a pier thrust into Boston harbor, the joint venture collapsed amid threats, recriminations and, in Ted Hager's words "lots of Sicilian shouting." Brountas, who later became NMC's corporate secretary and principal outside counsel, recalled that no one trusted anyone else, and he was at first bemused and later concerned that their hosts were tape recording the entire meeting. "It was bizarre, a real zoo!" Brountas reflected. "I kept looking for a way to get my guys out of there."

It was a jolt for Hampers and Hager. Nothing in their experience as physicians and academicians had prepared them for the rough and tumble negotiating that was part of determining who would invest, who would do the work, who controlled the operations, and how much each side would own in the resulting venture. McNeish decided to end the meeting when one of the principals, pointing at the Harvard doctors, demanded, "Who needs these guys, anyway? I'll get another two doctors." He obviously saw no reason to share part of the enterprise with Hampers and Hager, who weren't putting any of their money (and neither of them even had any money to invest) on the table. For their part, Hampers and Hager weren't even remotely interested in becoming part of a large ECF empire. They saw no other way to expand outpatient dialysis capacity, except by attaching it as part of a larger, ECF enterprise, since Massachusetts wouldn't license a free standing artificial kidney center. The ECF operators saw no reason to include Harvard kidney specialists in their new company, and the doctors weren't interested in running extended care facilities. The parties wisely went their separate ways - the businessmen kept the real estate and created Communicare, McNeish got the return of his investors' million dollars (including his own commission), and with Hager and Hampers, found another way to finance National Medical Care. As Hager said later, "We had to can the whole thing and start all over."

McNeish set to work trying to raise an additional $500,000 to add to the million dollars already invested by his clients with which to start NMC. McNeish wanted this deal for a small, select group of ten to a dozen well healed investors with whom he had done several past deals and with whom he had an on going relationship - people like Nate Corning, a Boston investor, who simply told McNeish after listening to the doctors for fifteen minutes, "I'll take 10%." State and federal securities laws also required a "private placement" group to be small, select and sophisticated. The process was all a mystery to Hager and Hampers. "They had to tell me what an investment banker was," Hampers later joked.

The doctors were represented by Henry Malkasian, a private practice attorney who represented several individual physicians, and who had met Hampers after Henry hired Joyce Hampers to work for him, right after the Hampers' had arrived in Boston in 1964. During those three and one-half years Malkasian had become immensely impressed with, and fond of, Gus and Joyce Hampers. Like Gus Hampers, Henry Malkasian was the son of immigrants, and had gone to college and law school by working hard and borrowing money. Joyce was raising a family, working in Henry's office and going to Boston College Law School, while Dr. Hampers was head of the dialysis service at the Brigham, teaching at Harvard, and taking care of patients at the Normandy House. All Henry Malkasian needed to know he knew from observing how hard they were working, and if there was a chance, he wanted to invest. "I told McNeish I wanted to invest in the company," Malkasian recalled. "But Dave told me it was too rich for my blood. They wanted guys who would buy minimum units of $25,000," Henry smiled. "I told him, 'I'll take two!'" Not only did Malkasian invest $50,000 as one of the original handful of NMC investors, but he never sold a share of NMC stock over the course of the following 16 years.

Henry Malkasian wasn't the only original stockholder that made out well with an investment in National Medical Care in 1968. McNeish negotiated a sweet deal for the investors and an even sweeter deal for himself. In exchange for their collective investment of $1.5 million, the investors received 51% of NMC, which was incorporated in Massachusetts on June 25, 1968. Of the remaining 49%, Hampers and Hager were awarded 34%, about 3% was set aside and granted to other early employees, and McNeish and his partners took away 12% of the company for their efforts in putting the transaction together. Paul Brountas did so well for his investment banking client, Breck, McNeish & Nagle, Inc., that Hampers and Hager retained him immediately to represent the fledgling company. "I wanted to hire Brountas to do for us what he did to us," Hampers explained. Never again would Hampers be reticent to challenge and bargain aggressively with investment bankers and large investors, and he later earned a reputation as a very tough negotiator when it came to fixing discounts, commissions and fees with underwriters.

One potential investor who decided not to buy shares in NMC was Joe Murray, the eminent Harvard surgeon who had been on the Brigham Hospital team that performed the world's first kidney transplant. "Dave McNeish and I were neighbors and friends," Dr. Murray recalled many years later, "and he offered me the opportunity to invest in this company that Ted and Gus were starting. I supported what they were doing, but I didn't want to put myself in that position," Murray explained. "But if I had, it would have made it a lot easier to pay my kids' tuitions," he laughed. Within a few months, however, Dr. Murray would help Hampers and Hager and NMC in a more substantial way than simply by investing money in the company. "I remember when certain people raised a stink about Gus and Ted and their dialysis business," Murray went on. "Dean Ebert [Dr. Robert Ebert, then Dean of the Harvard Medical School] asked me what I thought about it, and I told him to leave these guys alone. 'They're great doctors, excellent clinicians,' I told him, and I guess I felt I could say that to the Dean because I wasn't a stockholder, and I had no conflict of interest," Murray concluded.

The business plan for the company was to develop a combined ECF/dialysis center on Babcock Street, just off Commonwealth Avenue in Brookline, and to acquire options on real estate and recruit physician-managers to replicate the ECF/dialysis model in New Orleans, Miami and a couple other sites around the country. They had acquired the Babcock site from Sam Saitz and his partner who was in the catering business. Hager, who became the company's first president, joked that "We figured if we didn't make it at least we'd have a good deli." Neither Hager nor Hampers, NMC's first vice president, drew a salary. They hired three employees - Jane Eastin (who would later marry Dr. Hager), Vera Amos and David Randell - and set up an office across from Ted Hager's private practice office on Beacon Street, not far from the Brigham/Harvard campus. For most of the day Hampers and Hager would be busy seeing patients at the Brigham, and teaching and directing research at the medical school. "Around two or three in the afternoon, Hampers and Hager would arrive at the NMC office," Dave Lubrano, the company's first treasurer, recalled. "Hager would ask what was happening and we'd shrug and say 'not much,' at which he'd always respond, 'Well, damn it, let's make something happen,' and he did."

In January, 1969 things did start happening on Babcock Street as construction on the new facility began. Attorney Malkasian was drafting and pushing new Massachusetts regulations to cover the operation of out-of-hospital dialysis centers, which would allow the clinic to bill for its services, and these were promulgated by the Department of Public Health in 1969 and became effective the following year. Dr. Hager was pursuing leads for starting similar centers in other locations based on the ECF model. In the evenings Hampers and Hager looked in on patients at the Normandy House and tried to find dialysis spaces for the ever growing population of end-stage renal disease patients. In addition, Hampers, Hager and their colleagues spent an inordinate amount of time trying to find funding to pay for their patients' care.

George Bailey was particularly adept at finding money to insure and subsidize the care of these patients. The good news for a patient diagnosed with kidney failure in 1969 was that he wouldn't have to die, thanks to dialysis. The bad news was that dialysis would cost him $2400 every month, or twice that amount at a hospital like the Brigham. Bailey was shameless in pursuit of funding for his patients and through perseverance, guile and charm was largely successful. Dr. Bailey hit on a particularly rewarding funding mechanism in trying to find some financial support for one of his patients who lived in Rhode Island. Bailey argued before that state's rehabilitation commission that dialysis qualified as a prosthetic organ - the artificial kidney serving the same function as an artificial limb - and as such was covered by the rehabilitation program that tried to help patients regain or maintain their viability in the work force. It was an argument that succeeded in unlocking funds for many dialysis patients, not just in Rhode Island, but in other states as well, and eventually formed the rationale underlying the 1972 Medicare amendment that would create the federal End-Stage Renal Disease (ESRD) Program. According to Dr. Hager, "there was always money some-place; the trick was just to find it. No patient at the Brigham or the Normandy House was ever sent home to die because of money."

Things weren't happening quickly enough, however. The $1.5 million stake was running out fast. Dave Lubrano, who had audited NMC's books as an accountant at Arthur Andersen & Co., became the company's treasurer in mid-1969. "I was bored being a CPA and decided to take a leap of faith," Lubrano remembered. He immediately prepared a cash flow projection and could see that the initial investment would be gone by the end of that year. The venture capitalists were not a viable source for more funds, and no bank was going to lend NMC any money on the strength of its untested business plan without any track record of producing revenues. So Lubrano and Dave McNeish had yet another chore for Hampers and Hager - that of raising a substantial chunk of money before the start of 1970.

After one particularly gruelling and unsuccessful trip to solicit financial partners, McNeish and Hampers returned to Boston's Logan Airport around ten o'clock at night. "I'll never forget how tired I was," McNeish said, "but as soon as we stepped off the jetway, Gus looked at his watch, picked up the pace and told me he had to hurry because he had to drive out to Melrose and see patients at the Normandy House. I'll never understand where he got his energy," McNeish recalled.

Ted Hager had invited his friend, David Banker at The Pressprich Corporation, a New York investment banking firm, to compose a private placement memorandum that sought roughly $12 million from a limited number of institutional investors. NMC was offering to issue 25% of its common stock for three million dollars and senior, secured notes for an additional $ 9 million with an interest rate of 8 1/2%. For four or five months McNeish had been courting Travelers Insurance and was reasonably sure they would agree to a deal along those lines. In October 1969 ("Black Halloween" in Ted Hager's memory) the principals took their "dog and pony" show to Travelers in Hartford, made a presentation to the insurance company's chairman, and were turned down flat. "I went down to Hartford expecting to pick up a check," McNeish reflected, "and when he turned us down, I honestly didn't know what to do."

Things were looking desperate that November of 1969, when Dave Lubrano called Hal Bigler at Connecticut General Life Insurance Company. "Hal was a fraternity brother of mine from Brown," Lubrano recalled. "I was just making a cold call and was not at all prepared for the response I got." Bigler told Lubrano to meet with his assistant, Jim Tate, and Lubrano made the pitch to Tate, who brought in other investment officers from additional insurance companies headquartered in Hartford. A presentation from Hager and Hampers followed and went very well. Hampers and Hager took on the role of salesmen and appeared formidable, forthright, honest and precise. Exuding confidence without appearing cocky, Hager charmed the insurance executives, while Hampers overwhelmed them with intellect. Hager formed the emotional link with the audience, while Hampers commanded the details. "They fell in love with the company," Dave Lubrano beamed. As a result, Connecticut General, Connecticut Mutual Life Insurance Company, Phoenix Mutual Life Insurance Company, and Aetna Casualty and Surety Company invested $12.2 million in NMC in 1969. The terms, however, were harsher than anticipated by Pressprich. To secure $8.9 million in debt financing NMC agreed to pay an interest rate of 9 1/2% and in exchange for $3.3 million, issued the insurance companies one-third of NMC's common stock. As a necessary result, Hampers' and Hager's ownership was diluted from a third to less than 25%. Countervailing the dilution, which also affected the original investors, was the continued viability of NMC with a strong balance sheet and great prospects. The twelve million dollars enabled NMC to fulfill its business plans through 1971, including the opening and operation of ten dialysis centers.

4

The "BMA" Model

As Hampers and Hager experimented with the ECF model at the Normandy House and started NMC with private capital, Gene Schupak was busy in New York creating a different model for delivering outpatient dialysis. When he left Boston and the Brigham in 1964, Dr. Schupak fully expected to pursue a career in academic medicine. He accepted a faculty appointment at the Downstate Medical School and Brooklyn/Cumberland Hospitals, where he established its chronic dialysis program, drawing on his experience with Dr. Merrill at the Brigham and Dr. Kolff at the Cleveland Clinic. He also extended his pioneering efforts in treating patients at home, which he initiated in Boston, to a whole new, underserviced population in New York City. It was the first of its kind in New York, and drew a lot of attention, including a television newscast from a teenage patient's home, where the patient's mother, whom Dr. Schupak had trained, administered a dialysis treatment to her fourteen-year old daughter. Less than three years later, in 1967, Mt. Sinai Medical Center recruited Gene Schupak to leave Downstate and head its renal service. By then, the home care option, which originated with Schupak and Merrill in Boston, had attracted the interest and financial support of the federal government, and in 1967 the Public Health Service of the U.S. Department of Health, Education and Welfare began a program to study dialysis at home by creating ten programs at different centers across the United States. One was at the Brigham, by then run by Dr. Hampers, and another was Dr. Schupak's program at Mt. Sinai and its affiliated hospital, Elmhurst in Queens.

Elmhurst, a municipal hospital, not unlike Cook County in Chicago where Schupak and Hampers first met in 1961, cared for a large population of indigent patients from the greater metropolitan area. Unlike the patients from Boston's South Shore for whom Dr. Schupak first created a home dialysis alternative or Peter Stuyvesant, who had the means to employ skilled nurses like Ernie Lowrie, these Elmhurst patients had no private insurance, often had no family member who could be responsible for their care, and generally lived in public housing projects or substandard, inexpensive tenements, lacking the space, plumbing, electrical service and basic security that were necessary elements in treating a patient at home. In addition, the volume of patients was overwhelming the home program and the meager resources of area hospitals. It was clear that another alternative was desperately needed to keep these patients alive. Like his colleagues in Boston, Dr. Schupak went to the medical centers and the government as the most likely sources for funds with which to build more dialysis capacity. Like their requests, his entreaties - to the federal government, New York State health department and the City's Health and Hospitals corporation - were fruitless.

Dr. Schupak had kept in touch with Gus Hampers and Ted Hager and knew that they had begun treating patients, who were not good candidates for home care, outside the hospital at the Normandy House. Schupak started searching for capital and private investors who might be willing to help him start a free standing, outpatient dialysis center in New York. He faced a couple additional problems that made this job even more difficult than it had been for Hampers and Hager. First, the demographics of Schupak's patient base was overwhelmingly poor and dependent on Medicaid. There was no way he could charge Medicaid enough to cover the dialysis costs and still have sufficient income to pay interest or some form of return to investors, and only a small fraction of Schupak's patients had private insurance that could pickup the slack. Second, New York State law prevented corporations from investing in a healthcare facility. The law, which stated that "no corporation whose stock could be held by another corporation" could operate a healthcare provider, meant that such operations were limited to individuals or small restricted stock companies. The effect was to severely restrict the sources of potential capital. For instance, under the New York law, a company like Aetna Casualty and Surety could not invest in Schupak's facility. A third problem was presented by the fact that Dr. Schupak worked within a municipal hospital system that was bureaucratic and much less flexible than the Brigham. New York City's Health and Hospitals corporation which operated Elmhurst Hospital was not going to take the risks that Drs. Merrill, Thorn and Hassan accepted in supporting Hampers' and Hager's project.

Nonetheless, Gene Schupak sat down and calculated than if he could raise $250,000, he'd be able to start a much needed, out patient, maintenance dialysis facility somewhere in the Borough of Queens for patients who could not dialyze at home. He proposed a deal to some wealthy private investors to whom he had been introduced by his brother. Schupak offered them one-third of the enterprise in exchange for a quarter million dollar investment. They turned him down. He tried the approach that worked for Ted and Gus and negotiated with a nursing home operator, who wanted 75% of the enterprise. In addition, Schupak went to Howard Janneck, a top official at Baxter Travenol, the largest supplier of artificial kidneys, seeking help from Baxter, but was turned down flat by Baxter's CEO, Bill Graham, who was not interested in owning treatment centers. At about the same time, Hampers called Schupak, inviting him to become part of NMC and "take a smaller slice of a bigger pie." Gus and Ted Hager flew to New York and met Gene Schupak at a restaurant at La Guardia Airport, not far from Elmhurst Hospital. It was an auspicious meeting.

Hampers agreed that NMC would invest the needed capital to start the Queens Artificial Kidney Center in exchange for a 51% interest in a new corporation established by Gene Schupak, called Bio-Medical Applications, Inc. ("BMA") with Schupak owning the remaining 49%. In order to comply with New York State law, however, BMA could not actually own the Queens center, and it would be owned by Schupak directly as a sole proprietorship and operated by Schupak as an extension of his private practice. If anything went wrong, it was Dr. Schupak's license and liability insurance on the line. Eugene Schupak, M.D. dba the Queens Artificial Kidney Center, would sublease the real estate from BMA, lease the equipment from BMA, use BMA to manage the Queens center under a negotiated contract, and arrange with BMA to furnish all the necessary supplies from paper clips to artificial kidneys.

Essentially any profits or losses would be absorbed by BMA and 51% of these would accrue to NMC. In addition, in the future, Schupak had a "put," or the right to require NMC to buy, and NMC had a "call," or the right to require Schupak to sell, his 49% stake in BMA with the price set as a function of earnings with both a floor and ceiling on the price. These details were ironed out by lawyers many weeks after the La Guardia meeting, but the essence of that meeting was that Gene would be an equal partner in NMC with Ted and Gus. "I did it for one reason and only one reason," Schupak recalled. "It was based totally on my friendship with Gus. All our deals back then were handshake deals." Two years later, in early 1971, in anticipation of NMC's initial public offering of stock, NMC bought Dr. Schupak's 49% interest in BMA for 225,000 share of NMC common stock, representing about 7 1/2% of NMC's equity, which was less than the 8.7% held by each of Hampers and Hager. Years later Schupak observed, "I had no one to advise me; Gus was talking to [attorney Paul] Brountas and I was talking to myself, so I ended up with less than an equal share. They got the best of me."

Dr. Schupak secured the funds to start his center in Queens, but what he planned was different from the Normandy House-Babcock-ECF model. The Queens Artificial Kidney Center would be a barebones, dialysis only, outpatient, "storefront" facility, accessible for patients and staff and located close to a backup hospital. It became the model for hundreds of dialysis centers across the nation, both those owned by NMC and others that tried to emulate its efficiency. By the end of 1969 Dr. Schupak was not only supervising the construction of the Queens center, but on behalf of NMC was also promoting the idea of replicating his model to other doctors around the country, many of whom he and Hampers knew from their participation in the Public Health Service's dialysis home care project. Among these were Alan Hull in Dallas, Charles Swartz in Philadelphia, and Bill Anderson in Miami. "I remember that late in 1969 Gene Schupak called me," Alan Hull later recalled. "I asked him what I could do for him, and he said he was going to do something wonderful for me. It was hard to say no to Gene," Dr. Hull, who was then running the renal dialysis and transplant program at the Southwest Medical Center in Dallas, admitted.

The Babcock Center in Brookline, Massachusetts opened on February 21, 1970, and the Queens Center began operations as a 20-station artificial kidney center in Long Island City, New York two weeks later. By the time of its opening in early 1970, the Babcock model had evolved into something slightly different from the older Normandy House model. During 1969 while Babcock was under construction, Ted Hager entered into discussions with Dr. Sheldon D. Zigelbaum, a Boston psychiatrist and former dentist, about the same age as Hager and Hampers. The result of those discussions was the Human Resource Institute, Inc., an NMC subsidiary to be operated by Dr. Zigelbaum as a mental health center, offering both inpatient and outpatient services at the Babcock Center. Thus, in 1970 during its first year of operation, Babcock was a "triple threat" - a 20-station dialysis center, a 34-bed ECF and a 30-bed psychiatric hospital, all operating under the same roof. This three tiered model would later be replicated at NMC centers in Miami, Tampa, and Norfolk, Virginia.

The third NMC outpatient dialysis center, the Metropolitan Washington Renal Dialysis Center, opened in Bethesda, Maryland, just north of the District of Columbia, on July 14, 1970. It was modeled after Dr. Schupak's Queens Center, and was directed by a team of three kidney specialists based at Georgetown University Medical Center and the Walter Reed Army Medical Center. Jim Knepshield, one of the Army doctors, had visited Boston in the late 1960's and ran into his friend, George Bailey, who was then one of Hampers' renal fellows at the Brigham and was excited about the outpatient dialysis service that the Brigham doctors were providing at the Normandy House. A few months later, in 1969, while the Babcock Center was being planned, Dr. Bailey set up a meeting at the Shoreham Hotel in Washington among Knepshield and his Army cohort, Dr. William Cirksena, and Hampers and Hager. They, and subsequently, Gene Schupak, recruited Bill Cirksena and Jim Knepshield to open a center in the Washington area. However, since they were still Army doctors, they would not be able to direct the day-to-day clinical operations of the center. Moreover, neither Knepshield or Cirksena at that time had much clinical experience in providing chronic dialysis care, and they literally had no patient base. Their solution was to try to enlist Larry Siegel to join them and take on the responsibility of directing the new artificial kidney center.

Dr. Siegel was an outstanding choice, and became a valuable resource for NMC, not just in directing the Washington clinic, but also nationally in monitoring and crafting the federal government's response to the growing need for renal dialysis. Just a couple years younger than Gus Hampers, Larry Siegel shared a similar professional journey through medical school, the U.S. Navy, and a residency in internal medicine at the University of Cincinnati, where he first came in contact with kidney dialysis and the Kolff artificial kidney in the early 1960's. At the end of his residency in 1966 Siegel was accepted as a renal fellow at all three of the leading renal centers in the country - Seattle with Dr. Scribner, Boston with Dr. Merrill, and Georgetown with Dr. George Schreiner. He chose Georgetown and played the same supporting role to Dr. Schreiner as Hampers played to John Merrill at Harvard. Dr. Siegel had distinguished himself as both an exceptional research physician, winning a three-year research grant from the National Institutes of Health for his investigations concerning erythropoietin, a chemical produced by the healthy kidney that is critical in preventing hypoxia, and as a clinician at the Georgetown University Medical Center and at D.C. General Hospital, a municipal hospital with a large indigent population. Like Dr. Schupak in New York, Larry Siegel saw many patients die for lack of the facilities to care for them, and the overwhelming majority of these underserviced patients were poor.

When Bill Cirksena and Jim Knepshield asked for his help in running the planned NMC artificial kidney center, Siegel was ready and eager. He sought and received permission from Dr. Schreiner, his chief at Georgetown, and set out immediately to stamp his own mark on the new center. Working with Cirksena and Knepshield and NMC's new construction manager, Frank LaPlante, Siegel helped create a first rate, state-of-the-art facility in Bethesda, which would not only provide thrice weekly outpatient dialysis care, but would be a one stop comprehensive care center for patients. The center offered nutrition and diet counselling, family support, social services, and psychological assistance. Siegel understood the political and social factors that would influence the success of the new, for-profit dialysis center, especially one located in the nation's capital, just a few miles from the White House and Capitol Hill. Siegel's medical skills were matched by his public relations instincts and political acumen as well. Long before the center opened, Dr. Siegel and his Metropolitan Washington partners negotiated a favorable contract with the Medicaid programs in Maryland and the District of Columbia. They did not want the center to become a resource that was restricted to the insured, middle class only; it had to be accessible for the indigent as well. That meant a favorable contract with Medicaid, which they secured, largely because they offered dialysis at one-third the cost of the acute care hospitals.

As a result, right from the July 1970 grand opening, to which Siegel invited District, Maryland, and federal officials, the Metropolitan Washington Renal Dialysis Center was a high profile, public, integrated facility that cared for welfare patients and wealthy foreign nationals and everyone inbetween. By promoting their center so visibly in the days when advertising by doctors was deemed unethical, the MWRDC doctors incurred the wrath of the local medical societies, but they weathered that storm of protest by providing unimpeachably excellent care. Having a successful and visible presence in the nation's capital, which quickly engendered a lot of grassroots political support, was very useful a few years later when Congress considered a special Medicare program to assist kidney patients and came very close to excluding for-profit providers from the program. NMC was lucky to have a two-year track record of superior service to the community from the MWRD Center and to have Dr. Siegel to present that record to the legislation's drafters when that debate was joined in 1972.

National Medical Care's fourth artificial kidney center opened in October, 1970 in Philadelphia under the direction of Dr. Charles Swartz, a distinguished professor of medicine at Hahnemann Medical Center, who had been recruited by his friend Gene Schupak to operate the new dialysis center. In December, 1970 the Tampa artificial kidney center, the company's fifth dialysis clinic, opened. It was directed by Felix LoCicero, M.D. and Lawrence Kahana, M.D. At the end of 1970, NMC's first year of operations, the new company realized revenues from kidney dialysis, extended care and mental health services of slightly more than two million dollars and turned a profit of $265,546. It's interesting to note that private, third-party insurers and the patients themselves were the source of 58% of NMC's revenues from kidney dialysis in 1970, and that Medicare accounted for just 2% of dialysis revenues that year. The other sources were Medicaid, representing 16%, and other state and federal agencies (e.g., rehabilitation programs) for 24%. The private investors and insurance companies that furnished the capital for NMC's growth in those early years and the physicians that agreed to direct the first clinics had no expectation that the federal government would create a special end-stage renal disease program.

For better or worse, there were no businessmen involved in operating National Medical Care in its infancy. The officer/doctors - Schupak, Hampers, and Hager - worked for NMC only part-time. Similarly, the clinic directors - Zigelbaum, Siegel, Swartz, Kahana, and others - derived their income from non-NMC sources, largely from physician practice fees. David Lubrano, who joined the company in 1969, wore the business hat, but his experience was exclusively as an accountant. "I never raised a dollar before National Medical Care," Lubrano, who later raised millions for NMC, Apollo Computers, and Staples, confessed. As a result of this lack of business acumen, the doctors learned "how to" manage by themselves, and since they lacked experience, they could barely advise the clinic directors, whom they recruited to run the NMC facilities. Each medical director was accountable not only for the provision of high quality medical care, but also for the bottom-line operating results of his clinic. Knowledge came by trial and error. "We lost as much money as we made in the first six months," Bill Cirksena remembered. "For one thing, the inventory flew out the back door as soon as it was delivered," Dr. Cirksena admitted.

"Gene, Ted and I were learning right along with the other guys. We didn't really have anything to teach them about business," Hampers recalled. The doctors learned quickly, however, and what developed under the umbrella of the NMC organization, became a federation of entrepreneurships. The medical directors gained confidence as the months passed and took pride in their ability to provide quality care and to make a profit, as well. This was a liberating experience for these pioneering clinic directors, most of whom felt saddled with the restrictions and regulations of bureaucratic hospital administrations and medical schools. Thanks to NMC's investment, they had their own clinics, where they had the freedom to hire their own staff of nurses and technicians, contract with suppliers, schedule treatments, and decorate their own offices. The entrepreneurial style was reinforced by the NMC system of providing financial incentives for these medical directors based on the profits they made at the clinics. Rarely did NMC pay its medical directors a salary for all the work involved in running the center. Instead, from the outset, Schupak, Hampers and Hager instituted a system of profit sharing, originally by giving the directors a minority interest in the clinic, which NMC was then obligated to purchase after five years at a price based on the clinic's income. In later years (until the federal government outlawed such profit sharing by physicians) the stock repurchase plan was replaced by a straight forward profit sharing arrangement. As a result, clinic directors controlled their own expenses and in the pre-ESRD Program years, even set their own fees. "If we paid the director a salary, I'd be fighting with him every week about how much to pay his nurse," Hampers argued, "but if we paid him with a share of the profits, I didn't have to second guess him."

Consequently, at the corporate level, NMC didn't need a cadre of planners, managers, and businessmen to control operations. Alan Hull, a kidney specialist in Dallas, was flabergasted when he asked Gene Schupak how much he should charge for a dialysis treatment at his clinic which opened in 1971. "He said I could charge whatever I thought was best!" Dr. Hull, who later became President of the National Kidney Foundation, laughed. "I told him we were going to charge about half the hospital's fee, or about $185, and he said that sounded okay with him."

The negative fall out from this system of mini-entrepreneurships was that as NMC expanded in later years, gaining in experience and expertise, controlling the clinic directors became impossible, especially the early pioneers, who wore their battle scars proudly. Scores of NMC managers and corporate officers failed because they didn't understand that these directors were not in the habit of taking orders from the "Mother House," as Les Freeman, an early NMC administrator, phrased it. Of course, what looked like initiative to Hager, Hampers and Schupak looked like anarchy to many investors and potential investors on Wall Street, where there was a clear bias against doctor-businessmen. Increasingly, as time passed, the investment community demanded a more seasoned team of managers to run NMC, flying in the face of its early culture.

National Medical Care experienced tremendous growth in 1971, opening five more artificial kidney centers in Miami, Dallas, Pittsburgh, and Torrance and Beverly Hills, California. In 1971 NMC also commenced operations of new extended care and mental health facilities in Tampa, Miami, San Francisco, and Portland, Maine. The company was consuming the $12 million in capital invested by the Hartford insurance companies at a fast clip, and the NMC board was hoping that they could float an initial public offering ("IPO") of stock sometime before the end of that year. The business plan was to sell NMC stock to the public in the spring of 1971, but market factors were not suitable, and the company deferred the IPO until the fourth quarter of 1971. In the meantime, in order to secure sufficient capital with which to continue its expansion plans, and in anticipation of an IPO later that year, NMC sought $2 million in interim financing from the Ford Foundation and other investors in May, 1971. In exchange, NMC issued 8% debentures that were convertible into common stock at a conversion price of $5.50 per share. For its part under the terms of the debenture, NMC had the right to redeem the debt, without a premium, if the company successfully completed a public offering during 1971. As a result, because the company did consummate an IPO in December, 1971 at a public offering price of $12.00 per share, the debenture holders converted the debt into common stock, and the company had use of $2 million for seven months, interest free. And for their part, the May 1971 investors converted their $2 million of capital into $4,363,620 worth of NMC common stock - a 118% gain during the same seven month period.

The management team at NMC had evolved by 1971 into a collection of highly motivated specialists, each responsible for his or her segment of the business, with little overlap or back-up support. It was a lean, horizontal structure, with a great deal of responsibility delegated to the clinic medical directors. The NMC board of directors, which was assembled after the initial private placement, consisted of four "inside" officers -Drs. Schupak, Hager and Hampers and the company treasurer, Dave Lubrano - as well as Dave McNeish, Donald A. Gannon, and Frederick G. P. Thorne, who served as the company's outside, independent directors. McNeish was a founder of NMC and had put together the original venture capital. Fred Thorne, an investment adviser in Boston, and Don Gannon, the president of Stop & Shop, Inc., a large retail grocery chain, were both part of the group of initial investors convened by McNeish in 1968.

The three principal officers of NMC - Ted Hager as its president, Gus Hampers, its executive vice president, and Gene Schupak, its vice president - were still primarily engaged in the practice of medicine, teaching and research in 1971. Dr. Zigelbaum, who ran the mental health division of NMC, was a vice president, as were Dave Lubrano, the treasurer and resident "businessman," and Frank LaPlante, an engineer and construction manager, who joined NMC in the fall of 1969 to supervise the physical expansion of the company's centers. This small group of officers and a few other key employees, like Murray Matthews, the company's controller, and Jane Eastin (Hager), comprised the tiny core of National Medical Care. Most of the operating decisions, from what supplies to buy, to personnel issues, to setting charges, and negotiating with insurers and government payers, were delegated to the clinic directors, with predictably inconsistent results. Alan Hull, whose Dallas artificial kidney center opened in July of 1971, recalled that Hampers called him in early June, as Dr. Hull and his cohorts were preparing the center for its opening. "I was helping unload our first shipment of inventory," Hull remembered. "I asked Gus if I could call him back, and he said not to bother, but if I needed anything to give him a call. That was June. We opened the center in July, and I never heard from Gus again until October!" Rather than ride herd on these novice directors, Schupak, Hampers and Hager, who were busy enough running their own new centers and continuing to practice medicine, left them alone.

The model was one of collegiality, a loose confederation of kidney doctors, each in charge of his or her own domain. The structure - or lack thereof - resembled the model of the teaching hospital, which was the only template that Schupak, Hager and Hampers had experienced. Medical school, internships and residencies train doctors to take responsibility and make decisions, often very quick decisions. Respect for the integrity of their colleagues, and the circumstances in which they have to make life-and-death decisions instills a reluctance to second guess or contradict other physicians. That same reluctance and respect extended into the business of managing the clinics. Uniform personnel policies, inventory control procedures, purchasing parameters, and quality control guidelines were missing at NMC for a long time, at least through the first generation of clinics during the 1970 to 1974 period.

5

Success Breeds Scrutiny

One reason Ted Hager and Gus Hampers didn't have a lot of time to chat with the new NMC clinic directors was that they were besieged with bad public relations. The siege began with a front page article in the July 11, 1971 Boston Sunday Globe, written by Richard A. Knox, a reporter who covered healthcare issues. The story, entitled "Brigham's kidney center run for-profit," focused on the structure of the relationship between NMC's Babcock Artificial Kidney Center and the Peter Bent Brigham Hospital and whether that relationship fulfilled or violated the state health department's regulations governing the operation of out-of-hospital dialysis centers in Massachusetts. Dr. Ann Pettigrew, then the director of the division of medical care at the Department of Public Health, and in charge of enforcing the 10-month old regulations, which were adopted precisely to cover the Babcock-Brigham situation, baldly asserted that "our view is that the center [BAKC] is strictly illegal as it is now operating."

Knox built his article around that highly provocative quotation, pointing out that the Brigham, as a tax exempt, charitable hospital, was in an untenable position under the Pettigrew interpretation of the regulations, since it could not operate a for-profit clinic, and at the same time could not comply with the regulations, unless the clinic was "totally supervised" by the hospital and was operated as an "extension of the hospital." Dr. Pettigrew's interpretation was supported by Dr. David Kinloch, her predecessor at DPH who was in charge of the division of medical care when the regulations were being prepared in 1970, shortly after the Babcock center commenced operations. In the Globe article Dr. Kinloch amplified his view by provocatively observing that "we knew that these centers, if set up with a proprietary interest in mind, would be subject to all the abuses of nursing homes in general," that under the 1970 regulations "out-of-hospital dialysis units were to be extensions of hospitals," and that this interpretation was understood and accepted at the time by Hager, Hampers and the Brigham administration.

That was clearly not the case, since Hager and Hampers had been operating a for-profit, out-of-hospital dialysis clinic under the medical auspices of the Brigham since 1966, first at the Normandy House, and later at the Babcock center. The Massachusetts regulations were adopted in September 1970 at the behest of Hampers, Hager and the Brigham precisely to conform to that five-year reality and to avoid the dilemma that Knox describes in his article. In fact, the Brigham and Babcock group had urged the DPH to assert direct control over outpatient dialysis care by separately licensing, and thereby controlling, these centers. Instead, the DPH embraced ambiguity by ignoring reality and accepting a fantasy. What these public health bureaucrats wanted was for hospitals like the Brigham to provide outpatient dialysis, even though it was clear for at least five years that the hospitals did not have the capital or the desire to create the necessary dialysis capacity. Knowing that the Babcock center and its predecessor at the Normandy House, were owned by private investors, and not by charitable hospitals, DPH adopted vague regulations, which its staff later interpreted as proscribing the very circumstance that the rules were meant to cover. Under the Kinloch-Pettigrew interpretation, the Babcock center should have been closed in September 1970 and its 100 patients sent home to die, since there was no other dialysis facility available to care for them. Fortunately, Pettigrew's boss, Dr. Alfred Frechette, who had given Hampers the green light to proceed at the Normandy House, and had been health commissioner for over a dozen years since his appointment in 1959 by then governor Foster Furcolo, had a good memory and a better sense of reality.

Commissioner Frechette's staff at the Department of Public Health were pressing him and his colleagues on the Public Health Council to adopt their interpretation, shutting the Babcock center down and forcing the Brigham to care for the patients. Frechette saw this as unnecessary since no one had complained about the quality of patient care (and in fact, Knox's article notes that "the quality of care at the Babcock center is reputed to be impeccable") and unwise since, the Babcock charged much less for dialysis care than the Boston area hospitals (again, Knox acknowledged that the taxpayers would end up paying twice as much for the care of elderly and indigent patients under Medicare and Medicaid if the patients went to the hospital rather than to the Babcock center). Faced with resistance from their superior, DPH staff went to the press, and the Knox article was timed just days before the Public Health Council, whose members were appointed by the governor (at that time, Republican Frank Sargeant), were to meet. Dr. Hager challenged Pettigrew's regulatory interpretation, stating that the rules were intended to require the hospital to vouch for the quality of medical service at the clinic, not to operate it in all respects. "The Babcock center has followed these serpentine regulations right down the line," Hager asserted. For his part, Dr. Hampers, whose photo in the Globe piece misidentified him as "Dr. Hassan" (the Brigham's executive director), couldn't resist the opportunity to denigrate the bureaucrats - an arrogant attitude that won Hampers few friends in the public sector: "The state has no expertise in this area. I don't know if the state department of public health would know an artificial kidney machine from a turnip."

The state officials expressed a concern that, if they did not require hospitals to be responsible for all aspects of operating dialysis clinics and, instead, separately licensed artificial kidney centers, profiteers would make a lot of money from sick patients, and the DPH could not insure high quality care, leading to the "abuses" that Dr. Kinloch cited in his statement. The profiteering aversion became a dominant theme in public policy debates over kidney dialysis. The theory was that it was better for the public to pay, and to require patients and their third-party insurers to pay, a charitable hospital, which, because of its immense overhead, research and teaching expenses, could not provide outpatient dialysis very efficiently, more in charges than it was to pay an efficient, investor owned clinic less, if part of the clinic's charge was returned to the investors as profit. The basis for this aversion to profit making was economic ignorance, fostered by a system in which capital was "free," since it was either donated by wealthy benefactors (and subsidized by the tax system which allowed deductions for charity) or doled out by the government. This attitude that disavowed a role for capitalism in providing healthcare was especially prevalent in northeastern states like Massachusetts, which had never experienced investor owned hospitals at that time.

The second bias - that quality could be assured only if the parent-hospital put its license on the line - arose from an ironic lack of self-confidence by the public health sector in its own ability to recognize and eliminate poor quality. Rather than assert her own ability to protect patients from substandard care, Dr. Pettigrew's position was that the Brigham medical and administrative staffs had to accept this responsibility. On the one hand, public health officials were futilely trying to control the forces of a market economy, while on the other hand, refusing to keep abreast of medical advances by accepting responsibility for directly regulating the quality of chronic, maintenance dialysis care. The inability of state and federal government agencies to allow market forces to produce desirable and efficient means of delivering healthcare, and focusing government's efforts, instead, in the area of licensure of physicians, clinics and hospitals to insure high standards of quality seems to continue to plague the public sector today.

In late 1973, Massachusetts did follow the lead of other states and allowed separate licensure of outpatient dialysis centers, and neither of the perceived problems developed. The system was not overwhelmed by profit making facilities, and to the extent that other investor owned clinics were established, the competition thus introduced tended to hold prices down. Secondly, the quality of outpatient dialysis care did not suffer once hospitals were relieved of the responsibility of grafting these onto their own license. In 1971, however, the views of Dr. Pettigrew, as amplified by Richard Knox in the Globe stories, continued to challenge the authority of Commissioner Frechette and thwart the progress of NMC.

At its July 13, 1971 meeting, the Public Health Council, frightened by the charges asserted in the Globe article against the Brigham, and pressed by an overflow crowd of kidney patients and their family members, who wanted to speak in favor of the Brigham and the Babcock center, decided to support the recommendations of Commissioner Frechette over the unprecedented, mutinous opinions of Frechette's DPH staff. The Brigham-Babcock position was aggressively stated by the hospital's attorney, G. D'Andelot Belin. "We don't think the profit making is the problem...we have operated in conformity with Department of Public Health regulations from the start," he stated in the following day's edition of the Boston Herald Traveler. The Council asked the hospital and the kidney center to specify the nature of the supervisory role of the Brigham and the rights and responsibilities of the two entities in a formal written contract which the Department of Public Health would review to be sure it complied with the regulations. Much to the chagrin of high level DPH staff, the Council refused to require the Brigham to take over control of the Babcock operation. As later reported by Richard Knox, DPH legal counsel, Peter Hiam, described the arrangement as the first time that DPH had "allowed a hospital to contract out a portion of its direct patient care responsibility," and Dr. Ann Pettigrew fumed, "I consider this a very dangerous precedent." Nowhere in these reports was it suggested that the separate licensure of the Babcock center, which would have been the procedure followed by most states, would be a better solution for the clinic, the hospital and the public. Instead, the Public Health Council perpetuated an artificial arrangement which held the Brigham accountable for the operation of an independent, investor owned dialysis clinic over which it had no legal authority.

Having stirred the pot without changing the outcome at the July DPH meeting, Richard Knox and his Globe colleague, Charles M. Cobb, continued their investigative reporting of the Babcock Artificial Kidney Center, and the doctors affiliated with the clinic, throughout the summer and fall of 1971. In a July 25th article, Knox criticized George Bailey for accepting the position of administrator of the federally funded New England Regional Kidney Program ("NERKPRO"), while he continued to hold a small amount of NMC stock and was a (unsalaried) vice president of NMC. NERKPRO was a new project that was intended to coordinate the provision of kidney transplantation and dialysis at home and in hospitals and out-of-hospital clinics within New England to insure that appropriate resources and services were available for all patients in the six state region. Essentially, the project recognized and compensated Dr. Bailey for the work he had been doing to find facilities and funding for kidney patients since he arrived at the Brigham in 1965. The report asserted that Bailey would have a conflict-of-interest as an investor and officer of NMC in recommending or opposing the expansion of dialysis services which might complement or compete with NMC clinics. Ironically, his role as a staff physician at the Brigham was not viewed as a problem, even though his Brigham base was the source of his income and the Brigham dialysis and transplantation program dominated New England.

If NMC's center had been a not-for-profit clinic, Bailey's affiliation with it would have been seen as a strength, not a vulnerability. Dr. Leona Baumgartner, who, as the executive director of the Tri-State Regional Medical Program, was George Bailey's supervisor at NERKPRO, explained Dr. Bailey's "blind spot" regarding the alleged conflict in condescending, cultural terms, in one of the Globe articles, as follows: "You have to keep in mind that George is from the South, where profit making medical institutions are much more common than here." The fact that every doctor who derives income from caring for patients, is affiliated with one or more hospitals and clinics, and has a faculty appointment at a medical school has similar conflicts-of-interest, and the fact that any doctor who had none of these affiliations would be unqualified to run a program like NERKPRO, never impressed the "ethically-more-sensitive" northerners, or the Globe reporters. In December, 1971 Dr. Bailey resigned from NERKPRO and subsequently left the Babcock center, the Brigham and Boston, where he had been a trusted physician and beloved friend for scores of renal patients. He moved to New Orleans where he established a new NMC dialysis center in 1973.

Knox and Cobb kept hammering away. Stymied by the incontrovertible fact that at $160 per treatment, the Babcock center was the low cost provider in Boston, and by the uniform opinion of every renal specialist in the area that the quality of care at the NMC clinic was unimpeachable, the Globe reporters sought unfavorable comparisons and critical opinions from sources outside New England. A Minneapolis dialysis clinic, established by Dr. Fred Shapiro as a not-for-profit clinic, was cited by Knox to evidence profiteering by NMC, since Shapiro's center charged $107 per treatment, or 33% less than the Babcock center. Since Hampers and Hager refused to disclose their profit margin at the Babcock center, Knox implied that the $53 difference was profit. Of course, he failed to account for the large differences in labor and other costs between Minnesota and Massachusetts and, like many critics then and now, put no value on the capital needed to build and equip the center. In Dr. Shapiro's case the capital - over a quarter million dollars - was donated. In addition, the Minneapolis clinic was exempt from local, state and federal taxes.

The Globe article also described the situation at the state-owned Lakeville Hospital, a satellite of the Shattuck Hospital and located about 30 miles southwest of Boston. The Lakeville dialysis unit charged Medicaid $65 per treatment for its indigent patients. Rather than serving as an example of efficiency, however, the Lakeville clinic was a case study in mismanagement. The $65 charge was admittedly well below costs and simply represented shifting expenses from one government bureaucracy to another. In fact, when the Lakeville unit first opened, it charged Medicaid $192 per treatment. In addition, the capital to build and equip the center was "donated" by the state, and the center made no provision in its costs for depreciation. Obviously, it did not have to pay real estate or other taxes, either. Moreover, the Lakeville clinic did not pay the state for the use of its space, occupying the same rent-free. Finally, Lakeville had five, fully equipped dialysis stations that it could not use, despite overwhelming demand, because the Massachusetts legislature had not appropriated sufficient funds to hire and pay the requisite staff.

The Globe articles predictably provoked a spate of responses from physicians and patients. In fact, Richard Knox quoted a BAKC patient as a leadin to one of his anti-NMC articles. "I don't know what degree of profit they make. I don't know and I don't care, because they're keeping me alive. I'm happy to pay for it," said John Fogerty. Ellen Mason, a Babcock patient, wrote to the Globe: "The doctors from the Brigham that operate the kidney center have always put the patients first and any 'financial interest' some doctors may have is of no concern." Catherine Sweeney, the wife of another patient, also had a letter published, arguing, "Three years ago the doctors whom you attack and their associates accepted my husband who was in his 70th year for treatment for kidney failure. They were the only ones who would have considered treating him...If I called a plumber as often as I called them his bills would have far exceeded the fees of these doctors...I hope their venture will be successful. If they eventually receive some financial returns after giving the government its percentage [in taxes], they will deserve it."

Kidney patient Emily Thurow, then married to the renowned economics professor and writer, Lester Thurow, was particularly eloquent regarding the hypocrisy of those in government and the not-for-profit sector who had failed to solve the problem of inadequate facilities and then attacked the NMC doctors for solving the problem they had ignored. In December, 1971 she wrote to the Globe, "Politically I agree with the liberal stand the Globe takes on medical care and agree that the direction should be away from allowing individuals to become wealthy from the misfortunes of sick people. However, where was the government when we, who were saved by the corrupt system you criticize, were dying? It is only because of these doctors that we are still here," she continued. When Emily Thurow first came to the Brigham and was diagnosed with end-stage kidney failure, there was no maintenance dialysis slot available for her. Her choice was home dialysis or death. She and her husband accepted the burdens of home care until the Babcock offered an alternative. Even then, it was a continuous strain, physically, financially and emotionally. In fact, Lester Thurow is a professor at the Massachusetts Institute of Technology today, because he left Harvard University's faculty when the expense of Emily's care reached the maximum $50,000 limit under Harvard's health plan at that time, leaving them with no insurance coverage. Ms. Thurow knew what she was talking about when she wrote in her published letter, "Furthermore, there are other private dialysis facilities in other places in this country that do a worse job and charge more! Furthermore, there are parts of this country in which people with kidney disease are told that there is no hope and they are sent home to die." Emily was particularly incensed and hurt by the attacks on George Bailey who was her physician and had decided to leave the area after the Globe stories had criticized his motives and character. "You have been unsympathetic to one of the most humane men I have ever known, and you are making his life so difficult and bitter that we patients are about to lose the best doctor we have, one who has saved not only our lives but our morale," she concluded.

In his own response of July, 1971 to the Globe pieces, Dr. Bailey characteristically focused his concern on the effect these articles would have on the kidney patients, and he didn't mince his words in the process. "It is unfortunate that a leader of the press allows muckraking to frighten unnecessarily patients whose very lives are dependent on the facilities under attack. Since there are no other facilities adequate in size to absorb the 110 patients at Babcock, any talk of an uncertain future for Babcock is a threat to the future of each of those 110," Bailey wrote. He noted that before Hager and Hampers started dialysis at the Normandy House in September 1966, maintenance dialysis was unavailable and prohibitively expensive for all but a few patients, but that "[t]hrough the efforts of this team of physicians and businessmen the capacity for center dialysis in New England has been nearly doubled...If provision of impeccable care to greater numbers of persons for a lesser cost is a crime, then these dedicated men are guilty," he argued.

Other kidney doctors praised the care given to their patients at the Babcock center, and were unperturbed by the profit making structure. Dr. Robert Morrison, who ran the dialysis program at the state owned Shattuck Hospital told Richard Knox, "I agree that there are hazards in letting private enterprise do it, but the service doesn't appear to be provided anywhere else." Knox also quoted an unidentified kidney specialist: "I don't see anything wrong with it. How is it different from a doctor incorporating his practice as many are doing? he's making a profit there, too." Dr. Ted Steinman, a nephrologist at Boston's Beth Israel Hospital, stated at the time, "The quality of care at the Babcock has been and is excellent," and Dr. Nina Rubin, a kidney specialist practicing at the Massachusetts General Hospital, added, "National

Medical Care provides good care, so we sent our patients there."
Similarly, Dr. Martin Gelman, a kidney specialist with the Tufts
Medical School, reflected that "I think there's a bit of intellectual
snobbery and even a touch of jealousy at play in those accusa-
tions. It's not as noble to run the centers as a business as it is for
pure science, but I see nothing wrong with what's being done."

Still, the idea of doctors making profits from the provision of
highly sophisticated healthcare, touched a raw nerve for many. "It
is morally wrong, unethical as well as a slur on the medical profession for physicians to be involved with a profit making dialysis
program. Rather, such profits might be reinfused into further
research, establishment of more Dialysis Transplant Centers and
training programs to produce more physicians to cope adequately
with the ever increasing number of patients with end-stage renal
disease," wrote Dr. Thomas B. Graboys, an assistant resident in
medicine at Boston City Hospital at the time. As months passed,
Hager and Hampers became accustomed to these superficial
observations about their professional ethics and the accompany-
ing assaults on their characters, and they were able to develop
tough exteriors. In a January 31, 1972 article in Newsweek magazine Ted Hager observed, "Everybody screams in horror when they
see doctors making money by working to develop new systems of
healthcare, but who should do it - the mailman, the stockbroker,
the bus driver? With non-profit institutions, there is no incentive
to improve service or keep the costs down." It was an argument
that was lost on many 25 years ago, but today has much more relevance in light of the control of healthcare by corporations run,
not by doctors, but by insurance executives, drug manufacturers,
and lawyers. In the McGovern era of the early 1970's, doctor-
owned healthcare corporations were suspect. Dr. Hager and his
wife, Jane Eastin Hager, laughed when they recalled that at about
the time of the Knox Cobb articles in The Boston Globe, they decided to marry, and they went to a Unitarian minister in Boston to
ask him to perform the ceremony. "When he found out that Ted
was one of those awful doctors that he'd read about in the Globe,
he refused to conduct the wedding," Jane recalled, prompting Dr.
Hager's observation that "we were unfit to be tied!"

The Globe writers didn't stop with Drs. Hampers, Hager and

Bailey. They continued "up the food chain" to attack John Merrill and other officers at the Brigham and Harvard Medical School, and many people who had encouraged Hager and Hampers to take risks to help patients in the late 60's started to run for cover. In securing approval for the Normandy House dialysis project, Dr. Merrill, chief of the Brigham's cardio-renal service, assured the Public Health Department that the unit was an extension of the Brigham Hospital. Similarly, in February 1970 in preparing the Babcock for its opening, William E. Hassan, Jr., the chief administrative director of the Brigham, wrote the Public Health Department that the Babcock was "a part of the total dialysis-transplant program of this hospital." These statements were, of course, valid with respect to patient care and medical supervision, which were the principal concerns of Commissioner Frechette, who was well aware of the private ownership of both the Normandy House and the Babcock. The reason for this schizophrenic, "they-own-it-but-we-supervise-it" approach was that the Commonwealth would not separately license the Babcock, and under Massachusetts law at that time only hospitals could (but no hospitals would) operate dialysis facilities. The letters satisfied the artificial construct created by the state, while the separate ownership of the Babcock was disclosed to, and always known by, public health officials.

At the insistence of the Public Health Department the contract between the Brigham and the Babcock Artificial Kidney Center required that the supervising physician at the Brigham, who was to ensure quality of care and the appropriateness of all patient referrals to the Babcock, could have no financial interest in the profit making clinic. In practical terms this meant that Dr. Merrill could not own stock in, or otherwise be compensated by, National Medical Care. The contract was approved by the Department and executed by the hospital and the clinic on September 14, 1971. At about the same time, NMC was preparing a prospectus for its initial public offering of stock for public sale, and in a preliminary prospectus, NMC listed John Merrill as a member of its three-member Medical Advisory Board, along with Dr. George Thorn, the physician-in-chief at the Brigham, and Dr. Morton Maxwell, the chief of nephrology at Cedars-Sinai Medical Center in Los Angeles and a professor at UCLA. The prospectus stated that the medical advisors were paid a monthly fee by NMC. The disclosure precipitated another Globe article by Richard Knox on October 19, 1971, despite the fact that Dr. Merrill had already resigned his position on NMC's Medical Advisory Board.

In his characteristic fashion, Dr. Merrill assumed a condescending posture, and, refusing to become defensive, noted that the problem was in the eye of the beholder. "No matter what a man's stature or integrity is, if he has anything to do with money, he is subject to possible criticism for conflict of interest in our present climate. I hope to God this changes, but until it does it's something we've got to live with." In other words, since the public could not appreciate the incorruptible principles of men like himself and Dr. Thorn, he would eschew any financial considerations in order to satisfy their simplistic notions of motivation. It's unlikely that the larger audience understood his point, but Merrill was probably making the case, not for Knox and the general Globe readers, but for his professional colleagues.

Merrill's observation anticipated by two decades or more, the cynicism that the public has steadily acquired with respect to the motivations of doctors and other health professionals. In such a climate of cynicism, where greed is understood to motivate professionals and pervert their judgments, no amount of cleansing is sufficient to reestablish credibility. Unfortunately, if the public assumes that physicians make their medical decisions primarily or largely on the basis of how those decision affect their bank accounts, rather than how they affect their patients' health, it becomes virtually impossible to devise a healthcare delivery system which the public can trust. That's not to argue that medical degrees confer sainthood. However, there are many forces besides money that influence doctors - scientific research, prestige, politics, institutional pride, and risk avoidance, to name a few - to make decisions that might not be in the best interest of an individual patient. The recent, escalating tendency to attribute all imperfections in the healthcare system to a lust for-profit is simplistic and disabling to meaningful reformation. In casting money as the scapegoat, the critics elevate its importance and ignore many equally powerful influences.

As members of the medical establishment at the time, Gene Schupak, Ted Hager and Gus Hampers understood that money was the least virulent influence on prominent physicians like John Merrill. If the Brigham doctors (or their counterparts at any of the leading academic medical centers in the country at that time) had been primarily motivated by greed, they would not have sent kidney patients home to die. Expanding chronic dialysis capacity at these hospitals would have been profitable both to the nephrologists, who could have charged physician fees for more maintenance patients, and to the institutions, provided they were willing to adopt more efficient methods of delivering care. Indeed, the factors that motivated the medical leaders - expanding the frontiers of medical science and investigating and learning from the unusual, non-routine cases - harmed the unremarkable, but seriously ill, chronic kidney patients far more than a desire for more money would have. By failing to expand dialysis capacity and by opposing efforts to streamline and lower the costs of maintenance dialysis, service chiefs and administrators at hospitals all over the United States were not acting in the best interests of their kidney patients. As Ted Hager stated in a Globe article at the time, "We're in the business simply because the existing systems for delivery of medical care have failed to meet the need for people with kidney disease."

Dr. Hampers considered the failure of the hospitals to expand their dialysis capacity a result of a combination of laziness and fear to fight for funding. The patients were there, but securing payment for their care was time consuming and risky. "Almost every case was unique in terms of finding a funding source," Hampers recalled. "It demanded creativity, persistence, and a lot of time to persuade insurance companies, employers and government agencies to pay for dialysis for these beneficiaries. The hospitals weren't interested in making the effort," he concluded. The NMC founders and early medical directors weren't lazy or shy about securing dialysis funding, but it became increasingly galling to watch academic physicians walk away from their patients and then have the temerity to criticize their entrepreneurial counterparts for doing what they were unwilling or unable to do. For example, Dr. Hull, the founder of the Dallas clinic, remembered telling a large and prestigious Dallas employer that if they continued to refuse to cover dialysis services for their employees' beneficiaries, he would simply disclose this refusal to the media. As a result, the patients' bills were paid by the company's healthcare plan. That was not the sort of tactic that a teaching hospital would adopt.

Nevertheless, the public was aroused by an analysis that attributed questionable medical care to a quest for-profits, pure and simple. Moreover, the interests of the not-for-profit hospitals were served by scapegoating for-profit healthcare. Since they were not operated for-profit, their motivations were commendable and their failures, forgiveable.

An interesting and illustrative example of how this prejudice against profit in medicine operated arose in the context of charity care. Every doctor and medical institution provides a certain amount of charity care. In the case of not-for-profit centers, like the Brigham, it served their institutional mission, self-image and public relations to tout, and often inflate, the level of free care that they contributed to the community. The contrary was the case for centers operated for-profit - they provided free care but had no interest in telling the world about it.

Dr. Alan Hull recalled discussing the subject with Dr. Schupak and Dr. Hampers when Hull and his colleagues first opened NMC's Dallas center. Schupak told Hull that he should follow the same procedure he followed at the university hospital and treat the indigent, but the only difference was that he shouldn't tell anyone about it. In fact, Dr. Schupak's original dialysis center in Queens took care of so many charity and Medicaid cases in the early years before the Medicare ESRD Program started that the Queens center was one of the only, if not the only, dialysis center in the country that was penalized for the practice of charity care. The penalty arose, because the rule in setting the original Medicare rate was to allow $150 per treatment or the "usual and customary" charge, whichever was less. Unlike most hospitals and outpatient centers where the usual and customary charge was much higher than $150, Dr. Schupak's Queens Center had a usual and customary charge that was well below $150, because so many of his patients were indigent. Consequently, even though he was operating in the most expensive area of the country, Dr. Schupak's center was paid the least for each dialysis treatment.

This anti-profit prejudice turned logic on its head, under a cost reimbursement system such as the original Medicare and some state Medicaid and rate setting programs, and even under certain traditional Blue Cross-Blue Shield cost based systems prevalent twenty-five years ago. Under these systems, the non-profit provider was rewarded for inefficiency, since its rate was directly related to its costs, whereas the investor owned provider could only recover its costs and was not allowed to make a profit. In that context, in which profits were equated with venality and charity identified with purity, it was relatively simple to prejudice any audience by describing NMC as a for-profit enterprise. The label made NMC and its officers as welcome as skunks at public health lawn parties. The early public demonization of profit making healthcare in general and NMC in particular colored the corporation's reactions to the press, and instilled a defensive response by NMC officials to any public health inquiry. In a self-destructive sense, NMC began to fulfill the role in which it was miscast by the media in its adolescent stage.

The criticism reached its apogee during the second week of December, 1971 with the publication of a Paul Szep cartoon as the centerpiece of The Boston Globe's editorial page of December 10th. Ted Hager and Gus Hampers are portrayed attending a patient attached to a dialysis machine. To the patient's right side they appear as physicians, donning lab coats and stethoscopes, as Dr. Hampers asks, "How's the patient progressing?" On the patient's left side, Hager and Hampers, this time clothed as 19th century robber barons, with a wheel barrow catching coins produced by the kidney machine, grin broadly, as Dr. Hager responds, "Well... and so are we!" As with all pithy cartoons, this one captured the essence of the Knox-Cobb thesis which they had presented for several months, namely that it was unethical and somewhat ghoulish for doctors to make money from the misfortunes of their sick and dying patients. For thousands of Globe readers, who had not bothered to read the articles written for the past several months by Richard Knox and Charles Cobb or who had difficulty piecing together the conflicting opinions that were cited in those articles, the impression was immediate and indelible.

At about the same time, Cobb wrote a scathing article ("Kidney Center doctors may make millions") that described the approaching initial public offering of NMC's common stock. Astutely reporting the sales pitch that Hampers, Hager, Schupak and the NMC underwriters were delivering to Wall Street brokers and potential buyers, Cobb noted that as a result of the IPO, Hager and Hampers (and Gene Schupak, although, as a New Yorker, Dr. Schupak was not a target of Cobb's attack) would become multi-millionaires. Even though Hampers and Hager were preliminarily proposing to sell only 35,000 shares each at an IPO price (before underwriters' discounts) of $12 per share ($420,000), Cobb reported that by creating a public market for NMC common stock, the IPO would inflate the value of Hager's and Hampers' NMC holdings to $2.7 million each. (In fact, at the last minute, none of Hampers, Hager or Schupak decided to sell any stock in the IPO, but because the offering was oversubscribed, Hager and Hampers were required under their so called "green shoe" undertaking to sell somewhat less than 20,000 shares to the underwriters.)

Businessmen and Globe readers familiar with the restrictions on sales of stock by "corporate insiders" like Hager, Hampers and Schupak, and with the vagaries of prices for newly issued stock, were not unduly impressed. Most readers, however, lacked that cautionary acumen, and Cobb certainly made no attempt to qualify the drama of his story. Erroneously, Cobb wrote that Hampers and Hager decided whether and which Brigham kidney patients would be sent to and treated at the Babcock center. In fact, those decision were made by Dr. Merrill and other physicians and surgeons who were not affiliated with the Babcock clinic. The article of December 9, 1971 and the following day's cartoon created a sensation, and no where more so than within the ivy covered walls of Harvard Medical School and the Peter Bent Brigham Hospital. Harvard faculty members were not accustomed to seeing themselves caricatured in Boston's leading newspaper. On December 11th The Harvard Crimson, the university's campus newspaper, published a virtual reprint of Charles Cobb's piece, entitled "Brigham Doctors May Make Millions." The reactions were faster and as unconscious as the jerk of a knee when tapped with a doctor's rubber mallet. No less than three investigations were commissioned - one by Harvard, one by the Massachusetts Medical Society, and one by the Commonwealth of Massachusetts.

Within a week the executive committee of the department of medicine at the Harvard Medical School commenced an inquiry, and Dr. Kurt Isselbacher, the chairman of the executive committee, appointed an eight member subcommittee, headed by Dr. Claude Welch, to conduct the investigation into the conduct of Drs. Hager and Hampers. The issue for the medical school and its affiliated hospitals was whether Hager and Hampers had violated the limits that the medical school had set on the total income a faculty member could derive from his professional activities, and in the course of that inquiry, the committee would investigate whether the relationship between the Babcock center and Harvard faculty members created conflicts of interests. Against the advice of his lawyers, but in order to expedite the factual inquiry, Dr. Hampers submitted his tax returns to the committee, showing that he had received $30,000 in salary from NMC and a $17,000 stipend from the National Institutes of Health that flowed through the Brigham, and not a dollar from Harvard or the Brigham itself. In addition, all the physician fees for patient care delivered at the Normandy House had been paid to the Brigham Group, not directly to Hampers.

The Welch Committee met for the first time on January 11, 1972, at Boston's tony Harvard Club, after which Chairman Welch made it clear to Globe reporters that the committee's work would not be done in the glare of the public spotlight, and that its report would be privately transmitted to the executive committee of the department of medicine for further action, if any were necessary. After seven meetings and interviews with several witnesses, the Welch Committee submitted its seventeen page report on March 15, 1972, which is replete with factual findings, none of which was ever in dispute anyway, and a series of questions, but devoid of any conclusive recommendations. For example, the rules regarding compensation arrangement for medical school faculty were so arcane that the committee's report concluded that further studies would be necessary to clarify the meaning of "academic salary," "additional compensation," and "fulltime status." Clearly, if committee members didn't understand these concepts, they couldn't punish Hampers and Hager for misconstruing them. In Ted Hager's case, furthermore, the entire inquiry was indeed "academic," since he had not received any compensation during the relevant time period from either Harvard or from the Brigham Hospital. In Dr. Hampers' case, the question essentially was whether he had fulfilled his commitment as "fulltime" faculty, and whether his NMC salary was "additional compensation" subject to the limits set by Harvard. Hampers argued that his NMC job was as a businessman, not as a physician, and was no more a part of "additional compensation" than the investment or rental income that might be derived by other, older and wealthier faculty members. Seeing a can of worms before it, the committee posed, rather than answered, the question. The committee, in Hampers' words, became totally "tied up in its own underwear."

In the end, it was up to Dr. George W. Thorn, at that time completing his last of thirty years as Harvard's Hersey Professor of the Theory and Practice of Physic and Physician-in-Chief at the Brigham, to decide how to proceed, and on April 21, 1972 Dr. Thorn met with Hampers, Hager and Dr. Merrill and set forth his decision in a memorandum. Ted Hager's status was unchanged; his appointment as an (unpaid) part-time, clinical faculty member at Harvard would be reviewed and recommended on an annual basis. Dr. Hampers, however, had to surrender his directorship of the dialysis unit at the Brigham, which had been paid for by the National Institutes of Health. The responsibility and $17,000 annual stipend were transferred to Ed Lowrie. Hampers also lost his three-year faculty appointment as a fulltime, assistant professor of medicine at Harvard and was reduced in rank to the (unpaid) parttime, clinical faculty, reviewable annually. Dr. Hampers and Dr. Hager both lost admitting privileges for renal patients at the Brigham, and had to refer all their renal patients to Dr. Merrill, who would be responsible for their care (and entitled to physician fees) at the hospital. Nonetheless, Hampers' work at Harvard and the Brigham, including the preparation of the second edition of the standard textbook on hemodialysis, continued on an unpaid basis.

For Gus Hampers, the decision was at once liberating and disappointing. Freed from the strictures of compensation limits on faculty members at Harvard and released from responsibilities at the Brigham, which might have been construed to conflict with his interests as an officer, director and principal stockholder of NMC, Hampers had the opportunity to pursue his entrepreneurial talents and devote his skills and time to the expansion of National Medical Care. Nonetheless, for a 38-year old kidney specialist who had, after a dozen years of advanced training, finally hit his stride in the heady world of scholarly medicine at Harvard, his academic divestiture was difficult to accept, particularly because it was precipitated in Hampers' view, not by his actions or inactions, but by ignorant and jealous journalists. Hampers and Hager made a half hearted attempt to seek retribution from the Globe, and their attorney, Henry Malkasian, even wrote some threatening letters, but in the end, they were persuaded by Paul Brountas and by Jim St. Clair, a litigation partner at Hale and Dorr (and in 1974 the lawyer for embattled President Nixon), that such an action would be unproductive and an enormous waste of their time.

More than Dr. Hampers' status was in flux at the Harvard Medical School and the Brigham Hospital in the spring of 1972. The old guard, represented by Dr. Thorn and Dr. Merrill, who, along with Drs. Murray, Moore and Harrison, had made the Brigham into the world's leading kidney transplant dialysis center, was being replaced. Eugene Braunwald, M.D., an outstanding cardiologist, had been appointed to the Hersey chair and to lead the Brigham's medical staff commencing in July 1972. One of his first objectives was to untangle the relationship between the Brigham and National Medical Care. Dr. Braunwald and Dr. Hampers had crossed paths in San Diego, several months before Braunwald assumed the prestigious positions at Harvard and the Brigham. In 1971 the NMC doctors were trying to recruit Dr. Arnold Roland to start an NMC dialysis clinic in San Diego, and, as director of dialysis at University (University of California- San Diego) Hospital, Dr. Roland sought Hampers' assistance in securing the approval of Gene Braunwald, who was then his chief of medicine. The meeting, according to Hampers, was successful and Braunwald gave his blessing to the NMC-Roland proposal to establish a new out-of-hospital facility similar to Dr. Schupak's center in New York. Later, after NMC had spent thousands of dollars in designing and equipping the San Diego center, Braunwald reversed his position and opposed the new clinic, forcing Dr. Roland to resign his University Hospital position. Hampers and Roland believed that this change of heart resulted from Braunwald's review of the Globe articles during a late-1971 trip to Boston. Roland recalled an agitated Braunwald showing him a copy of the Globe story and telling him that the Boston situation was a disgrace and one that he would remedy once he took up his new position in Boston.

Dr. Braunwald's appointment as Dr. Thorn's successor in 1972 was not good news for Hager and Hampers. In short order, Braunwald displayed his intolerance for the cozy relationship that had developed between Dr. Thorn and the NMC doctors and made Thorn's emeritus status one without any political or professional influence. He also demoted Dr. Merrill and appointed a new renal chief, Dr. Barry Brenner, to replace the legendary "potentate of kidneys." Although he couldn't oust Merrill from the tenured chair endowed several years before by Dr. Hampers' patient, Peter Stuyvesant, Braunwald put Dr. Brenner, a highly skilled researcher from the University of California at San Francisco, in charge of the cardio-renal laboratory and hence in control of its program and research funds. According to Hampers, John Merrill was broken by this humiliation It was not long after, that Dr. Merrill died in a tragic accidental drowning. With Thorn and Merrill out of the loop, Hager and Hampers had no significant "inhouse" advocates at the top levels at Harvard or at the Brigham by the middle of 1972.

The third act in Braunwald's attempt to excommunicate Hampers and Hager from Harvard Medical School came in late 1972 when the new Physician-in-Chief declined to renew Hampers' academic appointment when its regular, one-year term expired, without any stated reasons and without notice, an unusual procedure that Hampers and his lawyer, Henry Malkasian, challenged over the course of the ensuing four years. In a letter of July 11, 1973 to Dr. Merrill, Dr. Braunwald cleverly stated his position, "I do not believe that his [Hampers'] appointment was actively terminated; rather his term of service was merely completed." Incessantly prodded by Malkasian, Harvard University's counsel, Daniel Steiner, recommended in 1974 that Braunwald's decision be reviewed by the executive committee of the department of medicine of the medical school (the same committee with Dr. Isselbacher as chair that reviewed the conduct of Hampers and Hager two years before, following the Globe series). Dr. Braunwald defended his decision not to reappoint Hampers as one of executive prerogative; since Hampers was not tenured, he had no right to reappointment, and Braunwald, like any department head, needed no reason to decline to reappoint an untenured faculty member, he contended. It was a solid argument that in the end was upheld by a special subcommittee of the Committee on Appointments and Promotions, but in the course of a long, defensive and largely superfluous memorandum to the executive committee, Dr. Braunwald revealed his underlying animus for ending Hampers' nine-year affiliation with Harvard Medical School:

...I hope that [the executive committee] will direct its attention to two... issues: The first deals with whether or not a Department Head can or should include a candidates's philosophy and attitudes toward academic medicine as well as his technical and clinical competence in his decision concerning ... reappointment. It seems to me that such qualities, while perhaps more difficult to define than clinical competence and research abilities are as important to the successful function of a department or of a University than the more easily documentable qualities. I believe that one of the responsibilities of a Department Head is to develop a set of values and attitudes for our students, house staff and fellows. While the Department Chairman must not exert 'thought control' over his staff, or prevent diversity of approaches, it is equally important that he not be forced to accept on his staff all attitudes regardless of how reprehensible he finds them. He must have the opportunity to draw the line at some point in the professional activities of his staff. For example, while he may not be pleased with occasional 'moonlighting' activities by members of his staff,...his hands should not be tied when he feels that this activity has gone out of control. It is here, of course, where the term appointment is so useful. Without having to discharge the faculty member whose para academic [sic] activities have gone 'out of control' and do not reflect well on the Department or the University, he can simply let the appointment lapse.

The pomposity of the statement was surprising, even for a physician-in-chief, and, further, disclosed that Braunwald viewed his annual in terrorem power of reappointment as an "useful" weapon, not only to control the income and outside activities of these physicians, but to alter their "reprehensible" attitudes concerning academia, as well. Hampers was disqualified from training Harvard students and fellows, not because his skills as a clinician and researcher were poor, but because he didn't share Braunwald's ideas about medical school doctors providing professional services outside the academy. It was clear that Braunwald was sensitive to the Globe series, and as the newly distinguished, Hersey Professor, Gene Braunwald was intent on protecting Harvard and his office by becoming one of Hampers' and NMC's harshest critics.

The Massachusetts Medical Society was, and remains, a venerable professional association of physicians and surgeons practicing medicine in the Commonwealth. Founded early in the nineteenth century, the MMS is renowned for its prestigious publication, The New England Journal of Medicine, a rival of the comparatively "parvenu" Journal of the American Medical Association. Publication in The New England Journal of Medicine was, and is, a mark of distinction, and its editorials establish the political and ethical standards for the profession. Under the editorial direction of Dr. Arnold ("Bud") Relman and Dr. Jerome Kassirer, The New England Journal of Medicine took a strong stand against the "corporatization" of medicine, in general and in opposition to the ownership and control of artificial kidney centers by National Medical Care, in particular. In late 1971, following the publication of the Globe articles about NMC, the Massachusetts Medical Society convened a panel to inquire into whether its ethical standards had been violated by the arrangements between and among the Babcock center, the Brigham, other referring hospitals, and the kidney specialists who practiced at the Babcock. Dr. Hampers and Dr. Hager were called to testify and answer the panel's questions, which focused on the propriety of what came to be called "self-referral," a practice later outlawed by the federal government in the Stark Act. The conflict that underlay the practice of self-referral was that doctors might be tempted to misdiagnose or overtreat their patients in order to reap personal financial gain by referring these patients to facilities in which they had an interest, and that even if the doctor never yielded to such temptations, the mere existence of the potential conflict would undermine the essential patient-trust relationship. Thus, doctors should avoid owning pharmacies, purveyors of wheelchairs and other durable medical equipment, and chronic dialysis facilities, if they were in a position to direct patients to purchase products or services from their own companies.

As applied to Drs. Hager and Hampers (and the same or similar inquiries were very often raised about other NMC clinic directors as these dialysis centers opened around the country), the issue was whether they were in a position to refer patients to the Babcock center (or other NMC clinics) in which they had a financial interest. With respect to patients who were referred to Babcock from hospitals other than the Brigham, like Massachusetts General or Beth Israel Hospital, the issue was clearly moot, since doctors outside the Brigham Group controlled the flow of patients. With respect to patients from the Brigham Hospital, Drs. Hager and Hampers had established a rigorous procedure whereby kidney doctors on the Brigham service, other than themselves, were responsible for advising the patients on the most appropriate therapy - transplantation, home hemodialysis, peritoneal dialysis, in hospital dialysis (largely available only for those in acute failure or in a pre or posttransplantation program), or out-of-hospital, assisted hemodialysis, such as that provided by Babcock and the other NMC centers. The fact that in the early years (1966 to 1975, or so) there were few alternatives to the NMC centers for those patients requiring assisted hemodialysis was not the fault of Hager, Schupak and Hampers. NMC existed precisely because the medical establishment and the government were so slow to respond to the crisis. Even after NMC had demonstrated that dialysis could be provided economically and safely in an out-of-hospital setting, the government in most states applied "determination of need" laws which impeded competition and established minimonopolies in the service areas.

End-stage renal disease does not allow leeway in diagnosis, where potentially healthy patients would be inappropriately sent to a dialysis clinic. Without transplantation or some form of dialysis these patients would expire. In fact, many experts now believe that in the 1970's doctors waited too long to initiate dialysis and that patients live longer with fewer health problems (lower morbidity) if they begin dialysis while there is still some residual kidney function. Moreover, once the patients were referred to the NMC center, they did not become the "captive" patients of Hager or Hampers. From the start, Babcock had an open staff policy whereby any qualified nephrologist could continue to care for her or his patients at the NMC. In any event, the Massachusetts Medical Society in its 1972 review could find no evidence of inappropriate referral of patients to Babcock or of unethical practices by Hampers or Hager. Nor was there any evidence that NMC made profits by cutting corners or providing patients with inadequate or substandard care. Indeed, most of the evidence introduced was that from other physicians attesting to the exceptionally high quality of care provided by the Babcock Artificial Kidney Center.

What seemed to bother the Globe reporters and editors, some health professionals, government regulators and elements of the public, at least in Massachusetts, was not that the Babcock center existed (it was clear that out-of-hospital dialysis was cheaper and more convenient for the patients), or that doctors from a major university hospital were controlling its operation (the high reputation of the Harvard/Brigham group was a source of pride for most people in Boston), nor that a very high proportion of the fees for dialysis were paid by the public (there has always been a generous public response to help end-stage renal disease patients at the state and federal levels). What irked NMC's critics was that the centers were operated for-profit.

If Hager, Hampers, and Schupak had received startup capital in the form of a bequest from a wealthy former kidney patient or his family, or from a foundation with an interest in creating a new form of healthcare delivery, or from the church, and there with established Babcock and the Queens facilities as non-profit clinics, there would have been three significantly different results. First, no taxes would have been paid on the income which would have accumulated and supported expansion. Second, the larger world of charity would have been reduced to the extent of the grant, that is, the money donated to Hampers and his colleagues would not have been available for gifts to the Harvard Medical School, homeless shelters, or symphony orchestras. And the third difference would have been a series of tributes to these three doctor/founders from the press, academia, the government, and the medical societies - the same institutions that held the inquests into NMC's operations in the 1971-72 period. What would not have been different was the quality of care for patients.

"Getting rich off sick people" was a sure fire method of condemning for-profit healthcare, yet no one seemed to be bothered that the executives and stockholders of Archer Daniels Midland or General Foods "get rich off hungry people" (particularly if they are starving foreign people), or that investors of Weyerhauser and Levi-Strauss "get rich off homeless people" or "get rich off naked people." Capitalism as a system for incenting investors to surrender their resources toward a common enterprise - sometimes socially useful like providing telephone services or sometimes frivolous like selling pet rocks - has been acknowledged as the most efficient and least intrusive economic system in the history of the world, particularly since the collapse of communism, in all areas except healthcare, where it continues to be suspect.

In addition to the Harvard investigations and the hearings before the Massachusetts Medical Society's peer review panel, in response to the series of Globe exposes, the Massachusetts legislature passed a resolution on October 6, 1971, appointing a seven-member special joint committee to investigate the provision of kidney dialysis in the Commonwealth, particularly with respect to the costs of providing dialysis to patients like the indigent, disabled and veterans, whose healthcare was subsidized by the taxpayers. Eventually this commission would endorse a bill that allowed and required separate licensure of dialysis facilities - an improvement that Hager and Hampers had been pursuing for several years.

For all his prowess in medicine and business, Gus Hampers was an inept politician and public relations manipulator. As a person who instinctively and by training based his decisions on cold facts, Hampers failed to understand the heated emotions that suggestions of physician profiteering could evoke. He failed to understand the dominance of appearances over reality, and whether dealing with academic deans or investment bankers, Hampers believed that they would act and react rationally, rather than politically. Sensing his lack of political acumen, his opponents and rivals could easily trap Hampers, because his reactions were predictable, and he did not make decisions that would necessarily please or appease an audience.

The reactions in Massachusetts against NMC's out-of-hospital, for-profit dialysis clinics may have been the most noticeable and virulent, but they weren't unique. Similar complaints were voiced in the media against Dr. Schupak's center in New York, and articles in The Washington Post raised the same issues when NMC's Bethesda facility opened in July 1970. Bill Cirksena and Larry Siegel met with Post reporter, Stuart Auerbach, at the time, and according to Dr. Cirksena, the Auerbach story, replete with inaccurate quotations from Dr. Siegel, bore scant resemblance to the interview conversation. In fact, Cirksena strongly urged Hampers and Schupak to engage the services of a top public relations firm like Hill and Knowlton to generate more accurate and sympathetic stories about the effort by NMC to provide dialysis to underserviced populations. Hampers failed to heed his advice and the attacks continued. Hampers and his colleagues did, however, heed the advice of Dr. George Schreiner, the chief of the renal service at Georgetown University Medical Center. Schreiner noted that the bad publicity was a blessing in disguise, insofar as it served as an early warning to the NMC doctors to set the standard of care at the highest possible level and that NMC's best - and ultimately, it's only - defense would be in providing dialysis care of unassailable quality. "It was the best single piece of advice we received in those early years," Ted Hager recalled.

Undaunted by the Globe stories and other media criticism and by the various investigations, the principal executives at NMC - Gene Schupak in New York and Ted Hager and Gus Hampers in Boston - kept their eyes and energies focused on the prize of making the brand new centers models of high quality, low cost care and of selling NMC common stock to the public in an initial public offering before the end of 1971. The seven million dollar proceeds from the IPO would be used by the company to replicate these models in more centers around the country. Keeping that focus amid their continuing patient care, research and academic responsibilities was arduous. In addition, Drs. Hampers and Hager experienced a series of personal tragedies in the midst of opening the first clinics, preparing for a public offering and responding to the adverse publicity. In a twelve month period between August 1971 and 1972, Gus Hampers' sister, father and mother all died unexpectedly. Hampers' sister, Liz, only 40-years old at the time with three young children, complained of back pain on a Thanksgiving visit to Hampers' home in 1970. She never returned to her own home from that visit, and died in Joyce and Gus Hampers' home from cancer in August, 1971. Within a few months, first his father and then Hampers' mother died. Around the same time Ted Hager lost his young sister, a victim of breast cancer. Not only did Hampers refuse to allow these upsetting personal ordeals to affect his work and plans, but he never shared the pain they caused him outside his immediate family. Friends and colleagues had no idea. Paul Brountas, NMC's general counsel, who talked with Hampers on a daily basis during the summer and fall of 1971 in preparing for the public sale of stock and responding to the media and other criticism, and who played tennis with Hampers every Sunday during that time period, never knew of Hampers' family losses.

Not surprising then were Hampers' comments in a report published a few months later in 1972: "Nothing outside the color of my underwear remains unexposed. I've met with Harvard committees and councils (all they decided was that full and part-time jobs should be better defined), have gone before a joint legislative committee (they didn't condemn me), Massachusetts Medical Society panels (they never felt any action was necessary) and the state rate setting commission (they want to reduce vocational rehabilitation payments to $100 a treatment, and will eventually settle on a figure between that and the $140 we now receive)." What seemed to keep Hampers, Schupak and Hager going was the unshakable self-assurance that they could make a difference and be successful in keeping patients with end-stage renal disease alive. Years later Hampers remarked, "Society often creates a culture of failure by nurturing a fear of success in others; if you succeed you'll be unhappy, criticized, outcast, they say. People need to learn not to fear success. If Gene and Ted and I had failed, they would have erected a statue. Since we succeeded, they had to tear us down."

By December 1971, National Medical Care was quickly running out of capital, having started ten artificial kidney centers (in Boston, New York, Washington, Philadelphia, Tampa, Miami, Dallas, Los Angeles, Beverly Hills and Pittsburgh), five mental health facilities and four extended care facilities over the course of the past twenty months. An additional dozen centers were in various stages of development. The initial public offering had been delayed several times due to bad market conditions on Wall Street and bad publicity in Boston. The principal underwriter, R.W. Pressprich & Co., which had tentatively agreed to sell NMC's common stock to the public at $12.00 a share, was, according to NMC treasurer Dave Lubrano, "getting nervous." The parties agreed on Tuesday, December 14, 1971, as the day of the offering, and all the necessary documents were prepared and filed with the Securities and Exchange Commission, except the "pricing amendment" which, as was customary in such cases, would be signed and filed just hours before the offering was to be effected. On Thursday, December 9th, the Globe ran one of its most critical articles, followed the next day by the scathing Szep cartoon of the "profiteering physicians." On the evening of December 13, 1971 the parties met to set the final price. Dave Lubrano recalled that the Pressprich executives listed all the downside factors and told the NMC doctors that they couldn't stick with $12.00, and would take the 600,000 shares the company proposed to sell at a price no more than $10 a share. "I remember it like it was yesterday," Lubrano said. "Gus came right out of his chair. I thought he was going to smack the guy!" Hampers insisted that Pressprich honor its $12.00 commitment, and wouldn't concede a reduction of even twenty-five cents a share. The NMC officers left the meeting and were on the street curb hailing a cab when a Pressprich officer recalled them. The next day the offering went off at $12 per share - about 45 times 1971 earnings - and was oversubscribed.

Gaining access to dialysis care for these patients was what made Hampers, Hager and Schupak fight so hard. The difference of $2.00 per share in the selling price meant an additional $1.2 million dialysis clinic and care for scores of patients who would otherwise be facing the system of rationing that the government and the hospitals had allowed to continue for nearly a decade.

Within a few weeks the price of NMC common stock soared beyond $20 a share. Collectively, Drs. Schupak, Hager and Hampers owned about 21% of a $73 million company, based on the market value of the 3.6 million shares of outstanding common stock. The company used about a third of the proceeds of the public offering to pay off debt and applied the remaining two-thirds toward the construction of more mental health, and artificial kidney centers, thereby expanding its dialysis capacity to provide care to an additional 1,000 end-stage renal disease patients at eight new locations in the United States.

6

Life Saving Legislation

In July, 1973 the federal government began the End-Stage Renal Disease Program, covering approximately 13,000 patients at an annual cost of $240 million. By 1999 expenditures had increased to approximately $18 billion (of which the ESRD Program contributed about $13 billion) to care for over 340,000 Americans disabled with kidney failure. Although savaged by its many critics over the past twenty-eight years, the ESRD Program has substantially achieved its objectives of providing quality care, accessible to all, at a reasonable cost. The program charts a logical course for the federal government's assumption of the financial risks of catastrophic disease and disability, but, like nearly all government programs, has failed to construct a strategy for its own demise, either by ending kidney disease as a chronic condition, or by shifting its financial burdens onto the private sector. In planning larger healthcare financing reforms in the future, the history of the ESRD Program is a very valuable prologue.

When they created National Medical Care and began operating the country's first out-of-hospital kidney dialysis facilities, Doctors Hager, Hampers and Schupak could never have imagined the federal government's eventual role in paying for dialysis and kidney transplantation services. In 1968 Medicare was a fledgling federal health insurance program for older Americans, enacted in 1965 in the full flush of President Johnson's Great Society initiatives. In NMC's founding year, total Medicare outlays were $3 billion (fiscal year 1967). Virtually none of these funds paid for dialysis, since Medicare beneficiaries were by definition too old to be considered for the rare, rationed, life saving therapies of dialysis and transplantation. In contrast, annual Medicare expenditures today are nearly $250 billion (fiscal year 1999), and the 1997 balanced budget initiative prescribes $115 billion just in savings over the five-year, 1998-2002 period from the Medicare program. Critics of National Medical Care, who claim that the company was created to milk the Medicare program, generally overlook the fact that by the time the End-Stage Renal Disease Program was implemented on July 1, 1973, NMC was already five-years old and was profitably operating fifteen artificial kidney centers around the country.

Some indigent patients were covered by the Medicaid program after 1965, depending on whether they lived in states that included renal care in their programs. For instance, in New York when Dr. Schupak began the Queens Center in 1970, dialysis was not covered for poor patients. After tough negotiations, Dr. Schupak managed to secure coverage at the rate of $90 per treatment, but only for four patients. Later, as patients arrived at the Queens Center, and Dr. Schupak threatened to go to the media with his patients, the Department of Health Economics of the New York State Health Department relented and approved dialysis for all its Medicaid patients in New York. The rate increased to $100 per treatment for a short time, and then, prior to the ESRD Program's enactment, was lowered to $75 per treatment.

Since mid-1973 the federal government's health insurance program for the aged and disabled (Medicare) has paid for virtually all the healthcare expenses of people with kidney failure. This so called End-Stage Renal Disease ("ESRD") Program of Medicare pays not only for physicians' services, hospital care, dialysis, drugs and other ancillary services and products that are required as part of the therapy for kidney disease, but the ESRD Program pays for all the healthcare needs of individuals who are covered by the program. Thus, a 40 year-old ESRD Program beneficiary who breaks his arm from a slip on the ice is entitled to have Medicare pay for the emergency room care in setting the fracture. Coverage is determined not by age but by disability caused by kidney failure. It was, when enacted in 1972, and remains today, the only universal, comprehensive federal health insurance program - it covers all services and products for all people who are diagnosed with end-stage renal disease (with some important, but relatively minor, exceptions), regardless of age, income, or residence.

On October 30, 1972, just eight days before his historic, land-slide reelection victory (and a little more than four months after the Watergate break-in that would result in the premature end of his presidency), President Richard Nixon signed Public Law 92-603, the Social Security Amendments Act, which among other provisions created the ESRD Program to become effective the following July. While the ESRD provision (section 229 I) was added during a rare Saturday session of the United States Senate during the floor debate of the Social Security bill, the ESRD Program thereby created was not without antecedents.

From 1960 to 1967 the Public Health Service, an arm of the Department of Health and Human Services (then, the Department of Health, Education and Welfare) had established several experimental and prototypical projects to determine whether dialysis and transplantation could become viable therapies for patients with chronic kidney failure. Known as the Kidney Disease Control Program, this federal project supported fourteen dialysis and transplantation centers in the United States. Beginning in 1967 the Public Health Service shifted its support in favor of a number of home care demonstration projects, several of which involved physicians who would later become the original medical directors of NMC outpatient centers in the 1970's, including Schupak, Hampers, Alan Hull in Dallas and Charles Swartz in Philadelphia. Under the KDC Program PHS contracted directly with the participating medical centers to provide the necessary hardware, home care training, medical and dietary services, dialysis supplies and back-up support for a certain number of home care patients for a three-year period. The patients who were selected to participate paid nothing for the care, but were responsible for their other medical needs not related to their renal failure. The PHS criteria mandated that older and sicker patients were not acceptable for this study. Thus, for example, diabetic patients were disqualified. These limits on participation and coverage were not replicated in the later Medicare ESRD program with the result that extrapolations from the experience in the old PHS model project grossly understated the cost of universal, comprehensive care. The cost of treating elderly patients and patients with other afflictions, such as diabetes, were far greater than the PHS experience would have predicted.

When the home dialysis demonstration project of the Public Health Service reached the end of its three-year term, the participating physicians, the medical facilities and the patients were left with few, if any, alternatives, even though the contracts with PHS required the participating home dialysis programs to develop additional sources of support. By 1970 it appeared that the federal government would simply end its financial support, and hundreds of chronic dialysis patients, who were being kept alive by home treatments, would be left without recourse. The backup hospitals were generally unable and unwilling to provide free care for these patients, and there were far too few viable kidney transplants available. New York City, under the direction of its then-Commissioner of Hospitals, Joseph Terenzio, was one of the few local governments that stepped into the breach and paid for the costs of its resident home care patients. The situation put tremendous pressure on physicians and facilities, as well as on state and federal elected and appointed government officials, to come up with a substitute program. Once the government intervened, patients, their physicians and their advocates could and would argue that ending that intervention was akin to a death sentence.

Another federal program that early on provided support to patients with kidney failure was the dialysis and transplantation program of the Veterans Administration centers. Veterans were covered for dialysis and transplantation care nearly from the initiation of these therapies. This also led to the anomalous and illogical situation where dialysis and transplantation were being rationed not only on the basis of age, other health factors, and wealth, but also on the basis of veterans status, although prior to the enactment of the ESRD Medicare Program, the VA did start to provide limited dialysis services to certain non-veterans and their dependents. Politicians quickly came to realize that the American public was not happy with rationing life saving care on these limiting bases. Once the federal government had provided kidney disease therapies for some, the public began demanding that these therapies be denied to none.

These three pioneering approaches toward funding kidney services in the 1960's extended federal dollars to institutions, rather than individual patients. The Kidney Disease Control Program and the Public Health Service's home care projects were in essence direct grants to "centers of excellence," similar to research grants from the National Institutes of Health. Patients who benefitted from these early federal programs were simply lucky to live near, and to be cared for by, these superior medical institutions. The patients themselves had no way to apply for support, and even under the Veterans Administration program, dialysis patients had to travel to VA hospitals in order to receive federally subsidized care, since, again, the hospitals, not the patients, received federal government support. Veterans with end-stage kidney failure, who lived hundreds of miles distant from a VA center, were no better off than their non-veteran counterparts who found themselves outside the catchment area of the KDCP's centers of excellence. In other words, federal funding for kidney services was not yet an entitlement to be claimed by individual patients.

An important shift occurred in the mid-sixties, thanks to the efforts of a determined politician from the tiny state of Rhode Island, which would form the basis of the Medicare ESRD Program several years later. John Edward Fogarty was a member of the U.S. House of Representatives from Rhode Island from 1941 until 1944, and again, after service in World War Two, from 1945 until 1967. During these 25 years in Congress, Rep. Fogarty, himself a former bricklayer and president of the Bricklayers Union, was a champion of the blue collar working man, an unreconstructed Roosevelt Democrat. By the mid-sixties Fogarty had become a senior member of the powerful House Appropriations Committee and the chairman of its subcommittee on vocational rehabilitation. Not long before his death at the age of fifty-four in 1967, Congressman Fogarty received a telephone call from George Bailey, Dr. Hampers' first renal fellow at the Brigham, concerning a 20-year old young man who had arrived at the Brigham, seeking care for irreversible kidney disease. He lived in Rep. Fogarty's district in Rhode Island, had no money or insurance, and the modest program at the Brigham was full. The hospital had decided to send him back to Rhode Island and certain death. Bailey and Hampers initiated emergency peritoneal dialysis and kept him as an inpatient at the Brigham, and Dr. Bailey placed the telephone call to Congressman Fogarty.

"George refused to let the kid leave the hospital," Hampers remembered. "He got Fogarty to agree to meet with us, and George and I flew to Washington to plead his case." The Brigham doctors explained the situation to Mr. Fogarty, who had no idea what kidney dialysis was about or how much it would cost. In the course of explaining the dialysis process, Bailey used the term "prosthesis" to describe the function of an artificial kidney, and a light went off in Rep. Fogarty's head. He immediately made the connection between the artificial kidney and an artificial limb, and realized that vocational rehabilitation programs that were funded by the federal government and administered by the fifty states might cover artificial kidneys, just as they covered artificial legs and arms. He called the Rhode Island rehabilitation commission, and at his urging it began paying for the care of Bailey's patient.

Thereafter, Congressman Fogarty visited Dr. Scribner's outpatient clinic in Seattle (which had opened in 1962), and became an advocate for a leading role by the federal government in the care of ESRD patients. Under his leadership the federal Vocational Rehabilitation Act was expanded to cover some dialysis patients. Similarly, the Crippled Children's Act was broadened during this period to provide limited pediatric renal care. Still, the vast majority of ESRD patients in the United States were not covered.

New ground had been broken in two places. First, the justification for federal government funding was based on the potential rehabilitation of patients; and second, the benefit was identified with the particular, individual patient, rather than the institution. The rehabilitation commission would pay for dialysis care for Bailey's patient whether it was delivered at the Brigham Hospital or anywhere else. The nexus with the medical center was not important under the Bailey-Fogarty analog, but was established between the government and the patient directly. This shifted the role of the federal government from one of helping certain, excellent medical centers to one of helping patients on their road to rehabilitation. The benefits were portable. Obviously, this would facilitate the growth of the NMC centers in the years to come, but at the time of this breakthrough, National Medical Care had not yet been imagined.

Healthcare policy analysts frequently argue that there is nothing unique about end-stage renal failure among all the other conditions and diseases that can be categorized as catastrophic and chronic, and therefore, that there is no reason that kidney failure should be treated so differently by the federal government from any of these other illnesses and disabilities. They are right. The different treatment is only explained, but in no way justified, by its history and the fact that Dr. Bailey and Congressman Fogarty reconceived of dialysis as a rehabilitation challenge to be addressed by a team consisting of the patient, his doctor, the state rehabilitation commissions and the federal government, rather than accepting the dead end concept of kidney disease as a fatal condition that could only be delayed by a medical facility with the financial support of the government. In looking toward any future reform of the ESRD Program specifically, and the federal government's role in healthcare in general, adopting the Bailey-Fogarty paradigm can lead to different and better prescriptions. As it has evolved over the past quarter century, the ESRD Program itself has neglected the rehabilitation objective, and, instead, has replicated the prevailing allopathic model of paying for therapies and drugs that reverse the effects of disease or disabilities, rather than incenting patients and providers to regain health. Funds flow freely to fight disease, but rarely to promote health.

A major factor in eliciting the unprecedented, special response of the federal government to end-stage renal disease was the media exposure the disease and its victims received from the popular, lay press. There were many examples of human interest stories, usually connected with fund raisers that were held in communities all over America to raise money to purchase an artificial kidney machine or to help pay for a patient and his family to travel to a distant medical center where he could receive a transplant. However, the single most influential article that captured and shaped the public's attitude was the November 9, 1962 cover story in Life Magazine describing the procedure adopted by Dr. Scribner and his colleagues to determine which ESRD patients would be accepted into the limited program at his newly opened outpatient dialysis clinic in Seattle. The idea that, in order to ration life saving dialysis care, a committee (referred to provocatively by the press as the "God-Committees") would evaluate the relative merit and social utility of several individual patients was anathema to the American public. Editorial writers, commentators, politicians and clergy expressed the popular dissatisfaction with rationing, and demanded that the government, especially the federal government, end rationing by expanding the supply of artificial kidneys for everyone who needed them.

As a result, between 1965 and 1972 over one hundred bills were filed in Congress to help the victims of kidney failure. These ranged from fairly modest suggestions for more federally supported research to the enactment of a large scale, national program of providing dialysis machines and transplantation services through government subsidized programs. None was as comprehensive, however, as the final recommendations of the Committee on Chronic Renal Disease, which was created in 1967 by the Bureau of the Budget and chaired by Dr. Carl W. Gottschalk, an expert in diseases of the kidney from the University of North Carolina Medical School. The "Gottschalk Commission" urged the creation of a national program to provide victims of irreversible renal failure with kidney transplant and dialysis therapies. Although the report of the Gottschalk Commission gathered dust and was initially ignored by the federal government, its insights, evaluations and recommendations formed the basis of the 1972 Medicare amendments that created the ESRD Program. The genius of the Gottschalk Commission's report was its boldness in arguing for a direct role for the federal government and the creation of a comprehensive, universal program that would end rationing of kidney care services. Consequently, more limited proposals seemed anemic, inadequate and unsupported by expert analysis and opinion. It's very curious, and indeed tragic, that after the enactment of the ESRD Program, the federal government, either under the auspices of the Department of Health and Human Services or the Office of Management and Budget, did not periodically recommission a Gottschalk-like committee of experts to reevaluate the Medicare program and make corrective or enhancing recommendations. Subsequent studies of the ESRD Program during its 28-year history focused on its costs and financing, rather than on its quality and access.

110

In the meantime, in 1965 Congress passed, and President Lyndon Johnson signed, the basic, comprehensive Medicare and Medicaid legislation that became effective the following year, thus blazing the path for the federal government's direct involvement in the healthcare delivery system. Simply put, these Social Security extensions provided health insurance to elderly and indigent Americans (and after the 1972 amendments, the disabled, as well), who previously had largely been responsible for their own medical bills, which is to say that, as a group, their medical needs were not being met. In its first fiscal year Medicare paid approximately $3 billion in claims. In fiscal year 1998 Medicare has grown to a $250 billion dollar program.

Under the 1972 Social Security Amendment, Medicare recognized disabled individuals, like elderly, retired Americans, as worthy of special consideration by the federal government. The assumption has been that the private health insurance market is unable to extend coverage to these groups, because their healthcare costs are high and their incomes are low, making them unable to pay premiums adequate to insure their risks. As a result, the elderly, disabled and indigent (under Medicaid) have been segregated into a distinct, high risk class of healthcare recipients who are separately insured by the government. Because the Medicare and Medicaid programs have their own coverage criteria and other regulations, the result has been that the elderly, poor and disabled actually receive a different level and quality of healthcare. The government could have chosen a different strategy, namely requiring private health insurers to include the elderly, disabled and poor into larger insured pool of the general population, thus raising the premiums for all insured individuals and groups. The federal government could then subsidize those elderly, poor and disabled individuals who were unable to pay through means testing criteria. Under such an alternative system, Grandma Jones would pay the same premium as her son, but might have part or all the premium subsidized by increasing her monthly Social Security stipend. There would then be no Medicare insurance system for high risk and poor Americans, and the government would provide premium subsidization, rather than a whole separate system of health insurance and the resulting, segregated system of healthcare.

In addition, from its inception in 1965 Medicare adopted the prevailing form of health insurance then available in the United States, namely the publicly chartered, hospital dominated Blue Cross/Blue Shield system. Medicare's "Part A" system mirrored the essential aspects of the various state Blue Cross collectives that covered hospital care under a system that reimbursed hospitals for their costs. Blue Cross itself was a not-for-profit corporation, specially chartered by the various state governments, and exempt from certain insurance regulations and anti-trust laws. It was a collective enterprise, dominated by the larger, charity and government operated hospitals, which were not responsive to investors and thus not profit oriented, and under its cost reimbursed system, which became the prototype for Medicare's Part A system, the hospitals were insulated from risk and deprived of incentives to economize. Similarly, Blue Shield, which was controlled by state medical associations, provided the basis for "Part B" of the new Medicare system. Like Blue Shield, Part B was not a cost reimbursed system, but set fees for physician services in advance. Individual doctors could either accept these fees from their Blue Shield insured patients or not. Since patients were not likely to pay premiums for a Blue Shield plan and pay their non-participating doctor separately (and additionally, since most doctors were unlikely to charge their Blue Shield patients less than the set fee), the system forced virtually all physicians to accept the Blue Shield fees. It was essentially a system of price fixing by, and for the benefit of, physicians.

Although substantial reforms in Medicare (as well as in the various Blue Cross/Blue Shield plans) were adopted in the mid-1980's, at the time that the ESRD Program was instituted, the Medicare system, into which it was melded, was essentially a system that reimbursed hospitals (or "providers," in terms of Medicare definitions) for their costs and paid doctors (and other so-called, "non-providers") their "reasonable and customary" fees, with an emphasis on the "reasonable," i.e., the fees deemed fair by Blue Shield and Medicare-Part B bureaucrats. In the 1960's and 1970's Medicare was a Blue Cross/Blue Shield system for the high risk, elderly and disabled patients.

When Congress and the Nixon Administration decided to respond to the pressure to end the rationing of dialysis and transplantation services for ESRD patients, the obvious and easiest route was to include these patients as part of the disabled pool under the Medicare system. Their healthcare would no longer be covered by private insurance systems (or not covered as was often the case), and all end-stage renal disease patients, regardless of age, wealth or income, location or other health conditions, would be Medicare beneficiaries. It was reasonably felt that compared to the general Medicare population, the ESRD population was relatively small, and there was no need to invent a separate system for these patients. What this meant was that their care in hospitals - all their care, not just care for their kidney-related condition - would be cost reimbursed under Part A (100%), and that their physicians' services - again all physician or "non-provider" services - would be handled by Part B of Medicare (80% with the patient responsible for the remaining 20%). However, unlike the general Medicare/Medicaid system, since the ESRD Program was a universal system for a specific disease group, there was no external market or pool of ESRD patients (except "comparable" ESRD populations in foreign countries) to which the adequacy of care and reimbursement could be compared, modeled, or measured.

Unwittingly, the Medicare ESRD Program became a monopsony - a system where there was one purchaser of services, with the additional complication of having the federal government, subject to the vicissitudes of political pressures, filling that sole purchaser role. The American free enterprise system is rarely confronted with the monopsonistic phenomenon - Standard Oil's dominance of refining in the post-Civil War period left oil producers with only one purchaser of their product, and the Department of Defense today sets the prices for a broad array of military hardware - and in the case of kidney dialysis and transplantation services, additional "buyers" were not likely to develop. A voucher system, whereby individual ESRD patients could purchase either healthcare insurance to cover their care in a competitive market, or directly contract with hospitals and doctors to deliver their care, would theoretically have eliminated the monopsony, but it would have required a well informed, motivated cadre of patient purchasers. Only now, after over 30 years of the Medicare system, are healthcare economists suggesting exactly that kind of deinstitutionalizing reform where Medicare beneficiaries can shop for indemnity insurance, health maintenance organizations or provider group plans that best suit their individual needs. However, in the early 1970's after only a couple years of Medicare/Medicaid experience, the problem of monopsony was not on the minds of healthcare economists, care providers, kidney patients, or politicians.

During 1972 in dramatic testimony before the relevant committees of the House of Representatives and the Senate, advocates of a comprehensive federal program for ESRD services brought dialysis patients into the hearing room and performed dialysis on a patient with end-stage renal failure, while he and his doctor testified in favor of federal assistance. For many legislators it was a transforming experience. Sheldon ("Shep") Glazier, the patient that testified and was dialyzed before the House Ways and Means Committee, was then president of the National Association of Patients on Hemodialysis Treatment and part of Gene Schupak's home dialysis program in New York City; his counterpart in the Senate Finance Committee hearings was a patient in the Georgetown program in Washington. Before their eyes, Congressmen could see dialysis at work, while they heard the heart breaking stories of people who had been denied this life saving therapy due to a lack of funding.

At the urging of Senator Russell Long, a senior Democratic member of the U.S. Senate from Louisiana and the Chairman of the Senate Finance Committee, Indiana Senator Vance Hartke [Rupert Vance Hartke served three terms in the Senate, 1959 to 1977. He was succeeded by Republican Richard Lugar.] introduced the so called "ESRD Amendment" to the Social Security Amendments Act of 1972 during a sparsely attended, rare Saturday session of the U.S. Senate on September 30, 1972. The amendment, adding section 229 I to the act, which would become designated as Public Law 92-603, was succinct and stated, in part:

Sec. 299I. Effective with respect to services provided on and after

July 1, 1973... every individual who (1) has not attained the age of 65; (2) is insured [under Social Security] or is entitled to monthly [Social Security] insurance benefits, or is the spouse or dependent child [of such a Social Security beneficiary]; and (3) is medically determined to have chronic renal disease and who requires hemodialysis or renal transplantation for such disease; shall be deemed to be disabled for purposes of coverage under parts A and B of Medicare... Medicare eligibility on the basis of chronic kidney failure shall begin with the third month after the month in which a course of renal dialysis is initiated...

The real effect of the amendment was to short circuit the Medicare law's requirements regarding eligibility on the basis of a disability. Generally, then and now, potential beneficiaries must demonstrate 24-months of disability. Other disabled Medicare beneficiaries must prove long term disability in terms of their inability to continue to work. The ESRD Amendment conclusively presumes disability - without regard to a person's work capacity - and, therefore, Medicare coverage, for all renal patients from and after their third month of chronic dialysis. Note also that the amendment does not limit coverage to kidney services, but treats ESRD patients in the same manner as if they had attained the age of 65, insofar as it covers all their medical services.

There was limited debate concerning the Hartke Amendment on the floor of the Senate that day. By unanimous consent, debate was limited to thirty minutes - fifteen minutes for each side, and even those few minutes were not entirely consumed. In addition to Senators Hartke and Long, the amendment was cosponsored by fellow Democrats Quentin Burdick of North Dakota and Lawton Chiles of Florida, as well as by Republican Senator Robert Dole of Kansas. The marginal opposition was bipartisan: Senator Samuel J. Ervin, Jr. (Dem. - N.C.) joined his Republican colleagues, James L. Buckley of New York and Wallace Foster Bennett of Utah in voting against the amendment, which passed on a 52 to 3 vote with 45 Senators not voting.

In support of his amendment, Senator Hartke noted, in part:

... more than 8,000 Americans will die this year from kidney disease this year [sic] because they cannot afford an artificial kidney machine or a kidney transplant...Each year, about 8 million Americans are afflicted with kidney diseases, the fifth leading cause of death in this country...In terms of indirect costs of mortality - lost future income - kidney disease is the highest ranking killer, costing the country $1.5 billion annually...Approximately 55,000 Americans are now suffering from chronic renal disease. Twenty to 25,000 of these people are prime candidates for dialysis or other life-saving kidney treatment...Final cost estimates for this vital amendment are now being worked out. Preliminary estimates indicate an annual cost of approximately $250 million at the end of the first 4 years with the first full year cost at about $75 million.

In fact, the program cost nearly $250 million in its first year of operation, and by 1977 (its fourth full year) the annual cost was approximately $640 million (without adjusting for inflation). Senator Hartke yielded to Senator Bob Dole, who noted that he had lived for 25 years with only one functioning kidney as a result of his World War II injuries; Dole went on to state:

I think that the one reservation - that could be raised to the amendment is in approaching some of these catastrophic illnesses on a piecemeal basis rather than on a broad basis. But I firmly believe that the Senator from Indiana's amendment is at least a step in the direction that will bring about some much needed progress.

In stating his opposition, Senator Bennett noted:

At risk of branding myself as one who is opposed to this program and, therefore, one who wants to see people die - which obviously I do not - there are one or two observations that must be made before the inevitable vote on this amendment is taken...[O]bviously, we are involved here in a new 'Christmas in September' program....If we are going to use this as a vehicle to bring out every worthy beneficial program and pile it onto this bill, I am not sure that the bill will be able to carry it....This amendment represents a move to pick out one particular phase of health care and bring it in ahead of the others and write it into law. There are a lot of other diseases that people are subject to which are as serious as the kidney problem....I want to make a slight protest against adding this additional straw to the financial burden that will break the back of the social security system.

In fairness, Senator Bennett shared the prevailing view in 1972 that after the election Congress and the Administration would address a broader, national healthcare bill. The relevant Congressional leaders had staked out positions on such a measure, as had President Nixon. It was nearly universally presumed at that time that the federal government would very soon become involved in providing health insurance for millions of Americans beyond the elderly, disabled and indigent.

On October 15, 1972 the House of Representatives and the Senate accepted the conference report for the omnibus 1972 Social Security bill, and Public Law 92-603 was enacted and signed by President Nixon on October 30, 1972, just eight days before his landslide, 49-state electoral victory over George McGovern. The law had many provisions of much broader effect than the ESRD provision, including a substantial social security payroll tax increase to pay for the many "Christmas in September" programs.

Contrary to subsequent assumptions, National Medical Care played no part in the enactment of Public Law 92-603, which was principally the product of lobbying by the National Kidney Foundation and other patient and medical interest groups. In fact, during the critical period in the fall of 1972 National Medical Care, which by then operated 13 artificial kidney centers in nine states, caring for approximately 500 dialysis patients, was preparing its second public offering of common stock. In the prospectus for this sale of stock by the company (260,000 shares) and its institutional investors and some of its individual stockholders (375,800 shares), NMC did not mention the passage of P.L. 92-603, even though the prospectus was issued November 2, 1972, three days after Nixon signed the law into effect.

The references in the 1972 prospectus to Medicare make it clear that the company's officials believed that the brand new ESRD Program would be administered under Part A cost reimbursement rules with which it was familiar from its general hospital and extended care facilities operations. "Under the present Medicare program, the federal government pays the allowed direct and indirect costs (including depreciation and interest) of the services furnished ... There have been a number of changes in the Medicare and Medicaid programs since their inception. The Company expects that there will be other legislative and regulatory changes in the future which could adversely [emphasis added] affect its reimbursement from such programs," the prospectus concluded. Since federal securities laws required the company, the selling stockholders and the underwriters to disclose in such prospectuses covering the sale of stock any "material" facts, and since the clear intent of P.L. 92-603 was to provide millions of dollars to pay for kidney dialysis, it's only logical to conclude that during the week in which the Medicare ESRD Program was created, NMC officials did not consider it "material" or relevant to NMC's prospects.

In fact, not everyone associated with NMC considered the new federal program a positive development. Dr. Hager, for one, believed that the company would have done better without federal intervention, by continuing to pressure private insurance and state kidney programs for the poor and uninsured to cover dialysis. In fact, during 1972, as disclosed in the November prospectus, over 50% of the company's revenues came from non-government sources. Little by little, private insurers were covering dialysis for their beneficiaries, just as in later years with the advances in medical therapies and technologies, insurers began covering heart and liver transplants and other expensive innovations. What the new ESRD Program did was to relieve these private insurers of that responsibility (except for the initial three months of dialysis) and coopt alternative systems. As a result, NMC and other dialysis providers would have no choice but conform to the Medicare rules and in some cases, its lower reimbursement rates. Dr. Cirksena in Washington and Dr. Hull in Dallas also noted that their clinics were thriving and profitable well before the ESRD Program began in July, 1973. In retrospect, however, Dr. Hampers' view has proved valid: "While in the short term, the Medicare takeover may have depressed revenues from some insured patients, in the long term, only with Medicare's universal system would we have reached the volumes of patients so quickly," he noted. Indeed, the primary reason the planners' 1972 estimates of ESRD Program costs were so low was the fact that no one knew how many thousands of patients were dying from renal failure and were potential beneficiaries of the new Medicare program.

Between November 1972 and the ESRD Program implementation date of July 1, 1973, NMC did, finally, get involved in the administrative process at the Department of Health, Education and Welfare of deciding just how the program would work. The enabling legislation stated in sub-section 299 I (g) that:

> The Secretary is authorized to limit reimbursement under Medicare for kidney transplant and dialysis to kidney disease treatment centers which meet such requirements as he may by regulation prescribe: Provided, that such requirements must include at least requirements for a minimal utilization rate for covered procedures and for a medical review board to screen the appropriateness of patients for the proposed treatment procedures.

Thus, it would be critical to NMC's continued existence to fit within whatever criteria the Secretary of HEW included in the implementing regulations. For starters, the term "kidney disease treatment centers" was undefined in the underlying legislation, and it was not at all clear that it would include either of NMC's two models, the outpatient clinic located within an extended care facility, like the Babcock Center in Boston, or the storefront, stand-alone clinic like Dr. Schupak's in New York. More importantly, the Secretary of HEW had very broad discretion in creating "requirements as he may by regulation prescribe." NMC had no regular lobbyists in Congress or at HEW at the time, and naturally turned to its local emissaries in Washington, D.C. The task of tracking and trying to influence the regulatory outcome fell to Dr. Larry Siegel, one of the codirectors of the center in Bethesda. He did an outstanding job, and his efforts to maintain the involvement and interest in the local center among the Washington political establishment, begun at the center's opening in July, 1970, paid off.

Dr. Siegel quickly determined that the drafting of the implementing regulations would be left to insiders, HEW bureaucrats, including Irving Wolkstein and Philip Jos, and a few selected experts from the staffs of Members of Congress most familiar with the program, such as Jim Mongan and Jay Constantine from the

Senate Finance Committee and Bill Fullerton from the House Ways and Means Committee. One of the first things Siegel and Hampers did was hire Charlie Plante, a lobbyist for the National Kidney Foundation, to act as NMC's lobbyist and to keep NMC executives advised of what was happening at HEW's Bureau of Health Insurance (now, HHS' Health Care Finance Administration) headquarters in Baltimore.

HEW officials realized that they had a problem implementing a Congressional mandate to provide dialysis and transplantation to all Americans with end-stage renal disease within the budgeted estimates of $250 million per year. It wasn't long before this insider problem became public. In a front page article in the January 11, 1973 edition of The New York Times, Richard D. Lyons reported that HEW officials were concerned that the ESRD Program might end up costing ten times the amount envisioned by Congress when it passed the bill three months before. Lyons quoted several Congressmen to the effect that they had been misled about the program's costs when they voted for the measure. Senate Finance Committee staffers stated that the lower estimates used by Senator Hartke in the legislative debate and in the House-Senate conference on the bill were furnished by the Bureau of Health Insurance, a claim denied by BHI officials in the Lyons' report. Lyons goes on to quote from an 18-page memo prepared by Dr. Ronald M. Klar, a special assistant for health policy development at HEW, that projected an annual price tag of $1 billion in the tenth year (1984) of the program. As Dr. Klar pointed out, the Senate Finance Committee report erroneously assumed a static or nearly stable number of ESRD patients receiving treatment without accounting for the cumulative effect of a growing pool of patients, as new patients were added each year to the existing population that would have died without the dialysis program.

As it later turned out, even Klar's dire predictions, as reported by Lyons in 1973, were low. In 1988, the ESRD Program cost was $ 3 billion (without adjusting for inflation). The bad news was that the program was costing four to five times more than envisioned. The good news was that by the late 1980's the program was keeping ten times the number of patients alive than had been estimated. ESRD Program critics emphasize the bad news, but rarely mention the good news.

Dr. Alan Hull, a recent past president of the National Kidney Foundation, and one of NMC's early medical directors, in his study of the ESRD Program, 1973-1997, discussed the reasons for the poor early estimates. First, in extrapolating from the limited 1962-1972 federal government's experience with chronic renal failure in both the centers of excellence and the model home care programs, the estimates did not properly account for the selection of healthier, younger patients, whose costs of care were relatively low. Second, the ESRD Program was comprehensive and covered non-kidney related healthcare costs, and there were no data on these rather large costs, particularly for the older and sicker patients. Third, the numbers of patients was much higher than anticipated. This was not the result of negligence; no one had ever seen such high incidence of renal failure before 1973. It was simply a hidden phenomenon. Finally, inflation in the 1970's was rampant and far exceeded anyone's estimates; in addition, healthcare inflation was much more severe than general inflation. These were the years of annual double digit inflation and interest rates.

As the weeks and months progressed and the commencement date of July 1, 1973 quickly approached, there were two major issues for HEW to settle. The first was whether the program would be limited to not-for-profit, charitable and government-operated providers. There was a considerable amount of pressure to make the ESRD dollars go further by eliminating any chance that providers or physicians could make profits from the program. The public criticism of NMC, largely from articles in The Boston Globe in the autumn of 1971, was fresh in the minds of these program planners, and the original regulations limited participation to non-profits. Larry Siegel remembered how hard he worked to persuade HEW to create a non-discriminatory system in which the form of the provider's ownership was irrelevant, so long as it met the price established by HEW. "It became a life consuming endeavor for several months," Dr. Siegel reflected. Alan Hull recalled an illustrative incident that occurred in the early 1970's, after he and Ron Prati had opened the Dallas center. Dr. Bob Berliner of the National Institutes of Health was visiting Parkland Memorial Hospital in Dallas and Dr. Hull told him about the new outpatient dialysis clinic. "He asked me how much we charged, and I told him $200," Hull noted. "He said, 'But that includes a profit - how much without a profit?' I looked at him straight on and said, 'Without a profit, it would cost $350.' He wasn't amused. I guess he thought I was a wise guy," Hull continued.

One of the reasons Dr. Siegel was successful in arguing to allow for-profit clinics to participate in the new ESRD Program was precisely because he could demonstrate that the for profit NMC centers in fact had been charging less than the comparable charitable hospitals. Moreover, many proprietary clinics had been reducing their charges as they became more efficient and in response to pressures from private insurers during the 1968-to-1973 period. Dallas had reduced its charge from $215 per treatment to $185, as had the Washington, D.C. clinic. Babcock was charging $160, and because of a large population of Medicaid patients, Dr. Schupak's Queens center's average rate was well below $150 per dialysis. It was clear to HEW bureaucrats that shutting these efficient providers out of the program and sending the patients to the higher cost hospitals would have actually increased program costs. If the hospitals had been slightly more efficient in providing dialysis during the pre-1973 period, and if the NMC and other for-profit dialysis clinics had been less responsive to public criticism and private insurance company pressure, the ESRD Program might well have shut the free enterprise providers out of the government's exclusive program.

The second issue for HEW was setting the price for out-of-hospital dialysis clinics under Medicare's Part B system. With respect to hospital-providers, Part A, which paid 100% of the hospital's "allowable" (a term of art that created a whole accounting subspecialty of Medicare cost accounting) costs, would control the provision of in hospital dialysis (both acute and chronic), as it did for every other hospital service under the Medicare system as then administered. However, HEW's Bureau of Health Insurance had to advise its various local agents on how to determine the "reasonable and customary" charge limits for chronic dialysis under Part B (only 80% of which would be paid by the Medicare ESRD Program) for the non-hospital providers, both those operated not-for-profit and the for-profit centers, like NMC's. The task was daunting, and made all the more difficult by the lack of hard data. Costs and charges ranged all over the lot, from a low of $6,000 to a high of $50,000 per year per patient; some clinics failed to include necessary cost elements, such as rent, because their affiliated hospital-landlords did not allocate these costs to the outpatient facility; other clinics did not create reserves for depreciation of equipment; while many clinics mixed the costs of chronic and acute care on the same books.

In addition to the facility's dialysis service charge, BHI had to set a Part B fee for physicians' services for attending these renal patients, since Medicare was required to pay the doctor's fees as well. Dr. Belding Scribner of Seattle, who had been the originator of using hemodialysis as a long term, chronic maintenance therapy, was urging HEW to deny physician fees to any nephrologist who had a proprietary interest in the outpatient dialysis facility. His was a draconian suggestion that would make doctors choose whether to be clinic-operators or attending physicians, but not both. Moreover, in setting these Part B charges for dialysis facilities and physicians, BHI would have to decide which services these fees covered, since no two ESRD patients were exactly alike and each patient-beneficiary would require a mix of medical, nursing, dietary, psychological, and rehabilitation services. As the process developed, it became evident that Medicare's reimbursement decisions regarding kidney transplantation, in hospital dialysis, outpatient dialysis, home dialysis and renal physicians' fees would in fact become major factors in therapeutic decisions. HEW would not just be deciding how much to pay, but which services would be covered, and therefore, actually delivered, to renal patients all over America. Since there were legitimate differences among nephrologists about the relative merits of different therapies and services, and since every patient presented different factors, setting universal policies that could and would skew medical decisions threatened the independence of renal physicians to prescribe the precise therapeutic regimen for their patients. The biases and preferences of these kidney experts began to influence reimbursement policy - a situation that would continue throughout the life of the ESRD Program.

At the same time, there were much broader implications in the way in which the federal government, kidney patient advocates and renal physicians developed these ESRD Program regulations, since the public and political leaders were looking at the kidney program as a model for a larger, general federal government involvement in the U.S. healthcare system. As Stuart Auerbach wrote in his June 24, 1973 report in The Washington Post, "Health planners, congressmen and doctors promise to give the kidney program close scrutiny for clues as to how well the government will be able to manage a national health insurance plan." Similarly, Harold M. Schmeck, Jr., writing for The New York Times on June 27, 1973 concluded, "... [T]he kidney regulations are widely considered a test case for Government [sic] coverage of catostrophic [sic] illness in general." The early and largely uninformed judgment of these groups concerning the ESRD Program was universally negative, and has remained negative throughout the twenty-eight year history of the program.

As the startup date approached, it became clear that final regulations for the implementation of the ESRD Program would not be ready on time. On June 26, 1973, a mere five days before the ESRD Program was to commence for approximately 13,000 renal patients across the United States, the federal government issued its "Interim Regulations," promising final regulations by the end of 1973. In fact, it would be over three years before final regulations were effective, on September 1, 1976.

The Interim Regulations imposed a ceiling on the Part B "reasonable and customary" fee for dialysis at $150 per treatment. With some rare exceptions - like Dr. Schupak's Queens Artificial Kidney Center which had a low "customary" charge because of the New York Medicaid rate it had accepted prior to 1973 - most dialysis clinics had to lower their charges to this $150 ceiling. Medicare would pay 80%, or $120 per treatment, and the remaining $30 would either be paid by the patient, his third-party insurer, a state kidney program, or written off as an uncollectible bad debt by the facility. Moreover, Medicare would not pay nephrologists any additional service fee for the dialysis session itself, even if the physician was attending the patient during the treatment, as was the case at all the NMC facilities. Instead, the facility had to pay the physician separately for his dialysis supervision. In general, NMC instituted a policy of paying its attending medical directors or their delegate-physicians a supervisory fee during this initial 1973 period of $15 per treatment, leaving $105 net for the clinic. In many cases, this treatment revenue represented a large reduction in fees, since these clinics were accustomed to receiving fees of $160 to $225 per treatment from private insurance sources. On the other hand, Medicare covered virtually every American, and over time, the amount lost on individual patients with private insurance was much less than the revenue gained from Medicare for patients who would not otherwise have been covered.

From the individual patient's perspective, the Medicare ESRD Program offered mixed blessings, and is a perfect, but sad, example of the old saw that one should be careful about what he ask for, because he may, in fact, get it. In lobbying for federal intervention, the National Kidney Foundation and patient groups like NAPHT, their constituent ESRD patients and their families, scarred and scared from years of fighting simply to survive, focused almost exclusively on access. The rationing of scarce viable kidney transplants and dialysis machines naturally made the renal care community eager to craft a solution that dealt first and foremost with scarcity and ended rationing. As a result, they pushed very hard for, and secured, universality - the federal program would cover virtually everyone. Less attention was paid to issues of quality, cost, innovation and patient and physician choice.

The flip side of the universality coin is exclusivity, and any exclusive system stifles diverse solutions. In covering all Americans with kidney disease the federal ESRD Program not only set prices, but necessarily established medical, nursing, and social protocols and standards that became calcified. The price of access for all was the same treatment for all. The government program co-opted the various state, city and private insurance programs, and it was constructed in such a way that innovations, in terms of treatment modalities, rehabilitation therapies, kidney harvesting, and research were circumscribed. Consider a fantastic analogy where telephones are scarce and rationed, with only the most wealthy able to telecommunicate. The federal government adopts a universal system of providing telephones and a telephone system for everyone, sets the price, lays down the specifications, and mandates that any telephone manufacturer or supplier that participates in the government's telephone program cannot provide telephones for a higher price, even if the customer is able and willing to pay more. Can we imagine innovations like cellular phones, cordless phones, extensions, call waiting, or answering machines under such a system? Other analogies are not so fantastic - public housing, public education, and Medicaid-subsidized nursing homes come readily to mind. The federal government's ESRD Program solved the access problem too well; it opened the door to all kidney patients regardless of income, while it sealed all the other doors shut.

Moreover, during the course of the history of the ESRD Program, the goal of maintaining universal access became so expensive, as the pool of patients living with end-stage renal failure expanded beyond anyone's estimates, it came to dominate other goals, such as quality of care for individual patients, kidney research, and more intense rehabilitation. There simply was no political will or pressure to increase the ESRD budget to fund experiments, or to require better dialysis, or to invest in an intense program of harvesting functioning kidneys for transplantation. In fact, ESRD Program administrators became obsessed with lowering the fees for dialysis and physician services, so that more people could be covered. Program bureaucrats convinced the patients, their physicians, providers and lobbyists, that pushing for more would be suicidal, since the ESRD Program consistently busted its budget estimates. Healthcare economists and government policy makers, as well as politicians, consistently labeled the ESRD Program a failure without a scintilla of sophisticated analysis.

Not only did the ESRD Program establish a single, segregated, static and exclusive system of universal healthcare for kidney patients, but the system provided comprehensive care. All the medical needs of kidney patients are covered, not just their kidney related needs. When the program was first set up in 1973, no one had any idea how costly this feature would become. Therefore, ESRD Program costs include all sorts of non-renal services, e.g., surgery, psychiatry, radiology, and gynecology, and, most significantly, hospitalizations, that would have been covered by the patients, their private insurers or Medicaid, if no kidney program had been created. It's worth noting in this regard that today, of the $13 billion spend per year under the ESRD Program, approximately 60% is paid to hospitals, over half of which is for in hospital (i.e., not chronic maintenance dialysis) care.

Finally, as part of the Medicare system, ESRD Program benefits are entitlements, and as such are outside the annual Congressional appropriations process. Thus, Congress and the President cannot limit how much the federal government will spend next year on the ESRD Program, since the government is obliged to extend benefits to all who qualify. What Congress and the President can do, and with increasing frequency have done, is to amend the underlying, authorizing statute to alter the mix of benefits for all ESRD patients, and hope that these alterations will result in an actual ESRD Program expense that squares with the budget estimates. The entitlement feature is good for individual patients, of course. Their entitlement is legally enforceable, and they don't have to worry that next year the federal government will limit growth and the services will once again be rationed.

However, there are downsides to entitlement status that ultimately affect patient care. Experimental or demonstration projects in trying new ways of delivering and financing renal services are less likely. Thus, for example, grants to leading hospitals as "centers of excellence" were eliminated as unnecessary under the entitlement only ESRD Program. Programs to make block grants to states to care for their ESRD patients in more cost effective, quality enhancing, and innovative ways were never considered. Devising a program of underwriting catastrophic risks with private health insurers was never attempted, nor direct patient vouchers. Instead, the entitlement system of comprehensive, universal coverage became immutable. Another problem with entitlements is that it forces the government to use the political process to make any significant changes at all, and the political process is awkward at best, and perverse at worst, in crafting solutions to healthcare delivery and financing challenges. For example, the political process dealt clumsily with the issue of the reuse of artificial kidneys, with providers like NMC on the one side and suppliers like Baxter on the other, and politicians making healthcare decisions based on public perceptions rather than science and economics.

Looking back twenty-eight years later, after two decades of general havoc in healthcare economics, we are able to see flaws in the comprehensive, universal, entitlement system that Public Law 92-603 created, but we have to remember that in 1972 it was viewed as a great triumph of compassion and beneficial government intervention to save lives. And, indeed, it did just that - it immediately paid for renal care services that previously had been available to only the lucky few. Also, the ESRD Program was seen as the vanguard of a national healthcare system that, as it turned out, never materialized. It wasn't long before the vanguard became the nomad.

7

Reform and the Politics of Profits

Within months after its implementation, the ESRD Program was being criticized, mainly for costing so much money, and attempts were soon mounted to alter the system by amending the statute. Hospitals were unhappy because they had to compete with free standing clinics in providing chronic dialysis. The proprietary clinics were unhappy because the hospitals and the not-for-profit clinics were exceeding the fee cap by seeking and receiving "exceptions" based on their actual costs. The suppliers were unhappy because their profit margins were being squeezed by aggressive clinic operators who were trying to reduce their costs. Many clinic workers and their union representatives were unhappy because the clinic managers tightened salaries and perks and re-arranged work shifts to promote efficiency. Physicians and patients were unhappy because their choices were limited.

In 1978, Congress passed, and President Carter signed, Public Law 95-292, an attempt to reform the five-year old, ESRD Program, improve patients' lives and save tax dollars by encouraging more renal patients to dialyze at home and to seek kidney transplants. It was seen as a direct assault by a Democratic President and Congress on NMC and other proprietary dialysis clinics. Known as the Rostenkowski Bill, after the then-chairman of the House Ways and Means Committee, P.L. 95-292 politicized NMC and its executive officers, as they sought Republican assistance to save them from the Democrats' attack on "for-profit medicine." Although enacted on June 13, 1978, the statute never went into effect.

During the first five years of the ESRD Program, National Medical Care grew by leaps and bounds, as more and more nephrologists joined the NMC enterprise. These physicians chafed under the direction of large, bureaucratic medical centers, and like Drs. Schupak, Hampers and Hager, wanted to "run their own show." Many were also, undoubtedly, interested in making more money, and NMC offered its medical directors a share in the profits of the clinics that they directed. Between July 1973 and June 1978, NMC's dialysis division grew from 15 artificial kidney centers to 90 such centers, and its operations were having an impact, not only on other dialysis providers, but on artificial kidney manufacturers and the administrators of the ESRD Program, whom NMC had taken to court on more than one occasion.

One lawsuit, Schupak v. Califano (during the long course of the litigation the defendant-Secretary of HEW changed to Weinberger and then Mathews), Dr. Schupak challenged the government's authority to collect cost data from outpatient dialysis centers like those owned by NMC. The basic argument was that since the dialysis fee was set administratively, the cost data were immaterial and its collection beyond the scope of HEW administrators. In another lawsuit, Erika vs. U.S., which was ultimately decided against NMC by the United States Supreme Court on a jurisdictional basis, the company also asserted its rights against what it perceived as over-reaching by HEW (later, HHS) officials. None of these actions endeared NMC to the Medicare bureaucrats or their Democratic allies in Congress.

In its original and intended form, the Rostenkowski Bill would have mandated that half, or 50%, of all chronic, maintenance dialysis patients be treated at home under a self-care program. It also corrected some anomalies in the law by paying for continuing care for patients who had received a successful kidney transplant (in the original statute, successfully transplanted patients were on their own shortly after the procedure, even though they would require considerable continuing care and medications). Advocates of the amendment, dubbed the "Scribner Amendment" after the famous Seattle nephrologist who believed strongly in the home care modality, included artificial kidney manufacturers and other suppliers, ESRD Program bureaucrats, but few patients and very few physicians. NMC and other clinic operators strongly opposed the bill. Physicians and clinic operators (and in NMC's case these were the same group of people) correctly viewed the proposal as a clumsy attempt to restrict therapies and severely limit patient choice. Clinical nephrologists, who were actually caring for patients, knew first hand that far fewer than 50% of them could handle home care, and no one more so than Gene Schupak, who had been the first to prescribe home care for his patients, or Gus Hampers who had extended the home care program at the Brigham in the mid-sixties.

By 1978 the ESRD patient population had changed dramatically. On average, they were older, sicker and poorer than the typical patient who was referred to the Brigham a decade or more before. Many didn't have the middle class amenities, advantages or education that were required to effect a home care program. Moreover, even those patients who might have been able to handle home care didn't want to. Given a choice between home care and death, home care meant survival, but given a choice between home care or incenter care, only a minority chose home care.

Of course, the impetus for this change was cost considerations. By 1978 the ESRD Program was costing the taxpayers approximately $ 800 million per year, or over 300 % of the original estimate, and the incidence (the number of new diagnoses) of renal failure had reached 16,000 new patients every year - twice the rate expected in 1973. The advocates of home care claimed it would save millions of Program dollars. They also argued that home care was actually better for patients' health, but the primary thrust was around saving money. Home care was not just cheap but better, they contended. Of course, the argument was logical and was endorsed by politicians and the media, and largely accepted as true by the public. Just as dining at home is cheaper than going to a restaurant (and probably better for you, too), do-it-yourself dialysis appeared more efficient. NMC pointed out that the cost savings were inflated, and to the extent they existed, resulted from the free labor of the spouse, or other unpaid family members or friends who were responsible for assisting the patient at home.

There are three roughly equivalent expense components in providing dialysis - labor, supplies and overhead, largely resulting from the cost of the facility and the equipment. Furnishing the same supplies to patients at home was inefficient and more costly (that's, of course, why manufacturers of artificial kidneys and suppliers of other disposable materials supported the Rostenkowski proposal). Buying dialysis equipment, chairs, water purification devices and plumbing and wiring the patients' homes, as well as paying competent technicians to periodically service, calibrate and inspect the equipment, was much more expensive than getting multiple uses from the same equipment at a central location (thus, support from companies selling these products and services). Therefore, the only way home care was marginally less expensive was by using the unpaid labor of a family member. Some families accepted this burden gladly, since home care provides more flexibility, but for these patients, no statutory amendments were necessary - they could always opt for home care and many did, at least temporarily.

Sue Faber, whose husband, Rick, began a chronic dialysis regimen at the Brigham in 1968, remembered the five years that Rick was a home patient as a time when their lives were constantly disrupted as their home was transformed into a dialysis clinic and their basement and garage became miniwarehouses for dialysis supplies. Sue's responsibilities encompassed much more than helping her husband with the actual treatment. Ordering supplies and being home to accept delivery, cleaning the treatment area, meeting with visiting nurses and technicians. And above all, the overwhelming knowledge that her husband's survival depended on her assistance. "People don't realize the profound effect home dialysis has on a family. The machine and supplies are always there. You can't forget about it even for an hour. And it affects the children," Sue recalled. Rick Faber, a college professor and in 1978 the president of the Kidney Transplant/Dialysis Association, with a smart, resourceful family and a comfortable suburban home, was one of those patients who would have likely been forced to dialyze at home under the 1978 Scribner Amendment as originally proposed. Instead, Rick has dialyzed at various clinics in the Boston area continuously for the past 25 years, preferring to keep his home life as normal as possible and pursuing his fulltime college teaching career.

In the 1978 amendment's final version, the strict 50% mandates were diluted to unenforceable, national goals that HHS was ordered to achieve by means of its own devising, including altering the reimbursement policies in order to encourage home dialysis. Although Congress seemed to accept the cost-saving argument, it did not have the political will to prescribe treatment modalities by statute. For the ensuing three years, which straddled the 1980 presidential election, HHS attempted, but failed, to promulgate regulations to implement Section 1881 (b) (2) (B) of Public Law 95-292. NMC became heavily involved in both the inside game of lobbying HHS officials and ranking members of Congress and their staffs on the relevant committees of the House and Senate, and the outside, public debate, that became very intense, as HHS considered shifting dialysis reimbursement dollars away from high cost hospitals toward free standing clinics, and away from all chronic dialysis facilities toward direct home suppliers in its quest to increase the incidence of home care. Millions of dollars were likely to be transferred from one set of providers and suppliers to another, based on these decisions.

On October 30, 1977 60 Minutes, then and now one of the top ten rated programs on television, aired a segment on the ESRD Program and its cost over-runs in general, and on the profits being made by National Medical Care, in particular. On the advice of counsel, NMC officials refused to speak with the CBS producers or correspondents. The broadcast sensationalized the debate over the cost of the five-year old federal kidney program and whether profit making from the program by clinics, such as those operated by NMC, was necessary and/or desirable. The broadcast also encouraged other reports, some more responsible and accurate than others.

In general the media shared and publicized the same, irrational syllogism. First, the ESRD Program was good - it kept very sick people alive. Second, the ESRD Program was in jeopardy because it cost too much money. Third, NMC and other proprietary clinics were making huge profits off the ESRD Program. The false conclusion was that, unless NMC and other for-profit operators were purged from the Program, the Program would collapse. Of course, wiser heads at HHS knew that without NMC the ESRD Program would have been even more expensive, but they allowed the scape goating to continue, because it provided a target for irate taxpayers and members of Congress.

The strategy of casting the low cost providers as the villains in the morality drama also resulted in elevating patient fears that the ESRD Program was broken and might be dismantled - all because of NMC greed. Every NMC patient had an anecdote evidencing that "greed" (others would call it efficiency) from the reuse of dialyzers to reductions in nurse-to-patient ratios to a shortage of blankets. It didn't matter that patients in charity hospitals had the same, or worse, complaints; what mattered was that in their view, profits were being made by squeezing the patients and the Program. HHS bureaucrats, hospital administrators, and dialysis supply companies were not interested in helping NMC out of this box. Neither were the patient organizations or the National Kidney Foundation, which had developed a somewhat irrational bias against proprietary dialysis operators. Where there should have been a strong alliance to extend and improve the ESRD Program, there was instead suspicion and distrust.

NMC and its leaders weren't always diplomatic in discussing these conflicts, and at times, fed the fears of patients and their allies at the NKF, as well as at HHS and in Congress. As noted, NMC didn't hesitate to file lawsuits against the government, thereby freezing relationships, and consuming a lot of time by HHS officials and lawyers, even though some of these suits appeared to be for reasons of delay and obstruction, rather than for substantive concerns. Although their interests were so closely allied, NMC never developed a strong bond with the patient associations, the NKF or the renal physicians groups, leaving this diplomacy to the individual doctors/medical directors. Financial contributions by NMC to these charities would have gone a long way to reversing images of greed and self-interest. Also, NMC chose political alliances with conservative Republicans like Bob Dole and Ronald Reagan. NMC hired John Sears, Reagan's 1976 presidential campaign manager, and later Lyn Nofzinger, Reagan's former advisor, to provide lobbying and government relations advice. These were not the natural allies of HHS bureaucrats or patients dependent on government largess, who, instead, sought protection and help from liberal Democrats. As they shed their lab coats for grey business suits, and spent more time on Wall Street than in hospitals, the NMC leaders became more closely associated with conservative politicians and disassociated from those whom the patients saw as their allies.

Nearly a year after the passage of P.L. 95-292, HHS finally proposed an incentive reimbursement system under the mandate of section 1881 (b)(2)(B). The hospitals were not pleased, as the first implementation plan called for a single rate of reimbursement for chronic dialysis, regardless of the setting and without exceptions. NMC liked this plan, because as the low cost provider, NMC expected to gain market share, as many high cost hospitals abandoned chronic dialysis, sold their clinics to NMC, or contracted with NMC to manage their dialysis facilities. NMC also anticipated that its profits would rise, since the single rate set by HHS would have to be high enough to keep at least some of the more efficient hospitals in the system.

The "reform" legislation of 1978 and the implementing regulations did not address an important issue. While focusing almost entirely on reducing costs by encouraging (some would say, forcing) patients to dialyze at home, and trying to eliminate the high-cost, mainly in hospital, providers from the system, the federal government failed to address the issue of quality of care. It was almost as if the government had decided that these ESRD patients should simply be grateful that they had a "free" government program to keep them alive. With a five-year history under its belt, HHS was interested exclusively in gathering cost data, but gave no thought to gathering medical data to find out whether these patients were being well cared for, adequately dialyzed, and whether there were measurable differences in clinical results between and among patients being dialyzed in costly hospital settings, at home, or in free standing clinics, and whether outcomes were different between not-for-profit and for-profit providers, or whether frequency of physician contact was a determinant in quality. One nagging question that was not addressed was why so many dialysis patients were being hospitalized and why such a large proportion of ESRD Program dollars was not paying for transplants or dialysis, but for in hospital services. Amazingly, even though the taxpayers were footing a $ 1 billion per year bill for the kidney program by 1978, there were no NIH or HHS grants being directed to determine why so many patients were so sick.

A second issue, also related to quality of care, that was ignored in reforming the ESRD Program after its first five years, was whether rehabilitation goals were being met, and how the ESRD Program could improve the rate of rehabilitating patients to become fully productive workers. Since a persuasive argument advanced before Congressional committees in 1972 was that with transplantation and dialysis therapies, the ESRD patient could resume a normal, working, taxpaying life, it's difficult to explain why the government didn't demand an accounting of rehabilitation successes and failures and redesign the program to facilitate patient rehabilitation. By 1978 the "typical" patient in a dialysis facility did not come close to resembling Shep Glazier who had testified before the House Ways and Means Committee in 1972.

Thirdly, in attempting to reform the ESRD Program in 1978, Congress and the Administration failed to analyze scientific, medical and technological advances that had been made during, and partly as a result of, the five-year old ESRD Program. Both transplantation and dialysis had progressed during those five years, but these innovations - high flux, capillary dialyzers, reuse technology, more effective immunosuppressant medications, bicarbonate dialysate, surgical advances, and central delivery systems, to name a few - were largely ignored. Rather than commissioning a group of experts, like the Gottschalk Commission of the late 1960's, to advise them on these advances and the likely advances in the succeeding five years, the policy makers viewed the system as static, and predictably, the reimbursement policies they adopted tended toward stasis. In fact, the original 1972 enabling legislation (P.L. 92-603) provided for a board of experts to advise HHS, but none was ever appointed.

Most significantly, the reform effort failed to address the single most important (and obvious) issue for the ESRD Program and for the lives of patients with irreversible kidney failure, and that was, and is, the insufficiency of kidneys for transplantation. In 1978 there were about 55,000 patients enrolled in the ESRD Program with end-stage renal disease; today there are about 340,000. The vast majority of these patients could live healthier and more productive lives, and the taxpayers could save billions of dollars, if functional kidneys could be transplanted rather than buried. By 1978, everyone knew that transplantation worked both with cadaver and living related kidneys, and that over the long-term it saved thousands, if not hundreds of thousands, of dollars for each patient, not to mention the vastly improved lives for patients freed from thrice weekly dialysis treatments. In 1978, and subsequently in each case when the federal government considered ESRD Program changes, it has avoided the most critical issue of encouraging more people to donate their kidneys.

Two other issues the 1978 ESRD Program reform ignored were whether and how Medicare could and should curb the universal and comprehensive features of the Program. With five years of data, HHS could have analyzed whether there were a number of patients whose care should be financed by their private insurers (or in the case of uninsured, wealthy individuals, out of their own pockets). Consider, for example the case of two hypothetical employees of XYZ Corp., both doing the same job for the same wage with the same benefits, including a family health insurance plan toward which each employee contributes the same premium. Employee A's wife is afflicted with end-stage renal failure, while Employee B's husband develops severe coronary disease. In the first case, Medicare pays for renal care, whereas in the second, the insurance plan pays. Each year the insurance company raises the premium, partly as a result of the enormous costs of financing Employee B's husband's care, and Employee A (along with every other employee in the group) pays a resulting premium increase. In 1972, the ESRD Program was passed in part because a national, universal healthcare system was expected to follow. However, by 1978, the ESRD Program was still unique, and plans for a broad, government financed system had been shelved. Why then, in 1978, didn't Congress and HHS consider a shift from the public back to the private sector for all but the indigent and elderly?

Or, if not a complete shift, why not a partial shift by eliminating the comprehensive feature? Back to our hypothetical example: Both the wife of Employee A and the husband of Employee B slip and fall on the ice, breaking their femurs. Medicare pays for the orthopedic care for A's wife, but B's husband's orthopedic needs are financed by the private health insurance plan. More significant than the question - why? - is the question, why didn't the government ask, why? A larger and larger share of the ESRD Program dollars was being spent on non-kidney related care, which, but for the ESRD Program's comprehensiveness, would have been otherwise financed either by the patient, the patient's private insurance or HMO or Medicaid (or, of course, Medicare, for the elderly). A significant part of the "catastrophic" program was being consumed by very routine and ordinary medical needs. In later years, Medicare would shift the financing burden back to private insurance by extending the initial pre-Medicare period, during which the private sector would finance renal care, from three months to 18 months to the current 30-month period. However, no attempt has been initiated to end the comprehensive feature of the ESRD Program, even though the percentage of ESRD Program costs spent for those in hospital services which are not kidney-related continues to increase.

In sum, the 1978 reform effort did not attempt to alter the aspects of the ESRD Program that were clearly costing the taxpayers much more money than Congress or HHS bureaucrats had anticipated five years before. Universal acceptance criteria that resulted in a sicker and older patient pool, deteriorating quality of care that resulted in more and longer hospitalizations, poor rehabilitation results, medical and technical advances, a dearth of transplant kidneys, the inequity of a universal system for one disease, and the illogic of comprehensive coverage in all cases, were largely ignored in their zeal to cut costs by forcing patients to accept home dialysis. Program cost over runs were the obvious manifestation of a financing system that required a major overhaul based on considerable five-year experience. Instead, accepting the simplistic diagnosis of Dr. Scribner and his acolytes, who were sure that the excess costs were going into the pockets of NMC medical directors and stockholders, the policy makers decided to cut costs by enslaving patients' family members to provide free (and often poor) care, and blamed this draconian solution on NMC's greed. Not surprisingly, the plan didn't work. Home hemodialysis rates continued to drop. Within a decade it would largely be the least significant form of care, having been supplanted for those who didn't want to be tied to a clinic by a different form of care entirely, known as continuous ambulatory peri-toneal dialysis ("CAPD").

The initial 1979 plan floated by HHS to implement the "prospective, incentive rate" system prescribed in P.L. 95-292 was promptly and vigorously shot down by the hospitals. What fol-lowed, in September, 1980, was a proposal from HHS for a dual rate system of reimbursement, one for hospitals and another for free standing clinics, like those operated by NMC. NMC and other clinics, including many non-profit clinics, objected vociferously, and jointly engaged counsel to challenge the proposal in court as being unauthorized and in fact, antithetical to the intent of the underlying 1978 legislation.

In November 1980 before final regulations were adopted under P.L. 95-292, Ronald Reagan was elected the 40th President of the United States, the same Reagan that had publicly defended National Medical Care and the single rate, incentive based system that it espoused. Moreover, the Republicans took control of the U.S. Senate, and Senator Bob Dole, another ally of NMC (and a co-sponsor of the originating ESRD Program legislation of 1972), became chairman of the Senate Finance Committee, to which all bills relating to Medicare were referred. Senator Dole, who had been Gerald Ford's vice president running mate in his unsuccess-ful, 1976 reelection campaign, sought and received early support from NMC executives in Dole's brief primary campaign against Reagan in 1980 (At the same time, Dr. Hager resigned from National Medical Care to run, unsuccessfully, as it turned out, for the U.S. Senate from New Hampshire). At a fund raiser organized by Dr. Hampers and his colleagues, Dole predicted accurately that the Republicans would win control of the U.S. Senate that November, and that supporting him for president was a no lose situation for NMC officers, since even if he lost the presidential nomination, "at worst" Dole would become chairman of the criti-cal Senate Finance Committee. And that's exactly what happened.

Things were looking much better for NMC, and in fact, the first signs from Reagan's Department of Health and Human Services, then headed by Richard Schweiker, former Senator from Pennsylvania (1969-1981), were most promising. At the May 1981 annual stockholders meeting Dr. Hampers confidently predicted that HHS would adopt a single, incentive rate, which was precisely what would help NMC most. In June, 1981, HHS in fact issued a proposal for a single, incentive rate for chronic, maintenance dialysis. At the same time, NMC began an aggressive marketing campaign among hospitals to manage their outpatient dialysis centers, maintaining that only an efficient provider like NMC could save their chronic dialysis programs which would otherwise become major loss centers for the hospitals under the June 1981 proposed rates. The hospitals, many of which probably weren't even aware of the proposed change in dialysis reimbursement, were thereby alerted and complained to HHS officials and politicians. NMC management again misread the political situation and pushed ahead prematurely. The aggressive tactics used by NMC were turned against the company by politicians who wanted to protect their local, community hospitals. The June 1981 regulations were never adopted.

Instead, Congress intervened in the summer of 1981, by inserting a provision in the Omnibus Budget Reconciliation Act of 1981 (Section 2145 of Public Law 97-35, August 13, 1981) that mandated separate, so called "composite" rates for free standing facilities and for hospitals. Just as even the most conservative members of Congress will authorize spending money against the advice of Pentagon officials in order to save a local military base, the 97th Congress quickly acted to help local hospitals. Congress settled the dual v. single rate issue in favor of a dual rate that allowed for higher costs for hospital based providers. Writing in The New England Journal of Medicine at the time (February 25, 1982) John K. Inglehart noted, "Congress has accepted the argument of hospitals that their costs are higher because they treat sicker patients, even though there is little or no evidence to substantiate that argument." Politics trumped economics.

The Congressional mandate also weighed in on the home care incentive issue by requiring a rate "composed" from cost data for delivering home care and for providing incenter care. The result was a strong financial incentive for home care suppliers. However, it had no significant effect in directing patients home and squeezed both hospital and free standing chronic dialysis providers by reducing their reimbursement rates. In fact, the composite rate was such a boon to suppliers like Baxter and other companies that Wall Street analysts and some NMC stockholders were incensed that Hampers and his team refused to accept the verdict and start sending patients home, which would have boosted NMC's earnings and stock price. As one analyst stated in the Fortune magazine article, "The trouble with National Medical Care is it's run by a doctor. A businessman would be saying, 'Hey, this is the coming thing, we'd better get into it.' Not Gus. He doesn't like this particular mode of therapy, so he turns his back on it. That is not the way to run a company." In fact, Hampers was as familiar with home care, including its limitations and the effect it had on the patient's health and family life, as any doctor in the country. Moreover, the investment community did not appreciate the fact that the patients' physicians, not NMC executives, decided on the form of therapy. Even if Hampers tried to enhance profits by encouraging home care under the new composite rate structure, he couldn't tell the doctors what to do. "If we could put a third of our patients home, why the hell wouldn't we?" Hampers stated in the Fortune article. "We'd make a fortune. But the fact is, they're not going."

It's ironic to note that in changing ESRD Program reimbursement policies, the politicians, aided by HCFA bureaucrats, used the capitalist assumption that behavior would be controlled by profit-making, in order to increase home care. Instead of educating doctors or patients on the advantages of home care (there weren't any), they attempted to require patients to go home by offering less money to clinic operators and more money to home suppliers. These policy makers assumed that the physicians would respond to the financial incentives. The ploy didn't work, largely because physicians put their patients' health and welfare above their own financial gain.

By the time the composite rate system was implemented two years later, the average hospital rate was trimmed by $18 per treatment and the free standing rate was sliced by $11 per dialysis, as shown in the following table:

Comparison of Average Reimbursement Rates for Outpatient Dialysis
(current, not constant dollars)

	1973-83	1983-86	1986-88	1989-90*	1991-
Hospitals	$159	$131	$129	$127	$128
Independent	$138	$127	$125	$123	$124

* $2 per Rx sequestered. In addition, $0.50/ Rx was deducted to fund the medical information system. Stated in constant inflation adjusted dollars, the current rates are less than one-third the original rates.

The reform attempt, begun in 1978 and concluded in 1983, did nothing to improve the quality of care, expand access, or create options for patients and their doctors. It didn't always protect local hospitals, either, and forced many high cost providers out of business. For purely budgetary reasons, the federal government squarely and forcefully inserted itself into the therapeutic debate concerning the merits of home care. Finally, it required dialysis facilities to use every possible means to cut costs and eschew quality enhancing changes, wherever these would add expenses. And in the end, it failed to slow down growth or save significant program costs.

Secretary Schweiker's Department of Health and Human Services announced its rates based on the 1981 legislation on November 25, 1981, the Wednesday preceding the Thanksgiving weekend. At Dr. Hampers' direction, within a few days NMC accountants prepared a list of NMC facilities that experienced costs in excess of their stipulated reimbursement rates. The list demonstrated that 60 of NMC's 160 centers then in operation would be reimbursed at levels below their true costs (the definition of costs became critical in this analysis, since the government and the company calculated costs in vastly different ways). Hampers then commenced an aggressive campaign to roll back the proposed rates, enlisting the help of other providers, nephrologists and patient organizations, arguing that he had a fiduciary obligation not to waste his stockholders' assets on losing endeavors and that the government was decimating the ESRD Program. Hampers felt betrayed by the Reagan Administration and his Republican friends, including Senator Bob Dole who easily forgot the campaign financing help he had received from Hampers and his cohorts and started denouncing fat cat doctors who drove around in their expensive Mercedes automobiles.

The fight became public, and the gloves came off. On December 21, 1981, NMC announced publicly that if the rates went into effect as proposed, NMC would close those 60 centers identified as underreimbursed, and the patients would be without dialysis. It was a dramatic gesture and one that those who knew Hampers well understood he would never implement. The steel grey suit only thinly covered the same doctor who used every means at his disposal to prevent the Brigham from sending patients home to die. The threat, however, naturally panicked the patients, their families, and their doctors, who in turn began pressuring Congress. The announcement had a depressing effect on NMC's stock price with a drop of over 10% on a single day. Schweiker was placed in an uncomfortable position, as members of Congress complained. As later described by Anne B. Fisher in Fortune magazine (July 25, 1983), "National's lobbying efforts against the new rates might be a textbook example of how not to make friends in Washington," and quoted one securities analyst to the effect that, "When you deal with Washington, you have to be humble. Humble, Hampers isn't."

Within 24 hours of NMC's threat to close 60 centers, Baxter, the largest domestic supplier of dialysis products and the leading proponent of home care, publicly called Hampers' bluff by offering to take over operations at the 60 centers, so that the patients would not have to worry. The following day NMC took up the challenge and probably sealed its fate on this issue by announcing publicly that it would sell the 60 centers to Baxter for $100 million. For politicians and HCFA bureaucrats, NMC's offer to sell the clinics for no less than $100 million was evidence that the company's threats were insubstantial. Hampers was caught between assuring his stockholders that he would not throw away their assets, and trying to convince policy makers that the $10-12 per treatment cuts would make the 60 clinics worthless. The harder Hampers tried to assure Wall Street that he would manage their investments in NMC, the harder it was for him and his lobbyists to convince Washington that the proposed rate cuts were devastating. In the same Fortune article, an unidentified HCFA official reiterates the non-sensical but prevalent argument that "the payment rates were really set too high in the first place. National's rapid expansion in the 1970's, from six clinics to 160, is empirical evidence of that." Using this central planning logic, rates should be raised only after clinics closed and demand exceeded supply, forcing rationing of the type experienced in the pre-1973 era. The bureaucrats forgot that the commodity at issue was life saving medical care, not potatoes, and what Hampers forgot was the fierce animus that the political establishment had against profit-making healthcare.

Eventually, the parties retreated to their neutral corners, temperatures declined and civility was restored, but NMC had lost face in the exchange. Lyn Nofzinger, architect of the 1980 Reagan victory, who had become a prominent Washington lobbyist and was advising Hampers in 1981, insisted that Hampers send Secretary Schweiker an apology and that he take a less visible role in the company's government relations. On February 12, 1982, the HCFA announced rates became official as part of a Notice of Proposed Rule-Making (NPRM), and in due course incorporated in Final Regulations on May 11, 1983, to become effective on August 11, 1983.

The debate, however, continued and continues yet today. Was the initial $138 rate set too high? Was the $11 cut appropriate? Is the proper measure of reimbursement the resulting profits of a subset of providers? In retrospect it's clear that the Program administrators and politicians were asking the wrong questions. Instead of trying to have a central bureaucracy set prices, they should have been creating a system that allowed the free market to set the price. Rather than worrying about the level of NMC's profits and the need to subsidize inefficient community hospitals, policy analysts ought to have been finding ways to ensure and enhance quality of care for patient-beneficiaries. Where HCFA was spending its resources on directing patients toward home care, they could have been studying ways to increase transplantation and curb the ever increasing incidence of renal failure through creative scientific, epidemiologic, and public health research and experimentation. These failures sadly continue today to plague the ESRD Program.

The effect of the intense fight over the 1978-83 ESRD Program "reform" effort on National Medical Care and Gus Hampers, who played a central, galvanizing and controversial role in that debate, was more significant than its effect on the health of kidney patients. It became clear that pleasing Wall Street with predictions and realizations of higher profits, while leading the charge to increase reimbursement rates for ESRD providers was impossible. As a publicly traded company, NMC was legally and morally required to disclose its earnings, and the factors that would or could influence those earnings. As the single largest dialysis provider in the country, NMC had a responsibility to improve the financial and clinical efficacy of the ESRD Program. High earnings reports that made stockholders happy made the bureaucrats and politicians antagonistic. Acquisition programs that increased NMC's market share were used as evidence of over reimbursement by ESRD Program critics. Dire predictions of funding inadequacies before Congressional committees resulted in a fall in the price of NMC's common stock. It became clear that NMC would be better off outside the public arena, perhaps as a private company or as part of a larger conglomerate.

In addition, by 1980 Hampers was operating alone. Dr. Schupak left NMC in July 1979, and Dr. Hager resigned to run for the Senate in March, 1980. When the controversy hit fever pitch in late 1981 and early 1982, the former Baxter executive, Peter Phildius, who had been hired in November 1978, largely to replace Gene Schupak in operating the products side of the company, had also resigned (October, 1981). Dr. Hampers, who always had a hard time delegating critical responsibilities to subordinates, was personally and solely attempting to promote the company to its investors and potential investors, lead the industry defense against the persistent attacks of the government and the media, support his medical directors in their quest for autonomy and independence, and simultaneously operate a $300 million dollar (annual revenues by late 1981) corporation. No constituency felt placated. The medical directors refused to deal with non-physician corporate employees, HCFA saw Hampers as a non-compliant combatant, ready to litigate at the drop of a hat, and Wall Street was uneasy with a doctor running a large corporation, particularly after Peter Phildius left the company. Gus Hampers was more conscious of these problems than anyone else, and realized that he needed one or more partners. Consequently, the 1978-83 reform controversy effected more changes at NMC than it did in the ESRD Program.

In the years since 1983, no one has seriously proposed reforming the ESRD Program. Instead, HCFA and Congress have fine tuned the Program, sequestering part of the payment during bad budget times, funding a much needed medical information system, and tinkering with the reimbursement rate in massive Budget Reconciliation Bills, usually completed in House-Senate conference reports, far from the pressures of lobbyists and the scrutiny of the public. Over the past fifteen years HCFA has tried to squeeze more services out of the providers and doctors for the same price, making the clinic operators decide whether to cut their margins (or in some case, increase their deficits) by providing quality enhancing drugs, laboratory tests, and nutritional supplements and other services, or maintain their margins by refusing to provide patients with these advances.

For its part, Congress has from time to time held oversight hearings that predictably castigate providers, and align the political establishment with patient-advocates, while masking the government's complicity in not funding much needed improvements in the ESRD Program. These are usually preceded by several well-placed critical articles in newspapers and broadcast media, reciting the stale mantra that the providers are ripping-off the taxpayers and hurting the patients. A typical example occurred in 1986 before the Special Senate Committee on Aging, chaired by Senator John Heinz of Pennsylvania, regarding the reuse of dialyzers. Bypassing the normal committee process (Medicare and health issues would normally be investigated by the Finance Committee or the Labor and Human Resources Committee or, perhaps, the Appropriations Committee's Subcommittee on Health) Chairman Heinz was responding to a sensational report in The Philadelphia Enquirer (entitled "Blood Money") that was largely based on the complaints of a patient that the system of reusing dialyzers was dangerous. The media covered the opening polemics from Heinz and other committee members, but gave scant attention to the testimony that followed from both healthcare providers as well as HCFA officials that reuse was common, safe, and efficient. Even The Philadelphia Enquirer later printed a clarification, short of a retraction, after Terry Daniels, an executive of W.R. Grace, which by 1986 owned a controlling interest in NMC, and Grace lawyers met with newspaper editors.

To reduce the ESRD Program costs, the federal government has amended the Program so that private insurers and HMO's stand as "primary" payors for longer periods of time, thus shifting the burden from taxpayers to the private sector. Today, the first thirty (30) months of treatment is paid by the patient's primary insurer (for those that have insurance or HMO plans) and Medicare takes a secondary ("MSP" - Medicare as Secondary Payor) position until the 31st month. For patients without private coverage, Medicare covers the costs from the outset. Since the private insurers generally pay more for treatments and ancillary services and prescriptions, the shift to an MSP system is encouraged by providers and physicians.

This lack of controversy and dearth of effort to enact major reforms in the ESRD Program since the mid-1980's has had both benign and harmful effects. On the one hand, the industry has matured and settled. The inefficient providers have been absorbed or replaced and there remains sufficient capacity to attend to the increasing dialysis demands from not just more patients, but older and increasingly sicker patients as well. No one would have predicted in 1972 that there would be 350,000 ESRD patients by the end of the twentieth century. Reimbursement has become predictable and assured and the providers and the government have been less antagonistic and more cooperative and civil. However, at the same time the system has tended toward an unhealthy, uncreative and numbing stasis. The patients, nephrologists, providers and government officials have avoided critical analysis. Where the ESRD Program was seen in its infancy as a fresh, exciting forerunner of healthcare reform, it has now become accepted as an embarrassment, almost like the crazy uncle in the attic of Medicare. Nephrology, once considered a challenging and worthy medical specialty, has been attracting too few qualified physicians, creating a shortage of kidney specialists. The serious problems - increasing morbidity, insufficient transplantation, higher costs, to name three - have simply been ignored. Complacency has replaced controversy.

After a quarter century, judgments about the ESRD Program have mellowed somewhat and are generally positive, particularly among those who lived through the pre-1973 era of scarcity and rationing. Eli A. Friedman, M.D., the chief of the Department of Medicine at the State University of New York Health Science Center in Brooklyn, and one of the pioneers of dialysis, wrote in 1996 (Journal of the American Medical Association,vol.275), "...the U.S. ESRD program should be viewed as a successful prototype of how an expensive and complex life sustaining regimen can be implemented universally with remarkable cost effectiveness." In fact Dr. Friedman cites the experience as justifying replication and expansion, "I conclude that the U.S. ESRD program is a splendid model of how a national healthcare system might serve all of us." The most accomplished analyst of the ESRD Program, Richard A. Rettig, formerly of the RAND Corporation, wrote in the 1991 study commissioned by the Institute of Medicine that, "although total ESRD Program costs are high, cost control for dialysis has been impressive." And specifically with respect to the role of for-profit clinics in providing care, Rettig concluded, "The committee [Committee for the Study of the Medicare End-Stage Renal Disease Program of the Division of Health Care Services of the IOM] is aware of no evidence that the shift from hospital based to independent and from not-for-profit to for-profit dialysis facilities has resulted in problems of access or quality."

Drs. Hampers and Hager offered their own earlier assessment of the program in an April 1979 issue of Dialysis & Transplantation (vol 8, no.4), which was considered by that journal's editors in 1996 as one of the landmark articles in its 25-year history. They wrote then that "...the objective evidence is overwhelming in establishing the incentive-based, proprietary sector as the key economic factor in the success of the ESRD Program...The growth of our country's ESRD Program is an excellent example of what can be achieved when the best of modern medical care is coupled with the best of modern business practices."

Shortly after the ESRD Program began, in an article published in Medical World News in August 1976, Dr. James C. Hunt, the president at that time of the National Kidney Foundation, and a specialist at the prestigious Mayo Clinic, questioned whether the ESRD Program was a "monstrosity" because it was costing so much more than anticipated. The view of this leading physician, who was as familiar as anyone in the country concerning the plight of renal patients and who, as president of the NKF, served as their spokesman, was "...there just aren't enough resources to provide all the care everybody needs." Fortunately, for thousands of kidney patients, Dr. Hunt's admonitions were ignored and the combination of government largess, medical ingenuity, and business acumen found and applied sufficient resources to "provide all the care everybody needed."

8

Visibility vs Viability

During the first decade of the Medicare End-Stage Renal Disease Program, 1973 to 1983, National Medical Care's artificial kidney division grew from twenty (20) outpatient dialysis clinics to 170, and its revenues increased nearly ten fold, from $35 million to $311 million per annum. NMC's earnings for 1973 were $ 2,058,000; ten years later, the last year for which NMC reported earnings as a public company, its earnings were $23,125,000. It was impossible for the ESRD regulators and the media to look at these spectacular returns and not conclude superficially that the taxpayers were getting a raw deal. On the flip side, by the early 1980's financial reporters and investment analysts believed that NMC's future prospects were limited and subject to the control of government bureaucrats and politicians, thereby depressing the value of NMC stock.

Gus Hampers spent a good part of the decade prior to 1984 trying to convince both sets of commentators that they were wrong. His case that both the government and the investors could benefit from NMC's expansion was an uphill struggle. His arguments contradicted the tenets of the zero sum paradigm that was shared by both Medicare experts and Wall Street insiders. Every piece of good news about NMC's financial success reported in the business pages was quoted by Congressional staff and Medicare officials to support ESRD Program cutbacks. Similarly, the government's short sighted initiatives to save expenses, such as promoting home care as a viable alternative, or rejecting ancillary services and charges, were seen by the investment community as threats to NMC's continued profitability. Securing capital from the public required full disclosure, but as the largest provider of kidney dialysis in a system with Medicare as the sole buyer, NMC's disclosure limited its growth and profitability. As Dr. Hampers recalled, "We were operating in a fishbowl where every flaw was not just perceptible, but became magnified."

Four possible avenues of escape from this dilemma suggested themselves. The most obvious avenue - returning to the status of a private company and financing operations and growth from a few major investors and loans from banks and insurance companies - was impossible in the 1970's and early 80's with double-digit interest rates devouring potential profits. Even if interest rates had been reasonable, there were no identifiable investors with enough capital to buy the stock from the public shareholders. In addition, setting a fair price for the stock that would pass the muster of the securities regulators would have been a huge challenge, given the fact that Hampers, Hager and Schupak, as NMC founders and controlling insiders, would be in a position of conflict of interest in attempting to purchase the company back from the public shareholders. If they paid too much, they would fail, and if they succeeded, they would have invited lawsuits. By 1976, NMC was already worth well over $100 million, and that value kept increasing as the years passed. Replacing the public investors with private financing was not a promising alternative at that time.

Eliminating the private financing solution meant that NMC could avoid the "fishbowl" dilemma by either becoming part of a larger corporation with operations that dwarfed and disguised NMC's dialysis business, thus making the profits from this Medicare purchased segment difficult, if not impossible, to compute, or by having NMC itself diversify into other, non-dialysis, lines of business to the same effect. Either strategy was intended to replace the spotlight with a flood light. The fourth, and final, strategy to deal with the dilemma of being penalized for being successful was not really an escape at all, but, instead, a strategy of combat. This latter tactic, combined with one or both of the other strategies, was to make NMC so large and dominant that neither Medicare nor Wall Street could control or ignore it.

None of the strategic responses was all together desirable or appropriate for National Medical Care and its executives, and all three strategies (setting the privatization strategy aside) shared the fundamental weakness of running counter to NMC's culture and underlying mission.

The approach of melding NMC into a larger entity essentially involved selling the company to a conglomerate and naturally invited the loss of control and integrity. The NMC founders knew that this approach could not only shorten their own business careers, but would alienate the medical directors and could lead to poor quality care. As a public company, however, NMC was essentially for sale every day on the stock exchange, and a willing buyer with sufficient funds could end up "owning" the company at any time. The challenge in pursuing a merger strategy was finding a company, large enough to shield dialysis earnings from the probing eyes of Medicare, but small enough and compatible enough to permit Hampers, Hager and Schupak the necessary measure of control.

The challenge of the diversification strategy was finding lines of business that were profitable, compatible with the core dialysis business, and controllable by the troika of nephrologist-executives in charge of NMC. At its founding, NMC included the operation of extended care (skilled nursing) facilities and mental health hospitals and outpatient centers. That experience, however, had taught Hampers and his cohorts that even within the medical field there were business they knew how to run and business that they were not adept at operating. As Hampers expressed in 1981 (Financial World, August 15, 1981), "We're getting out of mental health because we are just not innovative enough in the area. Besides we can use the capital elsewhere." As long as there was a strong demand for more outpatient dialysis clinics, a business in which NMC made good returns on invested capital, it was difficult to divert the capital into less productive uses. In addition, Hampers, Schupak and Hager had very different and irreconcilable opinions on diversification strategies.

Combat, which primarily involved resistance to the government's intrusion into the financial records and operations of NMC's business, was satisfying over the short term. Successive cadres of NMC lawyers and lobbyists made a lot of money staving off Medicare's often heavy handed attempts to audit and control NMC's operations, and these feisty responses to "big brother" pleased the entrepreneurial medical directors and the anti-government investment community, at least for the moment. The combat strategy allowed the company to delay the hard decisions about merging with another company or attracting enough new capital and executive talent to diversify NMC. In the long term, of course, the strategy of fighting the government offended the bureaucrats, frightened the patients, and baffled the more astute Wall Street analysts. Nonetheless, making the government work hard and long to secure cost data on dialysis operations (which the government would have used to reduce NMC's profits) gave NMC officers several years to enhance the value of the company and enlarge the company's reach. Combat also involved an aggressive acquisition strategy, confrontation with state and local health planning agencies and their hospital allies, and fierce suppression of any attempt by NMC's medical directors to leave the NMC clinics with their patients and compete with the company. By the 1980's the agenda of the annual medical director's meetings were more about the status of lawsuits and legislation than about the advances of dialysis and transplantation.

Another, somewhat irrational, but nevertheless compelling, reason that the combat strategy was adopted had to do with the different personalities and goals of the three NMC founders. As time went on, Dr. Schupak came to favor the strategy of selling the company to a larger entity, and was willing to cede control and even depart from the day-to-day operations for the right price. Ted Hager, ever the risk taker and research minded innovator, who had originated the concept of a multipurpose outpatient center for dialysis, psychiatry, day surgery and other services, was more willing to invest in a diversification strategy, and entertained a vision of National Medical Care as an entrepreneurial partner with doctors on the cutting edge of many different disciplines. Meanwhile, Gus Hampers was trying to find a way to get out of the public spotlight, retain tight control and regain a more significant share of the ownership of the company. Given these different goals, backed up by different personalities, the combat strategy had the appeal of being acceptable to all three NMC founders. Thus, the combat strategy bought time and allowed Schupak, Hager and Hampers to finesse their differences for a few years.

The NMC culture, originally one of risk taking and collegiality, almost as an extended partnership among smart, hard working physicians, was threatened by all three defensive strategies. Whether NMC pursued a sale to a larger conglomerate, diversification, or combat, or a combination of the three, centralization would be required, and this rubbed the medical directors, especially some of the pioneers, the wrong way. Increasingly, they saw themselves as pawns rather than as partners, and this feeling came to a head during the 1981 fight with Medicare over reimbursement rates, when NMC, without any input from these medical directors, threatened to close their dialysis facilities. Hampers was no longer their partner but their chief. Similarly, the mission of NMC - to provide high quality medical care in an efficient and physician controlled manner, was undermined, as the NMC executives pursued strategies to maximize the short term investment objectives of stockholders by either selling or diversifying the company. In the end, after both Hager and Schupak had left NMC, it was Gus Hampers' genius and good luck to save the NMC culture and advance its mission by finding a different way of shielding NMC from government control that did not involve either selling the company outright or diversifying it into an unfocused and inefficient holding company.

When NMC "went public" in December 1971 its three principal executives weren't thinking about exit or escape strategies from the glare of public scrutiny. In the first place, the Medicare ESRD Program had not yet been enacted. Further, the fact that ordinary individual and corporate investors were willing to exchange over $7 million in cash for a share in the future of National Medical Care, thereby enabling NMC to build its dialysis centers was more than worth the price of public disclosure to these doctors, who had all seen patients die for lack of dialysis and kidney transplantation options. They saw nothing to fear about public disclosure. In late 1972, they returned to the capitalist well to draw out an additional $4.3 million in financing with which to expand NMC. Again, there was no concern about the limits that public disclosure might impose on their future, even though by the date of the 1972 public offering the ESRD amendments had been signed into law and the program would commence the following July. In fact, at that time there was a sense that for-profit dialysis providers might not qualify to participate in the new Medicare ESRD Program.

While not necessary to NMC's survival or growth, the Medicare ESRD Program provided an enormous boost after mid-1973, when the Program went into effect. Between 1973 and 1974, the first full year of operating under the ESRD Program, NMC's centers leapt from 24 to 36 and its revenues increased by 32%. Similarly, in the following year, revenues increased 57% to $77.9 million in 1975. Following its successful registration and qualification for listing its stock for trading on the New York Stock Exchange on May 12, 1975, National Medical Care went to the public capital markets for the third time and raised an additional $5 million from the sale of common stock on October 22, 1975. These three sales of common stock in 1971, 1972 and 1975, together with profits generated from its operations, and a $30 million line of credit secured in early 1976, continued to fuel the growth of NMC. By early 1979 the company had 100 dialysis centers in operation, and another 30 in the planning stage.

Raising capital for, building and starting these outpatient dialysis centers kept the founding doctors and their medical director colleagues busy for several years. In addition, Drs. Hager, Hampers and Schupak were still seeing patients in both their base hospital settings, the outpatient dialysis clinics in New York and Boston, and in their private practices. By 1975, however, the "fishbowl" problem and its consequences on the ESRD Program's reimbursement scheme was becoming more apparent, and the three viable responsive strategies - sale, diversification and combat - began to be pursued.

The diversification strategy, which would allow the company to report aggregate sales and earnings from a variety of businesses, thereby making analysis of dialysis costs and operations more difficult for the government and other payers, was the most natural and least disruptive course. National Medical Care began life in 1968 as the operator of extended care nursing facilities with mental health and outpatient dialysis as ancillary lines of business. In addition, since its founding, in an attempt to save costs and not transfer all dialysis profits to the manufacturers of the artificial kidneys (Baxter Travenol and others), NMC had established subsidiaries that explored the reuse and reassembly of artificial kidneys and that played the role of bulk purchaser and redistributor of dialysis and other related medical supplies. Some of NMC's earliest employees were skilled in dialyzer engineering and design and in the sale of medical products.

Ted Hager, whom Dr. Hampers described as the "man with a hundred ideas a day," was particularly fond of this approach, and in the early (pre-Medicare ESRD Program) years between 1968 and 1972, Hager was the principal promoter of NMC among both the investment community and a mixed bag of medical entrepreneurs. He recruited a dentist turned psychiatrist, Sheldon Zigelbaum, to develop and run the mental health division of NMC, which emphasized a daycare, non-custodial model for providing services which was way ahead of its time. He promoted the incorporation of a day surgery center in Miami - one of the first of its kind in the country. Dr. Hager had no qualms about NMC's ability to operate general hospitals in New Orleans and Tampa, and these consumed an immense proportion of the initial capital raised in the late 1960's and early 1970's. And over the course of the decade of the 70's, Dr. Hager was often dispatched to the far corners of the United States to examine an innovative and unconventional idea of how to deliver a healthcare service or product more efficiently. Driven by an almost pathological aversion to the large urban, bureaucratic teaching hospital, Ted Hager saw very few potential innovations that he didn't like. Dr. Hager's mission was to use NMC to liberate creative physicians and other healthcare professionals from the bonds of institutional and socialistic servitude.

At times this "salad bowl" or smorgasbord approach could result in rather bizarre incidents. Housing psychiatric patients in the same building with octogenarians recovering from hip replacement surgery with the constant comings and goings of outpatients at the adjacent dialysis clinic could be disconcerting. Insurance companies providing liability coverage for NMC in those early years became very nervous. And allocating shared costs among the fee for service dialysis clinic and the cost reimbursed extended care facilities provoked many nightmares for the accountants.

After Dr. Schupak opened his storefront, stand alone, low cost dialysis clinic in New York City and introduced this so called "Bio-Medical Applications" model to NMC, it became increasingly difficult to justify spending large amounts of NMC's capital on real estate and other fixed assets. Nothing reached the level of profits that outpatient dialysis made for NMC. In addition, kidney dialysis was the area in which all three NMC leaders had tremendous expertise. Where an oral surgeon or a psychiatrist could make a convincing case for spending money on a new piece of equipment or hiring more therapists, the dialysis physician had a much tougher row to hoe in convincing the three nephrology pioneers, especially since many of the clinic directors had received their dialysis training from one of the NMC chiefs. Schupak and Hampers were more confident and comfortable in spending their investors' money on dialysis and also in not spending it in certain cases.

The early, Hager inspired diversification of NMC was a mixed bag. While the hospitals, surgical center, mental health division, and extended care facilities never made an adequate return on investment to expand these divisions, they were necessary to get NMC off the ground, and provide a home or base for the dialysis operations, which, prior to the Medicare ESRD Program was a highly speculative venture for most capitalists. In addition, it's hard to say that these ventures might not have out performed or performed as well as outpatient dialysis, if they had received greater capital, executive attention and the right management. In fact, during the same era, other proprietary hospital management companies such as Humana and National Medical Enterprises did very well. Nonetheless, NMC's early experience with diversification made its officers cautious about this strategy in the future. After a cat is burned once jumping on a hot stove, it never again jumps on any stove - hot or cold.

The area of greatest success in diversifying NMC's lines of business was the allied business of distributing medical supplies, primarily dialysis related supplies, and later the manufacture of certain products, including artificial kidneys, blood lines and dialysate solutions. The genesis of this business began even before NMC, when Gus Hampers and Ted Hager were directing the outpatient dialysis program for the Peter Bent Brigham Hospital at The Normandy House in 1967 and 1968. By purchasing in bulk and threatening to reuse dialyzers, they were able to force Baxter-Travenol to reduce its prices. Similarly, Gene Schupak saw the advantage of vertical integration once he opened his center in New York in 1970. The medical products division was named "Erika" (originally Erika Distributors, Inc) after one of Dr. Schupak's daughters, and in dividing responsibilities among the three NMC founders, Erika was assigned to Gene Schupak to operate. Gene knew he needed a staff to help run that end of the business, and he hired several people from Baxter with whom he had dealt over the years, including Dave Donlan, Howard Janneck, and Jesus Martinez. Almost overnight, NMC became a major competitor of Baxter in the dialysis supply arena, while at the same time remaining Baxter's largest, single dialysis customer. The Baxter salesmen had relationships with NMC's many medical and nursing directors in its various clinics that often pre-dated their affiliation with NMC. These relationships were being up ended by Erika and its sales force, and a lively competition ensued. This competition and the check it placed on prices of dialysis products had enormous benefits for the patients, their doctors, and the patient's insurers, including, after 1973, Medicare. Not only did the competition, fueled by Erika's aggressive pursuit of business from NMC's own clinics, as well as from hospitals and outpatient clinics not operated by NMC, reduce prices, but it also resulted in better and safer artificial kidneys.

However, there was a big, ugly fly in the Erika ointment, known as the "related organization principle." This "principle" was really an accounting procedure adopted by Part A of Medicare (the part of Medicare that at that time reimbursed hospitals on the basis on their actual costs of providing a service) that collapsed or eliminated the profit margins between entitites that were related by common ownership or control. Thus, hospitals that created a separate subsidiary to provide laundry service could pass onto Medicare the cost of providing the laundry service, not the markedup price paid by the hospital to its laundry subsidiary. The principle was an obvious means to escape the ruse of shifting costs from one corporate pocket to another, since at that time

Medicare paid only costs. This principle was one Medicare had inherited from similar Blue Cross plans that existed before Medicare came into effect. If applied in the NMC-Erika context, the related organization principle would squeeze the supply markup, or profit, from the cost of dialysis at an NMC clinic that purchased its supplies from Erika. Thus, if the clinic bought a $25 artificial kidney from Baxter, its cost for that item was $25, but if an NMC clinic bought its dialyzers at the same $25 price from Erika, which was a wholly owned subsidiary of NMC, it could only claim the cost of the dialyzer to Erika, before the Erika profit, say, $19 or $20 each.

Application of the "related organization principle" in the context of a Medicare Part B service, like outpatient dialysis, made no sense, since the price was established across-the-board at $138 per treatment (only 80% of which was paid by Medicare), regardless of the actual cost to the clinic. The clinic, whether NMC operated or hospital based, was allowed to keep any difference between its real costs and the $138 price, regardless of whether that profit went into the clinic's treasury or into the account of the Erika (or Baxter) supplier. In fact, the only reason that Medicare attempted to collect and audit cost data at all was in order to set prospective rates for the future. Nonetheless, the government's threatened application of the "related organization principle" in the NMC-Erika context led Dr. Schupak and his NMC colleagues to seriously consider the spin off of Erika in early 1975, thus allowing Erika to sink or swim as an independent manufacturing and supply company just like Baxter. The trick that NMC was never able to solve was how to ensure Erika's survival as an independent company competing against an enormously resourceful and competitive giant like Baxter. NMC and its lawyers attempted to contrive a long term supply agreement between NMC and the new, independent Erika that would insure Erika's viability and protect it from Baxter without falling into the "related organization principle" trap. Medicare auditors were smart enough to understand that even if common ownership was missing, the necessary control could exist through a tight, long term supply agreement.

Moreover, a long term supply agreement with Erika was risky for NMC, since, in fact, its dialysis clinics did often operate in the early 1970's as distinct entities outside NMC's central control. While Dr. Schupak could and did introduce Erika's sales force to NMC clinic directors, and while Dr. Hampers could and did encourage these directors to buy their supplies from Erika, if push came to shove, the clinic directors did what they wanted. That was the bottom line deal between these doctors and the NMC executives, and it was respected. Thus, NMC couldn't confidently predict how many Erika bloodlines or artificial kidneys it would need for its many clinics a few years into the future.

Gene Schupak had another reason to favor the Erika spin off, which had to do with his own dialysis center in Queens, N.Y. Because New York State law did not permit public corporations like NMC to own medical facilities, the Queens Artificial Kidney Center remained the sole proprietorship of Gene Schupak. Since Schupak was also an NMC "insider" (a term of art defined in federal securities law) and the chief operating officer of Erika, the related organization principal was applied to transactions between QAKC and Erika , not just by Medicare for prospective rate setting purposes, but also by New York State's Medicaid regulators under its actual cost reimbursement plan. Thus, the elimination of the Erika profit from QAKC's cost report actually ended up penalizing Dr. Schupak and NMC.

Finally, after several months of starts and stops, the Erika spin off was abandoned in the summer of 1975, and NMC decided to invest more capital in Erika to improve its sales force, commence a research and development program, improve manufacturing capacities, and beef-up its non-NMC advertising and marketing efforts. The problem of the "related organization principle" did not disappear, but NMC used a strategy of combat, specifically years of litigation, to retard its application by Medicare to NMC cost data. In 1979 NMC entered into a long term license and technology transfer agreement with Fresenius, AG, the leading German manufacturer of artificial kidneys, and in July 1980, Erika opened its plant in Ireland to manufacture and assemble a state-of-the-art hollow fibre dialyzer based on the Fresenius technology for import into the United States.

In 1975 and 1976, however, NMC decided to sell its general hospitals in New Orleans and Tampa, and use the capital proceeds to expand dialysis operations. Sam Saitz, an accountant, who had been the catalyzing agent in 1967, bringing Dr. Hager and the owner of the Normandy House into a partnership, and who had sold NMC the real estate that became the home of the Babcock Artificial Kidney Center, had become a fulltime employee of NMC, and was the business manager of NMC's "odds and ends," mostly all of Ted Hager's projects, including the mental health centers and the hospitals. Saitz's background as an expert in cost reimbursement accounting under the old Blus Cross and Medicare systems made him skilled at this task. In addition, Sam Saitz was fiercely loyal to Hager and Hampers, compassionate to anyone who had the good fortune to work for him, and as tough a negotiator and as tight fisted as any nineteenth century tycoon. In selling the hospitals, Saitz pushed himself to incredible lengths and took advantage of every loophole in the written sales contract to the benefit of "the doctors."

In the Tampa situation, the closing took well over a week, because Saitz insisted on taking a strict, item-by-item inventory, down to the last tongue depressor, claiming that the purchaser had to pay for this inventory in addition to the sales price of the hospital. The buyer, of course, claimed the inventory was part of the negotiated price. In a show-down, the buyer called Saitz's bluff by telling him that he wouldn't pay for the inventory, and Saitz could take it back to Boston with him (knowing full well that NMC had no use for the hospital supplies). Sam rose to the challenge by having his deputy, Jim Murphy, rent a huge U-Haul truck and back it up to the hospital loading dock. Now, the buyers began to sweat, since they weren't prepared to operate a hospital without any inventory of supplies. As a result, the buyers agreed to pay NMC an additional amount for the inventory ("I'm paying for it twice," one of the buyers remarked), and Saitz had Murphy return the truck, unused, to U-Haul. However, Saitz, did not beat a hasty departure. Even though the closing dragged on so long that he was likely to miss his airplane ride back to Boston in time to be home for the Jewish Sabbath, thereby requiring Saitz, who was observant, to stay in hot, humid Tampa an additional July day and a half, Saitz took the time after the closing to walk the halls of the hospital to personally thank every employee and wish them well.

When Sam Saitz closed the sale of the Saint Charles Hospital in New Orleans, he exhausted himself so badly that he became the first patient admitted to the hospital under its new owners! Fortunately for Sam and his family and for NMC, he recovered quickly and spent several more years taking care of the "miscellaneous" acquisitions and diversification investments of National Medical Care. Because Saitz was so trustworthy, Ted Hager and Gus Hampers could ask him to evaluate a potential acquisition or other opportunity, and be confident that Sam's answer would not be affected or skewed by Sam's own personal or professional interest in either the acquisition or the disposition of the business segment.

When National Medical Care decided to acquire a program for the control of obesity from Dr. Victor Vertes in late 1977, Hampers turned to Saitz to start the program, labelled the "Institute For Health Maintenance" (IHM), under NMC's ownership. As reported in leading medical journals, Dr. Vertes had developed the Risk Factor Obesity ("RFO") program for significant weight loss for morbidly obese patients (those at 120% or more of their ideal weight) that involved fasting and the substitution of a dietary supplement that Vertes had developed called "Optifast," under strict, regular physician supervision. The results of Dr. Vertes' work were impressive, with patients shedding literally hundreds of pounds safely, and his stature as a leading internist, based at Cleveland's Mt. Sinai Hospital and the Case Western Reserve Medical School, caught the attention of the academic medical community. What NMC acquired was Vertes' expert counsel and advice and his forbearance from developing the Optifast program commercially. And there was (and there still is) an enormous market in the United States for weight control programs. Hampers believed he could sell this program to the existing NMC dialysis doctors around the country to promote in their own cities. The response was lukewarm, at best. At a conference of the pioneering medical directors held in 1978 at NMC headquarters at the Hancock Tower in Boston, Dr. George Bailey, Hampers' first fellow at the Brigham Hospital, and a New Orleans gourmand, proud of his impressive avoirdupois, couldn't imagine people agreeing to fast in Louisiana. In late 1980 NMC was comfortable enough with the IHM program that the company purchased a similar program, including some centers that were already in operation from Morton Maxwell, M.D., another nephrology pioneer at UCLA, and his partner, Dr. Les Dornfeld.

By the end of 1981 NMC was operating 37 obesity control centers, generally under the IHM label (some had adopted more appealing and marketable names). Some of these centers shared space with existing NMC facilities, but most were housed in accessible offices, often in strip malls or near medical centers for the convenience of the doctors who directed them. In addition to the Optifast diet regimen, patients were engaged in classic behaviour modification programs. The cost of the program wasn't cheap and was largely self-pay, since third party reimbursement for weight-loss was very rare. The IHM division did provide revenues and meager profits to achieve the diversification strategy, but it was not sufficiently profitable to be useful to NMC in marketing itself to the investment community. The directors of these centers came from various backgrounds, and did not share the tight collegiality that was the hallmark of the dialysis operations. Some IHM directors were nephrologists who were also involved with NMC's dialysis division. Others were younger associates of these dialysis directors, while others were drawn from the behavioral sciences and were not connected to the world of hard science in which NMC thrived. Some were skilled at marketing, but most were not, and in the universe of weight loss, marketing was essential. The weight loss industry was far different from the closed world of nephrology. Patients were more likely to assert their preferences, and the system that NMC envisioned, that mainly involved doctor-to-doctor referrals, as in the dialysis community, could not be replicated in the obesity centers. Most importantly, Dr. Hampers (by 1980 both Dr. Hager and Dr. Schupak had left NMC) was not personally and professionally interested in the division, except as an investment that was required for diversification purposes only. He rarely attended the IHM medical directors meetings and spent little time supervising its operations.

Moreover, as time went on and the sensation of the first success stories faded (Oprah Winfrey being one of the most famous), the program developed problems. As long as patients stayed on the Optifast diet, they lost weight and kept their weight in check, but as soon as they began regular food again, they gained weight. Staying on Optifast was expensive, tedious, and for a few patients, harmful. Some were not following their doctor's prescriptions and supplementing Optifast with necessary vitamins and drugs, and as a result, there were a few, serious medical incidents, which were broadly publicized. The program developed by Dr. Vertes and promoted by NMC as a medical intervention to prevent high blood pressure, coronary disease, diabetes, and other obesity related conditions, was being turned into another diet fad.

Finally, NMC executives decided to replace Optifast with a similar product that was formulated to be as safe and effective as Optifast and also included some additional nutrients lacking in the Optifast formulation. However, the real impetus in creating a substitute for Optifast was to capture additional profits for NMC's IHM division. The doctors were convinced the new supplement was as good as, if not better than, Optifast, but they couldn't switch the patients. Hampers and his colleagues, so used to compliance by patients in accepting products and prescriptions recommended by their doctors, did not anticipate this patient consumer loyalty to the Optifast brand. This mistake, combined with the fact that a lack of any significant capital or health planning barriers to entry resulted in many imitators and competitors, led Hampers to decide by 1983 to exit the weight loss business. NMC divested the IHM division, closing some centers, selling others to the local medical directors, and finally selling most of the remaining IHM centers back to Drs. Maxwell and Dornfeld, from whom they had been purchased three years earlier. The experience reinforced Hampers' aversion to having NMC depart from the scientific universe of specialized medicine and technology controlled by highly trained physicians like himself.

In July, 1979 National Medical Care entered the respiratory care and home supply business with the purchase of Consolidated Medical Corporation, headquartered in Kansas City, along with its MedTech affiliates. Although there were certain "synergies" or compatible modes of doing business between the medical products division (Erika) of NMC, and the home care business, this, too, was largely a new endeavor for the dialysis doctors. In this case, however, Hampers and Schupak insisted that the executives, who had developed the MedTech business and sold it to NMC, be retained to continue operating the division. Unfortunately, the former owners found retirement more attractive, and they left NMC within a few months. The business consisted of selling and renting medical equipment, such as wheelchairs and hospital type beds, for use in patients' homes. If these purchases were justified by medical necessity, they might be covered by third-party insurance, but generally at a level that permitted very little profit. The division made profits, however, from the supply of oxygen and the equipment and personnel needed to administer oxygen therapy in the home setting. Contrary to NMC's expectations, this home supply business was not particularly amenable to national, corporate organization. It was essentially a local business that was fundamentally controlled by local physicians, not just the pulmonary specialists, but by the thousands of family doctors, who were basically most comfortable dealing with the local pharmacy or small medical supply company in their town or city. The critical factor was service and dependability, including a tie in with the local visiting nurse association or other home care providers. A national corporation, like NMC, brought very little to the table.

The barriers to entry were slight, and NMC's MedTech division soon became engaged in continuous contract disputes and trade wars with former employees, who would learn the business from NMC and then start their own competing enterprises. Lawsuits were instigated, but holding employees to a contract and preventing them from competing (or in their defense counsel's words, "of being able to earn a living") were not generally enforced by the civil courts, particularly where the plaintiff was a national corporation based in Boston and the defendant was a local "Rotary Club" member.

A particular characteristic of the home care business - and to a lesser extent, the obesity control business - was the myriad of problems that sprang from dealing with so many different healthcare insurance plans, HMO's, state Medicaid and federal Medicare plans, and self-pay patients. The sales force was disincented to reject any potential sale where the reimbursement looked questionable, passing the problem on to the business managers, accountants, and lawyers. As a result, supplies and services would be delivered to patients, the company would record accounts receivable on its books, collecting these receivables became difficult and time consuming, and more and more of company assets were being tied up in growing accounts receivable. This was very different from the dialysis service and supply business where there was one uniform Medicare ESRD program with which NMC employees, executives and even its stockholders, were intimately familiar. "We were fast becoming the busiest men in the poor house," Dr. Hampers frequently commented during divisional review meetings. Month after month, the home care managers would proudly emphasize the growth in sales, but quickly withered under Hampers' barrage of questions about when they would start to collect real cash on all those sales. Among the waggish employees at NMC the division became known as the "home scare" division.

What NMC was experiencing is a general condition in the U.S. healthcare system that impedes efficiency and inflates costs. With so many different healthcare reimbursement plans, it's difficult to impose rational and efficient organizational systems on the delivery of healthcare services and products. Even within a specific locality, a doctor's practice or a pharmacy may have to comply with billing and coverage regulations for scores of different plans. Within a given state or region, the permutations grow geometrically, and for a national company, even with computer assistance, compliance becomes a major obstacle. Instead, companies retain local control and compliance staff, which defeats any attempt to exploit economies-of-scale and to compare, and thereby improve, performance from region to region or center to center. In its core, dialysis business NMC knew that when it provided a treatment in one of its clinics, whether in California or in Michigan, it would be paid under the Medicare ESRD Program. The system was one of "entitlement" with the patient assigning his legally enforceable Medicare benefits to NMC. Home care was a whole different universe, and Dr. Hampers became very impatient with this uncertainty. A manager could never be sure whether a subordinate was truly faced with an insurmountable collection problem, or whether he was using the confusion as an excuse. That was not the way Hampers wanted to run a business.

Later, in 1983, NMC added a whole new dimension to its home care division by acquiring and adding home care infusion services and products, originally called "Theranutrix," to its lines of business. Until the early 1980's, infusion therapies were administered exclusively in hospitals, nursing homes or doctor's offices. These could include the provision of intravenous drugs, including chemotherapies for cancer, acute pain medications, saline drips, or enteral and parenteral nutrition therapies. Administering such therapies at home was an innovation, and it took many healthcare insurers and HMO's, including public insurers like Medicare and Medicaid, months, and sometimes, years, to accept and pay for these services. Even though much cheaper than in hospital care, these were not inexpensive services, and shifting expenses from carriers and plans that covered hospital services (like Blue Cross or Medicare Part A) to health plans that covered outpatient services (like Medicare Part B) was difficult. Again, the issues of providing services and not getting paid, while accumulating large accounts receivable, became a major issue.

An extreme example arose in 1985 when NMC's dialysis clinics began administering parenteral nutrition services (principally the intravenous infusion of nutritional supplements) to undernourished, or technically "starving," dialysis patients, many of whom had dysfunctional digestive systems, and simply could not eat. The service, called interdialytic parenteral nutrition, or "IDPN," was prescribed by the patients' doctors and was essential for the health, if not the survival, of these patients. The Health Care Financing Administration designated a single intermediary - Blue Cross/ Blue Shield of South Carolina - to process all of these Medicare IDPN claims for the eastern half of the United States. Under the Medicare guidelines at the time, only claims from patients who required parenteral nutrition every day to survive were covered. To the intermediary and its Medicare overseer a patient receiving these services only three times a week during his dialysis treatment meant that his claims were ipso facto invalid. In other words, to qualify for coverage the patient's physician would have to prescribe the service seven days per week. And indeed, as these patients deteriorated, that's exactly what would happen by necessity. It took several months for NMC to convince the intermediary to pay these claims. In the meantime, NMC's clinics delivered the services and bills were being sent, without any assurance of final payment. In short order IDPN accounts receivable grew to over $9 million. Dr. Hampers was not convinced the company would ever be paid, but he steadfastly refused to stop this service for patients. Terry Daniels, then a senior vice president at W.R. Grace, which by 1985 held a controlling majority of NMC stock, recalled, "I knew Gus was risking millions of dollars, but nonetheless I had to admire his refusal to jeopardize the patients' health."

The investment community, at least the sophisticated and analytical part of that community, could easily become suspicious of the earnings that NMC would report, where those earnings were increasingly dependent on accounts receivable from the sale of home care services and products. Knowing that not all these receivables would in fact be collected, NMC management created (and good accounting practice required NMC to create) reserves or "bad debt hedges" against these receivables, thereby reducing earnings to that degree. However, because of the uncertainty and lack of a clear track record, especially regarding new services like IDPN and other home infusion therapies, the amount of the reserves would be somewhat subjective, and debatable. And whenever, for whatever reasons, a corporation's management is allowed discretion to adjust company earnings based on a subjective judgment like how much to hold back in case all the receivables aren't collected, investors get very nervous. For example, if accounts receivable rose to, say, $30 million, and management decided to increase its bad debt reserve to hedge these receivables by, say, ten percent, or $3 million, then that reduction "drops straight to the bottom line," i.e., net earnings are reduced by $3 million. That can drastically affect the price of the stock. The suspicion is that in times when earnings aren't as good as expected, management will reserve less and thereby manipulate earnings upwards, and when times are good, management will conversely increase reserves in order to depress earnings and "lay away" a store of money for future, bad times.

Unlike the weight loss business, the home care enterprise, especially the more sophisticated aspects like respiratory care and infusion services, did meld fairly well into the NMC medical culture, and could, where properly managed, be very profitable. In large measure the home care business did succeed in implementing the diversification strategy: it grew large enough to add significant revenues, and it was profitable enough to justify the capital investment that would have otherwise gone to building more dialysis centers. Over time, there were some synergies to be exploited between home care and dialysis, and both divisions ultimately provided sophisticated technologically advanced services to very sick patients, who would have otherwise been cared for as inpatients at much higher costs to the system. Underlying both services was the mission of getting patients out of high cost hospitals.

The incorporation of the so called "Lifechem" subsidiary as part of Erika in 1979 was another natural addition to a vertically integrated and inclusive array of services for the dialysis patient and his physician. However, its genesis, though logical in retrospect, was the serendipitous result of a chance meeting of Gene Schupak and Bernie Kaplan during a vacation cruise. Shipboard conversations between Dr. Schupak and Kaplan, who was then in charge of a highly successful laboratory in the New York area, quickly led to a major, successful addition to NMC. Lifechem was a commercial, clinical laboratory, specializing in testing blood samples of dialysis patients. During the early years of its existence NMC relied on its local medical and nursing directors to engage laboratory services in their communities for the frequent and expensive assays that are required in treating kidney patients. The attending physicians required accurate and timely test results and were averse to using one lab in the NMC dialysis center and different labs in their private practices and at the hospitals. Very frequently, therefore, the labs that succeeded in getting NMC's business were the hospital labs, simply because this was most convenient for the doctors. Hospital labs, however, were expensive, and once the NMC medical directors saw how much money could be saved by using a central laboratory, they soon acquiesced in using Lifechem.

Transportation and communication advances made Lifechem viable, since using an overnight express mail service, combined with modern communications systems (facsimile, etc.) allowed Lifechem to receive the samples, perform the necessary tests, and get the results to the physicians as quickly as the local labs. Lifechem was also more efficient and less costly. (Its markups were also subject to the government's attempt to apply the "related organization principle," to the same degree and based on the same rationale as the Erika profits). As NMC's central laboratory for nearly all its dialysis, and later its obesity and diabetes control centers and its home care respiratory and infusion care business, Lifechem could provide NMC management and the medical directors with a significantly large sample of data about kidney patients that existed nowhere else in the world. These data allowed NMC executives and affiliated doctors to compare blood chemistries among different clinics, and among time periods. As a result, significant information about the effect of shorter dialysis sessions or the efficacy of different artificial kidneys or the changes caused by various drugs and other prescriptions could be analyzed. By the 1980's the Lifechem data and the resulting analyses were an attraction for many nephrologists to become part of the NMC system. Through NMC and Lifechem these specialists could learn much more about how to improve patient care than they could in their isolated centers.

Lifechem started as an "inhouse" substitute for local, expensive clinical laboratories, but it soon became a competitor in the growing, nationwide clinical laboratory business, acquiring additional business from outside the NMC system. When it began, there was an initial controversy about whether Lifchem should be located in Boston and be controlled by the dialysis services division, or whether it should be sited in New Jersey as part of Erika and the medical products division of NMC. Because Kaplan had a strong interest in remaining in the New York-New Jersey region, Lifechem became a close sibling to the products division, at that time managed by Dr. Schupak. After Schupak's departure in late 1979, however, the aggressive marketing culture of the products division began to dominate the Lifechem operation. This caused a lot of worry at NMC headquarters as the years transpired. It became difficult to police the salesmen to ensure that they were not "bundling" dialysis product discounts with Lifechem services in order to secure the laboratory business from its competitors. There would always be a temptation for product salesmen to "trade" the sale of NMC dialyzers and blood lines, for example, at a discounted price, in exchange for laboratory business from dialysis clinics outside the NMC system, since the lab services were paid by Medicare or other third party insurers. This was troubling, not only because it might be illegal, since it rewarded (by way of lower supply prices) the dialysis operator for directing Medicare-reimbursed business to the laboratory, but also was poor business, since it reallocated profits from one division to another, thus skewing management decisions about expansion and capital investments. Hampers was always concerned about maintaining a "stonewall" between these operations, which became a challenge when they were operated by the same managers at the same location. Other competing clinical laboratories and product manufacturers were just as aggressive in trying to "sniff out" and expose this kind of overreaching.

An additional diversification endeavor that failed to pan out for NMC was in the field of diabetes management. An increasing number of ESRD patients also suffered from diabetes mellitus, a condition caused by the failure of the pancreas to properly control the insulin glucose balance. If not properly managed, diabetic patients experience severe vascular deterioration, generally in the feet, retina (causing blindness) and the kidneys (causing kidney failure). In fact, today, diabetes is the leading cause of kidney failure in the United States. Thus, Dr. Hampers and the other NMC nephrologists were very familiar with the care of diabetic patients, and diabetic management looked like a promising new venture for the company. Researchers based at the Joslyn Clinic in Boston and elsewhere had developed a means for controlling insulin to better manage diabetes through the use of a pump worn by the patient that replaced the need to inject insulin at critical times. The device monitored the patient's metabolism and need for insulin in a dynamic and more precise way. National Medical Care started its Gluco-Med subsidiary to provide the insulin pump, training and related services to diabetic patients in 1981. The regimen, backed by hard science, was accepted by insurers, including Medicare, for reimbursement, and the startup costs were minimal. Gluco-Med operated two pilot programs, one in Boston and one in New York City. The company had all the necessary elements - good, well equipped offices, prominent medical directors, an excellent inhouse Lifechem laboratory, and reimbursement approvals. What it lacked and never attracted was patients.

In retrospect it was clear why the company didn't get the patient referrals it expected. Managing diabetic patients was and is the main stay for many internists and family physicians. Referring patients to the Gluco-Med center meant reducing the incomes of these doctors significantly. Once referred to the Gluco-Med medical director, the patients would not return to their original doctor. Moreover, the program that Gluco-Med offered could just as easily be provided by the family doctor, or a physician group. Again, NMC was not bringing anything to the table, since significant capital was not a barrier, and there was no need for any particular expertise in regulatory or reimbursement policies. The company even tried to attract diabetic patients directly through advertising and by offering other products and services that were hard for these patients to find. These techniques failed as well, except in one instance where NMC collaborated with a podiatrist to prescribe and provide special shoes for diabetic patients, who generally have circulatory problems in their feet making such special footwear necessary. This exception, however, was not the basis for a diversified business opportunity and was quickly abandoned.

In a sense, the most successful diversification strategy for NMC was finding ways to provide dialysis outside the U.S. Medicare system. Since the whole point of diversification was to diminish the relative significance of Medicare's "politically charged" ESRD Program revenues on the company's sales and earnings, selling dialysis products and services to clinics, doctors and patients who were not part of the Medicare system worked just as well as any other strategy. It also invested capital in NMC's strength. The company's earliest clinics in Boston, New York, Washington and elsewhere predated the ESRD Program and had experience negotiating contracts with Blue Cross/Blue Shield plans, other private insurers, some early HMO's like Kaiser, and even foreign countries. In Washington, D.C. especially, diplomats and other wealthy foreign nationals would seek dialysis treatments and pay the clinics directly. Dr. Cirksena, one of the co-directors in Washington, recalled some foreign patients paying with cash on each visit. Many centers outside Washington would from time to time care for foreigners and be paid with non-Medicare dollars.

After the ESRD Program began in 1973, however, finding non-Medicare dialysis revenue became almost impossible in the United States. NMC, therefore, began its international operations as early as 1975 with product sales in Europe and South America. Because these initial contacts with foreign nephrologists largely came through the process of selling dialysis products (also many younger foreign nephrologists had trained with Drs. Hampers, Hager and Schupak), Gene Schupak attempted to penetrate the European dialysis services market in the mid-1970's. Despite Schupak's considerable early success in convincing doctors to partner with NMC, the public healthcare systems in promising countries like Germany and France were dominated by state controlled insurance systems that were not amenable to an American invasion of this sort. By the time Dr. Schupak left NMC in 1979, the prospects of a foreign, dialysis service business were slight.

In 1980, however, Pete Phildius, who had become the company's president upon Schupak's departure, turned the good will he had established with doctors in Portugal and Spain during his earlier tenure at Baxter to NMC's advantage. It all started when the most prominent nephrologist in Lisbon was looking to retire, sell his dialysis operations, and at the same time minimize the tax bite that Portugal would impose on any such transfer. Since the doctor also owned the real estate that housed the clinic, the sale was structured primarily as a real estate transfer. After building a new center in Lisbon and consolidating its referrals and negotiating a long term contract with the Portuguese government, NMC expanded into other cities in Portugal and soon controlled 50% of the dialysis market in Portugal. After Portugal, purchasing existing centers and establishing new dialysis clinics in Spain was easier, but operating in foreign countries was never "easy." Nonetheless, these operations added considerable revenues and profits to NMC's base and, along with product sales, laboratory income, and non-dialysis home care products and services, filled out the diversification strategy for NMC. Years later, following the W.R. Grace financed, leveraged buyout, Peter Grace noted NMC's successful, but relatively marginal, results in Portugal and Spain, and asked Dr. Hampers at a Grace review meeting, "Why do you keep circling the airport?" With Grace's urging and support, after 1985, Hampers spent more and more time developing NMC's foreign presence, so that by 1996, NMC was operating 125 dialysis clinics in 17 countries outside the United States.

Any successful diversification strategy has to include finding senior-level managers, who have the skill and experience to operate the newly acquired or expanded lines of business, but who also share the essential values and mores of the dominant corporate culture. There were many reasons the diversification strategy did not always work for NMC, and one of the common reasons was the failure to recruit "new blood." The NMC founders had trouble operating diverse businesses themselves (mainly from lack of interest, not lack of skill), and had even more trouble delegating the task to other managers. On the other side, most of the managers recruited from the world of business harbored a bias against doctors as competent, corporate executives. In the end, Dr. Hampers, as the last of the NMC founders to continue in an executive role after 1980, was more successful in molding his loyalists with whom he was comfortable, to the task of running new divisions than he was in converting outside managers into loyalists. Only after NMC and Hampers were integrated into the much more diverse corporate culture at W.R. Grace did Hampers learn the skills of delegation from his new colleagues.

The early culture of NMC in the late-1960's and most of the 1970's was collegial for those with an "M.D." after their names, and strictly hierarchical for all others. Organized more like a teaching hospital than any other entity, the dialysis clinic directors were regarded as partners, or as specialty "chiefs," equal shareholders and autonomous. No one at the "mother house," as one early NMC business manager dubbed the Boston office, would in those days ever tell a medical director who to hire, how much to pay the head nurse, or what kind of artificial kidney to prescribe. On the other side, NMC's business managers were tightly controlled (Dr. Schupak would on occasion stand at the front door at 9 a.m. and record the names of all tardy employees, whether they were typists or product engineers, and Dr. Hager would get a bucket of soapy water and show the janitor how he wanted the office walls scrubbed, as if it were an operating room.)

One anecdote illustrates the dichotomy and the genesis of this cultural bias. On February 6, 1978, Boston experienced a disabling, record breaking, 24-inch plus snow storm that came to be known as the "Blizzard of '78." NMC's corporate office at the time was on the 50th floor of the John Hancock Tower in Boston's Back Bay. As the storm began, the Tower swayed in heavy winds so violent that the water in the toilets sloshed onto the floor, and the glass panes that clad the Tower pulsed with every gust. About midday, after checking with public safety officials, the human resource director advised Dr. Hager that employees should be dismissed so they could start their commutes early. Hager was dumb founded. "What do you expect? It's winter in New England," he announced. "Let them go home when the snow reaches the window sill," Hager laughed, gazing out his 50th floor window. The next day the roads were impassable, and Governor Dukakis ordered the public to stay home and off the streets, banning all but emergency vehicles. Dr. Hampers, equipped with "MD" license plates made it to the office and was annoyed that no one else was there. He proceeded to the dialysis center, where he directed efforts to get both staff and patients to the clinic so the life saving dialysis treatments could be administered. The following week Drs. Hampers and Hager issued a memo directing all home office employees to make up the four days lost from the blizzard by working the following four Saturdays. In their minds, NMC's job was to provide dialysis, day and night, good weather or bad, and even employees in the corporate office had to show-up for work or face the consequences, regardless of what Governor Dukakis or any other public official had to say.

It was also very clear to all NMC employees that staff members who had labored at the dialysis clinics and then later transferred to office jobs at headquarters were viewed differently by, and had a totally different relationship with, the founding doctors. The earlier their association with the doctors, the more favorably they were treated. More than one "Johnny-come-lately," business-school graduated, Wall Street oriented manager experienced Hampers' over reaching to take the side of a subordinate whom Hampers knew from the "old days at the Babcock." In return, these "front line" employees were fiercely loyal to Hampers, Hager and Schupak, and knew that they could take their concerns directly to the founders, without regard to the corporate pyramid.

It's only a slight exaggeration to report that the NMC culture, at least until the mid-1980's, divided the world of NMC employees into three camps. First and foremost, were the medical directors who were regarded as partners. The second were the clinical staff who cared for patients. Everyone else was in the third category, and the distinctions between MBA's and mailroom clerks were not critical to the founding directors. Those "outsiders," who grasped these cultural distinctions and were able to adapt to them, survived, and in many cases thrived. The many others who tried to fight it did not.

In its earliest years, even before the advent of the ESRD Program, National Medical Care was blessed with the talents of self-directed managers who thrived in the entrepreneurial ethos of the new company. While the founders were spending most of their time seeing patients and directing the new dialysis clinics, these few managers were left to their own devices to "take care of business." David Lubrano, as treasurer and chief financial officer, Murray Matthews, as the chief accounting officer, Frank LaPlante, an engineer who oversaw the construction of the new clinics, Sam Saitz, who managed the early, non-dialysis operations, and Dave Donlan, who put together the first medical products marketing and sales strategy, formed the core of the non-clinical staff. And all of these pioneers stayed with the company throughout its first decade.

In early 1974, the three doctor-founders, motivated in part by the non-employee, "outside" members of NMC's Board of Directors, representing the interests of the stockholders, decided it was prudent to recruit professional business managers to operate the company. They hired Joel Mahran, a successful executive from Comsat in Washington, D.C., and his deputy, Sam Scialabba. Mahran, who spent the first year at the company studying its financials and operating plans, analyzing its legal, audit, and personnel policies, writing strategic plans, manuals, and other memorandum, never gained the confidence of the doctors, and was the first in a long series of top professionals who failed to "fit in" and establish a trust relationship with Hampers, Schupak and Hager. Sam Scialabba, on the other hand, was sensitive to the needs of the doctors, both at the headquarters and in the clinics, listened more often than spoke, and adapted seamlessly into the NMC culture, where he took on a variety of roles for the next 14 years.

The key to success at NMC for those managers like Scialabba who did not come from the clinical setting, was learning to anticipate the expectations and needs of the founders, rather than asserting a personal agenda. In addition, it was critical to these doctors to have all the relevant data, good and bad, as soon as possible, just as it would be for a physician to have all the data that might affect his diagnosis and prescription. Omitting, eliding, or glossing over bad results could lead to mistakes and fatalities, both in medicine and in business. Hampers, Hager and Schupak didn't simply want to know what decision the manager had made, but what facts and assumptions supported the decision; they wanted the data, not the diagnosis, preferring to reach their own conclusions.

Business professional hired to work for Hampers found it maddening to have to justify the most insignificant decisions. The accountants had to explain why certain expenses were or were not capitalized; lawyers had to cite precedent to rationalize their conclusions to include a particular fact in a stockholder proxy statement; human resource managers had to produce the survey results to justify a particular salary increase, and so on. Of course, many staff members made the mistake of justifying a particular decision or conclusion by offering only the supporting data and deleting any facts that were "contraindicators." Generally they didn't survive to make the mistake twice. Moreover, not only did Hampers, Hager and Schupak "second guess" their senior staff members, but they had no problem contradicting them or reversing their decisions. They were no more likely to backup a senior manager for the sake of consistency and morale than they were to endorse a bad diagnosis and prescription by a resident on their medical service. As a result of this process, the doctors, especially Hampers, acquired a tremendous education in areas well beyond their original expertise. Hampers never forgot a contract provision, an accounting principle, a engineering cost study, a tax hedge, or a clever acquisition strategy. Hampers allowed, and in fact expected, his subordinates to make mistakes, but he wouldn't tolerate fakes. Even in his years in training as an intern, resident and fellow, his poker playing abilities were renowned. "Gus remembered every card that was played, and he could detect a bluff a mile away," Ed Lowrie recalled.

Not until 1976 were the business managers permitted to analyze, compare and grade the business performance of the individual dialysis clinics. Before, then, Schupak, Hampers and Hager saw no point in the exercise, since the individual medical directors expected and were promised autonomy. In fact, it was encouragement from these medical directors themselves, who wanted business guidance in order to improve their operations, that motivated the NMC executives to measure performance and set standards. Hampers and Scialabba recruited Ernie Lowrie, who had been a dialysis nurse assisting Hampers since the mid-sixties, and was by 1976 the administrator of NMC's Boston clinic, to assume a corporate role of assessing the efficiency of the various clinics around the country. Mrs. Lowrie and Scialabba focused on personnel and supply costs and their findings represented the first intrusion of the business managers into the clinical world. Because she was a nurse with over a decade's experience in caring for kidney patients and collaborating with nephrologists, the NMC medical directors (or at least the vast majority of them) accepted Mrs. Lowrie's findings. Moreover, without this study and the cost savings that it produced, the company would not have prospered, as the ESRD Program began cutting reimbursement in the early 1980's and as personnel and supply costs continued to rise. Still, it was not an easy sell. As Scialabba stated, "It took almost eighteen months to convince the doctors to change their operations."

By 1978 the investment community as represented by two or three dialysis industry analysts and few major shareholders and business journalists were clamoring for NMC to enlist the assistance of one or more seasoned business professionals who had experience operating a public company and were more in tune with the expectations of the media, the public and the investment community. The original NMC stockholders, many of whom like Henry Malkasian were still part of the NMC family, held Hampers, Hager and Schupak in awe. Their investments were not just motivated by financial expectations but by the appeal of helping provide a vital, socially desirable service. They were, however, in the minority in believing that NMC was best operated by the founding doctors. Three events in particular precipitated the cry for new, outside management. The first was the January 1977 bid by Becton Dickinson to acquire NMC and, more especially, the way the potential merger was handled or was perceived to have been handled. The second was the passage of Public Law 95-292, intended to cut dialysis reimbursement, and the negative fallout from that legislative effort. And the third was Dr. Schupak's resignation from NMC.

Peter P. Phildius, an 18-year veteran at Baxter International, and its third ranking executive in charge of about 60% of Baxter's sales by 1978, came to National Medical Care in November, 1978, and was elected its president and chief operating officer in December of that year. He had been courted principally by Gene Schupak who was planning his own departure, and, according to Phildius, wanted him to protect Schupak's interests and the interests of the medical products division. At each negotiation, Phildius recalled, he asked for more - more authority and control, more money, more stock options - more than even he ever expected to receive. Hampers and Schupak readily agreed, almost too readily, Phildius later reflected. He had second thoughts from the first day he arrived at the Hancock Tower office in Boston.

One incident in particular stood out in Phildius' memory from that first day, as Gus Hampers walked him around the 50th floor office suite, introducing him to key employees and orienting him to the operations. The last stop was at the far corner at the office of Ernie Lowrie. Phildius knew Mrs. Lowrie from his years trying to sell her Baxter products, and he admired her intelligence and business savvy. After exchanging pleasantries (after all, Mrs.

Lowrie, along with her boss, Sam Scialabba, would henceforth be reporting to Phildius, not Hampers), Mrs. Lowrie turned to Hampers and reminded him that she had requested his permission to purchase a file cabinet for her office and she was waiting for a decision. Instead of deciding, Hampers turned to Phildius and threw him the question - did he, Phildius, think Mrs. Lowrie should buy a new cabinet? At first Phildius thought it was a joke, and he laughed, but when Hampers and Lowrie continued to wait for his response, he realized he had to make a decision, so he responded by saying that anyone who had the experience and authority that Ernie Lowrie had over the entire dialysis division of NMC should be trusted to make her own decision about whether or not to buy a file cabinet. As Mrs. Lowrie grinned, Gus Hampers led Phildius back to his office. Once there, Phildius recalled, Hampers lectured Phildius on the NMC philosophy: "We earn money around here by not spending it," Phildius quoted Hampers. "I knew then that there was a major difference between us," Phildius later mused. "Gus believed you had to save in order to earn. I believed just the opposite - that you had to spend money on good investments in order to earn more in the future."

Pete Phildius made significant contributions to NMC's diversification efforts in the three years that he stayed at NMC, especially in improving the operations at the medical products division and acquiring rights to the Fresenius artificial kidney technology for the U.S. market, by acquiring the nucleus of the home care division, and by orchestrating the purchase of the Portuguese dialysis operations. However, he never managed to win Hampers' trust, and the "file cabinet" story was an early portent. To Phildius, the incident showed Hampers' limits in delving into the details and missing the big picture. To Hampers, the incident meant that Phildius was willing to let subordinates make decisions without checking on the underlying facts or requiring them to justify their conclusions. No one respected Ernie Lowrie's abilities more than Hampers, but that didn't mean that he would permit her to make a decision without making a convincing case, whether it was about the amount of heparin to administer or the amount to spend on a file cabinet.

Phildius also successfully recruited a cadre of business planners and professional managers, some, like Greg Prada and Austin ("Chip") Broadhurst, Jr., from Baxter, and others from business schools and corporate America beyond the healthcare sector. Being one step removed from Dr. Hampers, these executives never understood or were understood by, Gus Hampers. Two competing camps of senior level employees sprang up: one, loyal to Phildius, viewed Hampers as the smart, but crazy founder in the corner office; the other, dedicated to Hampers, saw Phildius and his recruits as interlopers. The situation was aggravated by Hampers' uncharacteristic withdrawal and disengagement from day-to-day operations in 1979. Whether fall out from the departure of Schupak and Hager, or whether motivated by his desire to allow Phildius to have a freer rein, Hampers was not for awhile intervening on behalf of his loyalists in their continuing battles with Phildius and the "new wave." At the same time Phildius knew how to charm and reward even the most intransigent "old timers" by giving them more staff, recommending salary increases and backing them up - behavior that these veterans had never experienced from Hampers. There were frequent rumors that Hampers would soon be following his founding colleagues, and security for senior staff meant collaborating with the new president.

Tensions came to a boiling point in 1980, jolting Hampers from his self-imposed management hibernation. Sam Scialabba was operating the core dialysis division, assisted by Ernie Lowrie, and had been very sternly warned by Phildius that he was not to talk to Hampers about decisions or seek his advice; Sam was to allow Phildius, alone, to keep Hampers informed, following the chain of command. This was very uncomfortable for Scialabba and Lowrie who had worked with Hampers for many years, and it became increasingly clear to Scialabba at least that this chain-of-command principle was not one that Hampers was aware of or certainly endorsed. When Phildius decided that all divisional controllers would henceforth report to the corporate controller and through him to the chief financial officer and Phildius, rather than to the divisional chiefs, Scialabba objected. He wrote a memorandum to Phildius making the case that such an extra divisional hierarchy would undermine his ability to control and manage his division, and in a bold move sent a copy to Hampers. Over

Phildius' objections, Hampers summarily agreed with Scialabba and shot down the president's plans. As Scialabba recalled, "I took a big risk, because if Hampers ignored me or took Pete's side, I was history. I was lucky."

Phildius, of course, had a different perspective. "I was outside the Sam-Ernie-Gus loop," he later remembered. "I became a non-entity, especially among the dialysis clinic medical directors," he continued. Phildius recalled that at a medical directors' annual meeting in Puerto Rico he felt excluded from all the important discussions. "It was embarrassing, almost a joke," he concluded. Phildius realized that Hampers was not going to surrender control of NMC to him and that he'd have to be more aggressive and attempt to take it with the assistance of NMC's outside directors, principally Paul Paganucci, the leader of the non-officer members of the NMC Board. He made his move at the December 1980 Board meeting, demanding that he be designated the presumptive CEO and that Hampers be eased into an emeritus position. At the time the Board consisted of seven members, including Phildius. He needed the support of the outside directors to trump the three votes held by Drs. Hampers, Hager, and Ed Lowrie, who was elected to the Board at the same December, 1980 meeting to replace Dr. Schupak who had by then resigned from the Board. (Even though Dr. Hager left NMC's employment in April, 1980 to run unsuccessfully for the United States Senate from New Hampshire, he remained on the NMC Board of Directors.) Phildius failed, and Hampers' control was reaffirmed by the Board. "I wasn't surprised," Phildius reflected. "But I had to try; I really had nothing to lose." Phildius was counting on his appeal to the investment community, which continued to view Hampers skeptically, believing that the outside directors would be unable to explain why an accomplished business executive like Phildius should not be put in charge of NMC. Mr. Paganucci, who had been on NMC's Board and had known Gus Hampers since 1973, remembered Phildius as being very solicitous of the outside directors, but in the end, he felt only Hampers could maintain the loyalty of the NMC medical directors, and that Hampers was not only the past, but also the future, of NMC. However, in a move to keep Hampers somewhat in check, the Board also voted at the December 1980 to expand to eight members, adding a fourth outside director. Pete Phildius left NMC in the fall of 1981, but for all intents and purposes, his wings had been clipped at the 1980 year end Board meeting.

Hampers prevailed in the December 1980 Board showdown with Phildius, in spite of his sometimes cavalier treatment of the outside directors. These directors, particularly Paul Paganucci, were concerned by the manner in which Hampers and Schupak had kept them uninformed in the 1977 near takeover by Becton-Dickinson. There were also lesser slights that grated on the directors. Typically, the Board meetings were scheduled as luncheons and started at noon. However, there were no cocktails, no catered hot meals, and no time for socializing, just a platter of sandwiches and cans of soda laid out on the sideboard, which Hampers grudgingly provided but never consumed. From Hampers point of view a "good Board meeting" was over by 1:30 p.m., before they had finished the cookies. At exactly twelve o'clock Hampers would begin the meeting, whether the directors were ready or not. "Gus never even let us eat our sandwiches," Paganucci later laughingly recalled. "He'd ask if there were any questions while our mouths were full, and hearing nothing but chewing, he'd move on to the next item." When Hampers began the December 1980 Board meeting with the nomination of Dr. Lowrie to fill the seat on the Board recently vacated by Gene Schupak, the outside directors were surprised, since they had not been previously notified or briefed by Hampers. "I made a mistake," Hampers later conceded. The outside directors wanted Schupak's seat on the Board to go to an additional, outside director, not a company officer like Lowrie, who would be under Hampers' control. The Board meeting had already been extended by the time taken to discuss and dispose of the Phildius challenge, and now the debate about an additional outside director had thrown Hampers off his tight, carefully planned schedule. "I had a five o'clock plane to catch to Los Angeles," Hampers noted. "So I stood up and told them I had to leave and they could let me know what they decided." They immediately voted to seat Lowrie on the Board and expand the Board by an additional seat, which was filled in the Spring of 1981 by Carl Tiedemann, a former executive at Donaldson, Lufkin & Jenrette.

For the next several years, 1981 to 1984, when the W.R. Grace leveraged buyout was implemented, NMC continued to recruit other executive talent, and largely failed to significantly augment the indigenous senior staff that had been bred in the dialysis clinical setting. The husband-and-wife, doctor-and-nurse team of Ed and Ernie Lowrie, and their recruits, like Chris Ford, who had started at the old NMC extended care facility when he was still a college student and his mother was head nurse in the late-1960's, and Bill Whittaker, who was picked by Dr. Lowrie to run the medical products division, became the principal lieutenants for Hampers. This phenomenon was both the result and the cause of an unsuccessful diversification strategy.

In addition to diversification, National Medical Care also pursued a strategy of aggression or combat during the years (roughly, 1974-84) it prospered as a public company, heavily dependent on a single, federal government program. These strategies were directed at the government itself, at actual and potential competitors, and at the media. The basic thrust of this NMC aggression was to upset any assumptions by either government bureaucrats or by investment analysts that National Medical Care was some sort of quasi-public authority, like a utility in the days before de-regulation, whose revenues and profits would be controlled by the Health Care Financing Administration (HCFA). These strategies included extending NMC's market share and therefore increasing its influence in the dialysis marketplace, and resisting all federal efforts to secure sensitive cost and other financial data.

NMC's willingness to defy government officials had a history that pre-dated the Medicare ESRD Program. In Boston as early as 1966, Dr. Hampers was warned by the Public Health Commissioner that opening an outpatient facility at the Normandy House would put his personal medical license on the line should anything go amiss. Later, in 1971 and again in 1973 and 1975, when NMC's requests for expanding its complement of dialysis stations were denied by the supervising Peter Bent Brigham Hospital and by the Massachusetts Department of Public Health, NMC went ahead and added the additional stations anyway. The principals were routinely scolded at public hearings and before the hospital governing bodies, acknowledged their sins, were in at least one case fined $5,000, and went about their business. Their defense always rested on the ends-justify-the-means argument: they knew what they were doing was wrong, but as physicians confronting the choice between seeing critically ill patients turned away, or following the dictates of bureaucrats, they had to defy the authorities and face the consequences.

In order to be able to deal with Medicare on a more equal basis, the larger NMC was, the better its chances of defying the government. As its relative importance increased, it would be harder for the government to ignore NMC's protests. Ultimately, NMC could implicitly or explicitly threaten to close all or some of its facilities in order to pressure Medicare. That kind of tactic would only be credible if NMC was viewed as large and aggressive. That's exactly what the combat strategy produced. It's not an exaggeration to note that the federal and state governments had to fight NMC for every piece of data and concession that other operators routinely surrendered. It would often take years before the government was able to obtain the information it wanted. It didn't matter to NMC that much that it generally lost these struggles to the government, since delay itself was its own reward.

In 1978, NMC began litigation, Erika v. United States, with the federal government over the pricing of heparin, a drug that impedes blood clotting and is vital to the dialysis process. Years later, after an earlier, proNMC ruling at the Court of Claims, the case was decided by a unanimous Supreme Court of the United States in favor of the government (456 U.S. 201, 1982). Nonetheless, NMC had made the point that it would not accept the cavalier pricing dictates of the federal government, and was willing to pursue the matter all the way to the highest court in the country, if necessary.

Shortly after the start of the ESRD Program in July 1973, the federal government sought cost data from participating facilities in order to set prospective rates. Other facilities complied as a matter of course, but not NMC. In 1975 Dr. Schupak as the proprietor of the Queens Artificial Kidney Center filed a lawsuit challenging the authority of the government to seek this data in litigation that was supported by NMC. The case, which began life as Schupak v. Weinberger, and was pursued through the tenure of several Secretary's of Health Education and Welfare, lasted over two years in the District Court and the Circuit Court of Appeals for the D.C. Circuit. NMC argued that since the ESRD Program was a Medicare "Part B" program, paying only 80% of reasonable and customary charges (similar to the program that paid physicians for services to Medicare beneficiaries), costs were irrelevant, and if irrelevant and unnecessary to the government's role, could not be demanded by Medicare. Schupak and NMC lost the case, but the tactic delayed the data transfer for several years. In addition to this major lawsuit, there were all sorts of "skirmishes" along the way. One involved the demand by the Inspector General of HHS for cost information from Erika, Inc., NMC's medical products subsidiary, in order to apply the "related party principle," and thereby shrink NMC's costs by eliminating the Erika markup, and, presumably lower prospective reimbursement rates. Again, NMC resisted.

During the 1978-1982 fight over ESRD Program reform, there were several battles between the government and NMC, culminating in NMC's December 1981 threat to close sixty dialysis centers if the government instituted its "dual rate" reimbursement system in order to help the high cost hospital providers. A few months later, on April 21, 1982, Chairman Charles Rangel of New York held a House Ways and Means Committee hearing and took the opportunity to lecture NMC's counsel that the company's aggressive tactics, especially in agitating patients with the threatened closure announcement were counter productive and not appreciated by Congress. As Dr. Hampers watched and listened at the back of the hearing room, Bob Green, the CEO of an NMC competitor, Community Dialysis Centers, unexpectedly told the Rangel committee that NMC should be praised, not criticized, for challenging HCFA's plans, which in his view were unauthorized and wasteful of taxpayers' resources.

Mr. Green's defense of NMC was surprising, because, throughout the first decade of the ESRD Program's life, other proprietary dialysis clinics, some operated as doctors' offices and some as part of corporate chains, generally permitted NMC to fight the government on its own. Although the delays and concessions that NMC won also benefited these other clinics, as well as doctors, patients and taxpayers, NMC had few, if any, allies. To be sure, NMC was pursuing these aggressive strategies out of its own, corporate, self-interest, and NMC was not known for coalition building and welcoming others to join the battle, but nonetheless there were important medical, financial and public policy issues at stake that affected a much larger community. In fact, NMC was more often criticized by physician and patient groups than helped by them.

What NMC was seeking was the most efficient and least intrusive government financed system for end-stage renal disease. In NMC's view, HCFA's decision to pay hospitals more for a dialysis treatment than it paid an NMC center was not just discriminatory, but wasteful, costing the taxpayers more than necessary. NMC fought to have Medicare pay more attention to the quality of care that was being delivered to the patients than focusing on NMC's profits. It was maddening for Drs. Schupak, Hager and Hampers to hear bureaucrats and politicians justify price cuts with the argument that so long as NMC kept building new centers, prices could be cut. Faced with such illogical syllogisms, NMC's officers felt the government was begging them to threaten closure of some facilities. What the government was not doing was assessing whether the patients were getting the care they deserved. While the bureaucrats were trying to save thousands of dollars by reducing the basic dialysis charge, they were spending millions of dollars for the hospitalizations of patients who were regularly admitted to correct poor care. There should be no mistake that NMC's protracted fights with the government were financially motivated, but the principles for which NMC was fighting were worthy of support by patient and physician groups.

NMC also pursued an aggressive course in expanding its dialysis services business, whether through startups or acquisition of existing clinics. In its early years, NMC had all it could do to build dialysis clinics fast enough to satisfy the demands of nephrologists all over the country who wanted their own centers. The openings of NMC centers, like the early ones in Washington, D.C. and Dallas, were often heralded in human interest stories in the local media, and politicians gladly showed up at the ribbon cutting ceremonies. After the ESRD Program began, however, NMC more likely had to fight its way into a local market and contend with a "certificate of need" (CoN) process that could take months, and sometimes years, to complete and was rife with conflicts of interest and local favoritism. Now largely extinct, the CoN laws adopted by most states in the 1970's were an attempt by state governments (encouraged by the federal government) to curb excess supply ("over bedding," it was often called) which, in an era of cost-reimbursement, meant higher costs, prices, insurance premiums and taxes. Thus, if there was no "need" for additional ICU beds, or MRI scanners, in a particular city, adding more of the same would result in higher per unit costs, which would have to be paid by the patients and their private or public (taxpayer) insurers. Instead of allowing over supply to naturally result in lower prices, these Blue Cross and Medicare/Medicaid insurers stuck with a cost reimbursement system, which turned the law of supply and demand on its head, i.e., increasing supply resulted in higher, not lower prices as capital costs were spread over smaller numbers of treatments.

The application of CoN laws to building dialysis clinics, especially after the introduction of the ESRD Program in 1973, was illogical, and was mainly used by existing suppliers to extend their monopolies or shared monopolies. NMC fought aggressively against CoN laws, when these were being used to keep NMC out of a new market, and just as aggressively to apply these CoN laws to keep potential competitors out of markets that it already dominated. These battles were extremely expensive in terms of both money and time. In the heyday of CoN laws in process obsessed states like Massachusetts and California, it could take several years to build a new dialysis center, years in which patients, who would otherwise have been served by a new center, would have to travel hours to far distant centers for their dialysis care.

Typically, the battles would begin at local "health service agencies" (HSA's) which were supported by the federal government's Public Health Service. The HSA's were by law composed of provider representatives (like the local hospital which would have a conflict of interest in judging the need for a potential competitor), consumer advocates, and a few experts from academia and public interest lawyers. In almost every case there was an inherent bias against profit making providers. These HSA's had their own staff experts whose recommendations were rarely disputed.

The HSA would review applications, hold hearings and make recommendations to the state health planning agency, usually the state health department officials plus one or two political appointees. The state agencies also had professional staff, and would hold one or more hearings on the applications after a long, tedious process. Under most CoN laws "affected parties" (a defined term, which was often disputed) had a right to intervene in the process, thereby entitling these parties to notice, and opportunities to argue and be heard. Often, there could be as many as six or eight parties testifying at final hearings: the state agency staff, the HSA staff, the applicant, competing hospitals and facilities, patients and doctors, all wanted, and were entitled to, their say. In extremely controversial cases local and state politicians would show up and add their "two cents," and all of these proceedings would be open to the public and reported by the media.

Although intended to be quasi-judicial, they tended to become political, legislative debates. In Massachusetts in the mid-1970's even a non-controversial project would take nine to twelve months to approve. Even after a decision was made by the state agency, the disappointed party (parties) would inevitably appeal, first to a health facilities appeals board, and perhaps later, to court. The battle could take years for final resolution.

Thousands of people - HSA staff, state agency staff, lawyers, planners, demographers and accountants - made a good living from this process. NMC had its own staff of CoN specialists within its law department who worked full time on these applications and became experts at avoiding and using these CoN laws in nearly every state in the nation. Every year the company spent hundreds of thousands of dollars complying with these laws. NMC lawyers established the precedent of "comparative review" in the CoN process where there were two or more applicants for the same service during the same application period. Thus, by the late 1970's all applications that sought to provide outpatient dialysis in the same "catchment" area during a six month period, would be bundled together, and simultaneously considered and decided, using a comparative process, similar to the process used by the Federal Communications Commission in awarding broadcast licenses. In effect, a CoN award was a government granted charter to monopolize.

Two examples from 1979 illustrate these efforts that were repeated nearly every time NMC tried to start a new dialysis clinic. They both involved NMC's competitor, Dialysis Clinics, Inc. (DCI), a company that was organized as a not-for-profit corporation, by doctors and businessmen affiliated with Vanderbilt University and its medical school in Nashville. In 1979 NMC "invaded" DCI's original catchment area by proposing to build and operate a dialysis clinic in conjunction with a nephrologist affiliated with Meharry Medical College and Hubbard Hospital, both institutions founded to provide medical education and service to the African American community in Nashville. The DCI-Vanderbilt establishment opposed the NMC effort with vigor. NMC and its local affiliates, led by the aggressive and charismatic, proposed medical director, W. Hermsworth Gardner, M.D., who had trained in Detroit under the supervision of Frank McDonald, one of NMC's pioneering medical directors, pushed forward with equal vigor. DCI and Vanderbilt contended there was no "need" and used statistics showing that there were more than enough dialysis stations in the Nashville area to service the anticipated population. NMC and Dr. Gardner advanced a different and unique theory of need - one that focused on the need of Meharry medical students to have a clinical experience with dialysis that did not then exist and the need of physicians based at Hubbard and the Meharry faculty, both largely African American, to be permitted to offer their patients "continuity of care." What continuity of care really meant for these doctors was the ability to take care of (and be compensated for) their patients in an outpatient setting, and not having to refer them to a DCI center. For the HSA hearing Dr. Gardner hired buses and transported scores of Meharry faculty and medical students to the hearing room. He had also alerted the local television news reporters. To the casual viewer it looked as though black doctors and patients and their NMC ally were being denied something that the white establishment had. As a result, the NMC clinic was approved.

DCI turned the tables on NMC in the same year - 1979 - when it teamed up with the Tufts University Medical Center to propose a new outpatient dialysis center in downtown Boston. In applying for a new center in Framingham, Massachusetts, NMC was trying to protect its existing dominance in the greater Boston outpatient dialysis market against the same rival it faced in Nashville. In the Boston situation there was a need for more dialysis stations. NMC's Kidney Center (formerly the "Babcock" center) was running around the clock, six days per week. The argument came down to whether the additional stations should be placed in Boston proper, as DCI proposed, or in Framingham, which would siphon off patients living in the affluent western suburbs of Boston, relieving them of the thrice weekly commute to the city. NMC used a model borrowed from the trucking industry in computing and comparing the patient miles saved under both plans. The suburban plan won out, but the entire process, including appeals took nearly three years to complete. By then, the need was great enough to justify both new centers.

These CoN disputes were repeated in nearly every state in the country as NMC tried to expand and also tried to protect its base. In his authoritative review of the ESRD Program, Richard Rettig concluded that the application of state CoN laws added, rather than lessened, costs, and should be abandoned with respect to outpatient dialysis.

At the same time NMC was protecting its base from potential competitors and establishing new centers around the country through the thickets of certificate of need laws, it was also engaged in an aggressive acquisition strategy. Acquisition of existing dialysis centers had a couple distinct advantages. One was the avoidance of the full review certificate of need process, and its attendant costs in terms of time (generally, nine to 18 months) and money. Most CoN laws required review of the transfer of ownership of a healthcare facility like a dialysis center, but generally such a review was an expeditious, non-combative, administrative examination of the proposed transferee, a process in which the other local dialysis providers did not have standing to intervene. Since the acquired facility already existed, the state was not going to reassess the "need" for the operation. Also, NMC's acquisitions involved a long term contract with the existing medical director(s) of the acquired center, and a non-competition agreement with the seller. Often the seller was also the medical director who saw a greater advantage in joining NMC than in fighting the national company. For many years, NMC was the only buyer in the market, thus keeping the price in check. Also, Congress, particularly Rep. Fortney "Pete" Stark (D-Cal) and the subcommittee on health (of the House Ways and Means Committee), which he chaired, would occasionally propose ending the ability of doctors to send patients to facilities that they owned, thus adding impetus to the trend for the nephrologist-owners to cash in their investments. Helping NMC grow was certainly an unintended consequence of those promoting that legislation. Finally, for some physician-owners, the profit margins were too slim, the cost of compliance with regulations and other non-medical aspects of running a business too time-consuming, and the capital gains too tempting to resist NMC's offers. Other sellers saw affiliation with NMC as having distinct benefits for their patients and their own practice of medicine.

National Medical Care was always on the look out for acquisitions in the dialysis area and by 1980 had set up a separate department within the company devoted to these purchases. The assessments, "due diligence" procedures, contracts, licensure transfers and other aspects of these acquisitions became routinized, and an acquisition could be effected in a very short time period by NMC's staff. The purchases could be of a single center, or of multiple centers from an entrepreneur-doctor, like the purchase of three centers from Dr. Schreiber in Miami in 1980, or of a competing corporate chain of outpatient centers, like the acquisition of several centers, most located in New Jersey, from IHC also in early 1980. As soon as the purchase was effected, a special team of NMC nurses, engineers, and administrative staff would convert the newly acquired centers to the NMC "system." Those most damaged and incensed by this aggressive tactic were the suppliers of the acquired centers, like Baxter, which were very often either replaced as supplier by the NMC products division, or had their profits trimmed by being forced to sell supplies at reduced, NMC negotiated prices. The operation of outpatient dialysis centers was clearly amenable to economies-of-scale, and in evaluating an acquisition, NMC was less concerned with the profits (or losses) the centers had generated in the past, than in the revenues it was, or could be, generating, since NMC would apply its standardized costs going forward. An acquired center no longer needed its own administrative staff, accountants, lawyers, engineers, or billing specialists. NMC administrators and head nurses were trained to manage more than one center in their localities, and complex regulatory compliance, legal, accounting, inventory control and warehousing, engineering, and other non-medical problems were handled by central NMC staff. These services were spread over more and more treatments and helped enormously in holding costs down for the ESRD Program. In this sense alone, NMC saved Medicare millions of dollars. Of course, NMC's critics and cynics of the ESRD Program saw this activity differently. In their view, if NMC could pay premiums for these centers, then the reimbursement rate must be too high, they argued, and federal taxpayers were being bilked to inflate NMC's profits and stockholder value.

Revenues were directly related to the number of patients. Dr. Hampers and his lieutenants at NMC could generally price an acquisition simply from the patient census. Under the ESRD Program in the 1970's, a patient would generate base revenues (not adding ancillary service and product revenues) of $20,700 per annum (150 Rx's X $138 per Rx), and the estimate of profits that NMC could make by applying its program to the center could easily be calculated. The capital costs of acquiring these centers far exceeded the assessed value of the real estate, equipment and other fixed, depreciable assets, and the difference resulted in ever-increasing amounts of "goodwill" on NMC's books. Goodwill is the acquisition premium - the amount the buyer pays over and above the "book value" of the tangible assets of the business. As NMC became larger and as its medical information system became more sophisticated, the company was able to look at the patient census and determine how long it would take to recoup the acquisition premium from the profits generated by treating these patients. Since the patients would not be at the center forever, with some having transplants, and others leaving the clinic for a variety of reasons, and still others expiring, the businessmen and accountants at NMC realized that this "goodwill" was not permanent, but in fact, depleted over time. From there it was an easy step to begin writing off the goodwill assets over time, thus reducing both reportable earnings and taxable income. It would take many years before the IRS would accept this reduction of taxable income by NMC, but the process of depleting the goodwill account was critical to the eventual sale of NMC to a small group of investors headed by W.R. Grace.

In addition to its acquisition program, NMC began to offer management contracts to hospitals, permitting NMC to operate outpatient dialysis facilities owned by these largely non-profit medical centers. The advantages to the hospitals included an up-front infusion of badly needed capital, usually in the form of a new, well equipped clinic space, and an end to operating losses associated with running high cost centers. These deals were especially pushed during 1981, when it appeared likely that the Reagan Administration would favor a single, incentive reimbursement system for outpatient dialysis and an end to the system that paid hospitals more than NMC-type centers. However, with the passage of Public Law 97-35 (the Omnibus Budget Reconciliation Act of 1981), HCFA was required to create the so called "dual rate" system of dialysis reimbursement, which resulted in a higher payment to hospitals, and a virtual end to NMC's management scheme.

The aggressive use of CoN laws to construct new centers and prevent others from competing, the very successful, but expensive, acquisition program, and the hospital management project were all intended to complement a combat strategy that held the monopsonistic Medicare ESRD Program at least partially in check. NMC's growing market share was, however, vulnerable from disaffected medical directors, who might bolt the NMC system and set up their own competing clinics. NMC assiduously resisted these attempts to break away and dissolve the non-competition agreements these doctors had executed. Hampers felt it was critical to NMC's continued success to beat these insurrections mercilessly, or face the consequences of growing disaffection, mutiny, and a shift in negotiating leverage in favor of the doctors. The physicians held the patients, almost literally in their hands. Very few dialysis patients would stay at a clinic if his or her doctor practiced elsewhere. In addition to splits with the medical directors, NMC could be hurt materially by the disaffection from the younger cadre of attending physicians who referred their patients to the NMC clinics, but were not bound by any contract with NMC. They could, and often did, leave to start their own clinics.

Preventing medical directors from competing was difficult. Courts generally disfavor tough non-competition arrangements, viewing these as coercive and inimical to public policy, especially in the case of physicians. The challenge for the NMC lawyers in these cases was to convince the judge that NMC was not seeking to limit the practice of medicine, but only the pursuit of business opportunities by these entrepreneurial medical directors. Since many of the same judges who were in awe of physicians also held the view that doctors shouldn't mix medicine with business, they were often persuaded by these arguments. As a result, NMC was successful enough to at least create a huge barrier for disaffected medical directors from starting their own centers. Not only would they have to raise several hundred thousand dollars to construct and equip a center, but they would have to commit an additional bank roll to defend themselves in court, and that was before adding the cost of pursuing a certificate of need in face of certain NMC opposition. By combining aggressive tactics to enforce the non-competition agreements and providing sweeteners in terms of financial incentives to stay within the NMC system, Hampers was very successful, over all, in maintaining the loyalty of the medical directors over a very long period of time. Many of the business managers hired by NMC never understood the vulnerability of NMC's enterprise to these medical directors. It was certainly NMC's "Achilles heel," and the doctors knew it.

Maintaining the loyalty of the growing number of referring and attending physicians to NMC's clinics was another matter. These doctors were not under contract to NMC and had never agreed not to establish their own centers. Hampers expected the medical directors to find ways to keep these other physicians happy. "It was the medical director's job to keep his house in order," Hampers explained. In the early years the medical directors were able to control these doctors through a combination of severe, but largely unarticulated, tactics. First, most of the medical directors were also chiefs of the renal service at the affiliated teaching hospitals. A nephrology novice could not afford to cross these powerful gatekeepers to the hospitals. Second, many directors were the mentors of these younger doctors, whose advancement in academic medicine depended on nothing less than perfect recommendations from their seasoned superiors. Part of their control also involved access to research grants and coveted clinical appointments at the medical schools. Finally, there was often the implicit promise that if the newer physicians "toed the line," the medical directors would take them in as future partners to their lucrative private practices, including their share in the NMC clinics. This latter point was particularly critical, as time elapsed. These younger doctors wanted a piece of the action as well. Some clinic directors did this well, and some did not, often putting NMC in the very uncomfortable position of having to choose sides between the medical director and his disaffected junior colleagues. In the later years, the medical directors attended fewer and fewer patients, and the non-affiliated, younger physicians would control the majority of the patients. Those were explosive situations that would predictably lead to potential competition.

In three cases the explosions had major repercussions for NMC. Although the circumstances in San Diego, San Antonio, and Alexandria (Virginia) were very different, all three presented substantial threats to NMC's hegemony, and all three required skillful management. Arnold Roland, M.D., the medical director of the San Diego clinic, was one of NMC's pioneer medical directors, and typical of the breed. Dr. Roland developed a thriving private practice to complement his responsibilities at the University of California - San Diego Hospital Center. Like Hampers and Schupak, Roland mentored a cadre of fellows who began carrying more and more of the load at the San Diego center. Confronted by their demands to share in the profits of the clinic, Dr. Roland denied that he received any profit shares, but was contradicted by clinic staff. Naturally this led to a protracted and very nasty intramural battle that became public when the parties went to court. The image of doctors fighting over profits from a dialysis center was additional grist for the anti-NMC publicity mill. NMC had an interest in maintaining the goodwill of both sides and tried valiantly to negotiate a truce among the factions. It was a "no win" situation.

In the San Antonio case, the company sided with the original medical director, Gordon Bilbrey, M.D., in litigation brought by his cross town rival, Dr. Steven Rosenblatt, but later was able to negotiate a truce and accommodation that saw all parties prosper. In fact, for a short period in the early 1990's Dr. Rosenblatt became an NMC officer at its headquarters office. San Antonio, thanks in part to the very skillful diplomacy of Marianne Szalay, NMC's regional administrator at that time, was a "win win" situation.

National Medical Care acquired the Alexandria center from its founder, Dr. Osheroff, in the late 1970's and retained Dr. Osheroff as its medical director. When Dr. Osheroff became ill and was hospitalized, his junior associate, Bob Greenspan, M.D., whose wife Bonnie had been the head nurse at NMC's Columbus, Ohio clinic while Dr. Greenspan was studying at Ohio State, took over the direction of the Osheroff clinics. Upon Dr. Osheroff's return, Greenspan resisted Osheroff's control, and a pair of lawsuits ensued. Osheroff sued Greenspan for essentially "stealing his practice," and Dr. Greenspan countered with antitrust litigation directed at Osheroff and NMC. NMC stuck by Osheroff and eventually prevailed, but in the process made Greenspan into a fervent and resourceful enemy of the company.

The drama and negative fall out from these disputes among NMC's doctors could temporarily overshadow the relative harmony of the NMC system, particularly as magnified and hyperbolized by the media. Better than a cat fight was a lawsuit among physicians over patient fees and clinic profits. Nonetheless, considering the size of the NMC network, and the size of the ego's of the medical directors, it was remarkable that there were so few disputes. Moreover, Dr. Hampers had an uncanny ability to disengage from these fights whenever it appeared that the costs outweighed the gains. "Why get into a pissing contest with a skunk?" Hampers often cautioned his senior advisors. Keeping his eye on the bottom line, Hampers could stun his lawyers and business colleagues by hopping on an airplane in the midst of a contentious, drawn out dispute with a medical director, and settle the controversy in a 20-minute conversation at an airport conference room without any lawyers present, and be back in Boston for dinner. Emotions were checked at the door, and the former opponents were welcomed back into the fold. The brush fires never expanded into full scale conflagrations, and Hampers was able to direct his medical directors' attention away from puerile battles over territory and respect, and back to the important matter of making money.

In attempting to escape the dilemma of operating as a public company, largely dependent on a single, government funded program, National Medical Care's diversification strategy was only partly successful, and its combat strategy was no more than a temporary fix. A thorough and permanent solution would have to involve a combination with another large entity. Finding the right partner was the challenge.

As a public company whose common stock was traded freely on the New York Stock Exchange ever since May 12, 1975 (and on NASDAQ's "over-the-counter" system from 1971 to its NYSE listing), National Medical Care was not wholly in control of its destiny in this regard. NMC executives could not restrict the ability of its stockholders to sell their shares, and hence could not prevent a wealthy investor, either an individual or another corporation, from acquiring a dominant ownership position. By the end of 1975, moreover, the three founding physicians together controlled only ten percent of the common shares of NMC. The remaining 90% were tradable, and hence acquirable. Still, these senior NMC executives were not without leverage, primarily in leading the group of medical directors, without whom the company would be valueless. The prevailing wisdom was that any potential acquiring entity would have to court and secure the favor of Drs. Schupak, Hager and Hampers in order to maintain the loyalty of the clinic directors and to prevent them from walking away from NMC and competing with any new owner. "They can buy the stock, but they can't make us work for them," Hampers was fond of reminding his colleagues. A hostile takeover was, therefore, largely discounted as a threat.

On January 26, 1977, during the first week of the Carter Administration, Becton, Dickinson and Company, a New Jersey-based manufacturer and distributor of a broad array of healthcare products and equipment, announced a merger bid for National Medical Care with NMC stockholders receiving Becton Dickinson stock worth $143 million, or $31.825 per NMC share, which was a 50% premium over its $20.50 trading price at that time. Becton Dickinson with annual revenues of about $600 million was nearly six times the size of NMC, and would have ended the exposure of NMC's dialysis revenues and income to public and government scrutiny. Becton Dickinson was a good fit in terms of product lines; it manufactured and sold syringes, blood collecting equipment, thermometers, bandages (including the popular "ACE" brand), surgical gloves, surgical blades, and an array of clinical laboratory equipment and supplies. NMC would have been its first service subsidiary. Becton Dickinson had just completed an acquisition of Drake Willock, a manufacturer of dialysis equipment, primarily a central dialysate delivery system, and was also manufacturing its own brand of artificial kidney machines and other dialysis products. In fact, the "fit" might have been too close in terms of its anti-competitive impacts in the dialysis industry, requiring a premerger filing with the Federal Trade Commission.

The FTC never ruled on the matter, since the acquisition was abandoned by Becton Dickinson on March 4, 1977, just five weeks after it was announced.

This embarrassing reversal was dictated more by internal politics at Becton Dickinson than by any discomfort about National Medical Care's prospects or by a concern with violating state and federal anti-trust laws. When Wesley "Jack" Howe, the CEO of Becton Dickinson, proposed the merger with NMC, Fairleigh S. ("Dick") Dickinson, Jr., the board chairman and former CEO, took the opportunity to raise questions about the wisdom of the transaction, in a clear attempt to embarrass Howe and his management team. Dick Dickinson went so far as to hire Salomon Brothers to investigate and opine on the proposed merger. In a February 14, 1977 letter to Dickinson which Dickinson then passed along to Howe two days later, William R. Salomon wrote "While the issues memorandum is neither exhaustive nor conclusory [sic], it raises such fundamental issues concerning the propriety and terms of the proposed National Medical Care-Becton, Dickinson combination that Salomon Brothers recommends that no action on this merger should be taken by the Becton, Dickinson Board of Directors unless and until the matters are satisfactorily resolved."

The Salomon memorandum raised a series of questions in five

areas: NMC's accounting practices and procedures; legal and public relations concerns; the relationship between NMC and its Erika subsidiary; NMC's dependency on the Medicare ESRD Program; and Becton Dickinson's ability to manage a multilocation service business. In addition, in an eight page attachment, the Salomon memorandum posited over 100 specific questions. Some of these would be addressed in any premerger, "due diligence" investigation, such as whether any patent infringement actions had been filed against NMC. Others were irrelevant and dilatory, such as providing the transcripts of all NMC stockholders meetings, 1970-1976. Still other inquiries were clearly instigated by someone advising Salomon with a very specific and detailed knowledge of renal dialysis, and the government's ESRD Program, e.g., seeking clinic staffing categories and turnover rates, and asking for the number of board eligible and board certified M.D.'s at the dialysis centers, segmented by medical specialty (a question that would only occur to an academic physician). At that time Dr. Belding H. Scribner, the Seattle nephrologist who had initiated chronic hemodialysis as a maintenance therapy in the early 1960's (and whom Gene Schupak, as John Merrill's fellow, had visited in 1962), was a member of the eight member Scientific Advisory Board of Becton Dickinson. Dr. Scribner and Mr. Dickinson were close colleagues, and the NMC executives speculated that it was Scribner who was whispering in Dickinson's ear, in an attempt to squelch the merger. Dr. Charles C. Edwards, a former Assistant Secretary for Health and then a member of the Becton Dickinson board and president of the Scripps Clinic and Research Foundation, advised Hampers that Scribner had lobbied Dick Dickinson to resist the merger with NMC. In the end, Jack Howe's priorities shifted from acquiring NMC to disposing of Dick Dickinson, and he decided to abandon the NMC merger.

A month or so after rejecting NMC, Howe ousted Dickinson as chairman and removed him from the Becton Dickinson payroll, but within a few short months Dickinson struck a deal with Sun Company, Inc, the oil refining corporation. Sun offered to acquire Becton Dickinson and restore Dick Dickinson to the leadership position at the company his father had co-founded.

Despite the fact that NMC's common stock price rebounded to

its pre-January 26 level within a day after the March 4th announcement, the company's prospects of finding a suitable partner for a friendly combination suffered a set back. At the time Gus Hampers joked, "We looked to all the world like the bride who had been rejected when the groom removed the veil!" In fact the joke was on the Becton Dickinson board who had rejected a dowry that within seven years was worth over $350 million. In addition to the unfavorable public impression caused by the Becton Dickinson rejection, the intense and unsatisfactory 5-week interlude in early 1977, brought several issues to the forefront of the attention of Drs. Hampers, Schupak and Hager.

First, several of the issues raised by Mr. Dickinson and his Salomon advisors were legitimate concerns that had been brushed away and denied by NMC's management. In order to find a successful suitor and effect a winning combination, NMC had to address these issues. In that sense the close examination served as a "wake-up call" to the NMC principals. Second, the experience made Hampers and his colleagues a little more chary of friendly overtures and come-on's, and particularly cautious when it came to premature public announcements that built expectations, and resulting pressure to make a deal at any cost. Third, Hampers, in particular, learned to approach any possible merger or combination discussion with a clear agenda of goals that NMC needed to achieve and chief among these was his continuing role in operating NMC and his new role in the combined entity. Once he had agreed to a deal without nailing down the terms of his own ongoing role, he would have lost important leverage.

Fourth, it was clear that one of the issues that Hampers, Hager and Schupak had purposefully ignored for years would emerge at once in any serious combination proposal, namely, the relationship among the three founders and the issue of hierarchy and succession. Over the course of their NMC involvement since 1968, Schupak, Hampers and Hager had shifted and shared titles and assigned themselves and each other various responsibilities in a logical, if seemingly serendipitous, manner. Early on, Hager was chairman, Schupak, president, and Hampers, executive vice president. By 1977 Hampers was chairman, Hager, chairman of the executive committee, and Schupak, president, and operating responsibility was allocated according to the intensity of relationship between the individual clinic's medical director and one of the three principals. For example, the Detroit clinic was supervised by Hampers because of his close relationship with Dr. McDonald in Detroit, whereas, Schupak's long relationship with Charles Swartz led him to manage Swartz's Philadelphia clinic. Hampers took the lead in the Becton Dickinson negotiations, and it became evident that Jack Howe wanted Gus Hampers to operate NMC as a Becton Dickinson subsidiary. Moreover, NMC would be allotted one seat on the Becton Dickinson board of directors, and Howe was clear that he wanted Hampers, not Hager or Schupak, on his board. While the issue became moot after Becton Dickinson made its exit, it hovered, unresolved, for the next two years. "I think Gene felt that I should have demanded a second seat on the B-D board for him," Hampers later speculated. "After the B-D episode, it was clear that Gene was looking for a way to leave NMC," Hampers continued.

In fact, by mid-1977, Gene Schupak had transferred the ownership of the Queens Artificial Kidney Center to his junior colleague, Bob Slifkin. Partly this move, which was effected on May 9, 1977, was responsive to the "related organization principle." With a new owner QAKC could file cost reports with Medicare and Medicaid without eliminating the product "markup's" from Erika and the profit transfers to NMC under its management contracts with QAKC. This put the Queens center on a more equal footing with comparable centers in New York City, which were receiving much higher reimbursement rates for the same dialysis services. The transfer also was partly motivated by Dr. Schupak's search for an exit strategy that was precipitated by the Becton Dickinson episode. If the Becton Dickinson deal had been perfected Dr. Schupak would have received about $5.3 million in readily disposable B-D stock. That was a tempting exit bonus, and in fact, Dr. Schupak was growing less and less interested in the day-to-day operations. His disenchantment was aggravated by a CBS 60 Minutes report, highly critical of NMC, Erika and the three founders, that aired on October 30, 1977. During the filming of the CBS expose, persuading Dr. Schupak to decline an interview and keeping him away from the TV camera, as the CBS van cruised in front of Dr. Schupak's New Jersey office at Erika's headquarters, was a major challenge for NMC's legal counsel.

As a result, Schupak became more aggressive in pursuing the combination or sale strategy. Following the Becton Dickinson rejection, Dr. Schupak investigated at least two other possible sales of NMC, one to Warner Lambert and the other to Bristol-Meyers, both large, profitable pharmaceutical companies. In February 1978 Dr. Schupak sold 45,000 NMC shares he held (about 27% of his holdings) for $25 per share, and during the summer and fall of that year he recruited Pete Phildius to leave Baxter International and take over as president of NMC. In November of 1978, shortly after Phildius began his tenure at NMC, Hampers and Schupak spent a weekend at Hampers' home in New Hampshire, where Hampers successfully persuaded Schupak not to leave NMC. However, the respite was temporary, and Gene Schupak left the regular employ of NMC on July 1, 1979, staying on the board of directors until the fall of 1980, when he sold all his remaining shares of NMC stock. In the interim, in March of 1980 Ted Hager also left the company payroll in order to run for the U.S. Senate from New Hampshire, a quest that failed, resulting in the election of Warren Rudman to the Senate. Within the brief space of eight months, two of the three physician-founders had left National Medical Care.

Not only did the Becton Dickinson experience "sort out" the relationship among the three founders, leaving Hampers solely in charge by the beginning of the 1980's, but it also accelerated the push to diversify the company, in an attempt to enhance shareholder value and its attraction to potential merger partners. In late 1977 NMC started its weight loss program, followed in 1979 by the home care acquisition and the clinical laboratory business. In 1980 NMC invested in dialysis operations in Portugal. In addition, partly as a result of the retirement of Schupak and Hager, and partly as a result of investor pressure, NMC began hiring outside business executives, starting in 1978 with Pete Phildius. In a sense, the company's entire orientation changed after the Becton Dickinson incident. In large measure the company had achieved its mission and goal for the 1970's by dominating the chronic dialysis market. Under Hampers' direction, it would pursue a collateral goal of maximizing stockholder value in the 1980's.

If the 1977 relationship between NMC and Becton Dickinson appeared as a short engagement without a wedding, the 1984 episode between National Medical Care (NMC) and National Medical Enterprises, Inc. (NME) was little more than a "hot date." Not only did the two corporations have a similar name, but they shared a similar history, having both been founded in the late 1960's, and a similar philosophy, forging a role for investor-owned healthcare facilities, services and products that challenged the traditional eleemosynary models. The principals of the two companies - John Bedrosian and Dick Eamer at NME and Hampers, Hager and Schupak at NMC - were well acquainted long before 1984. NME was about six times the size of NMC with 1983 revenues of $2 billion and net income of $93 million, compared to NMC's $311 million revenues and $23 million in earnings during that period. NME had grown in the early 1980's by leaps and bounds, pursuing a very aggressive acquisition program. By the end of 1983 NME operated 339 hospitals, of which 249 were long-term care facilities. It also mirrored NMC in respiratory care, durable medical equipment sales and rentals, and other home care services. It even had a small (15 clinics) outpatient dialysis operation in four states.

The merger discussion was short lived but intense, starting on March 27 and ending April 10, 1984. This time there were no public announcements, although there was a great deal of speculation, and on April 15, 1984 The Boston Globe noted that merger talks between NMC and "another company" had ended without a proposal. The teams of lawyers, accountants and business managers worked quickly and furtively. The NMC team was coordinated by the ever faithful Sam Saitz and outside attorneys at Hale and Dorr led by Paul Brountas. The proposed merger agreement and preliminary due diligence were completed within two weeks with the boards of both companies slated to meet on April 10, 1984 to approve the terms of the deal under which NMC stockholders would receive 0.95 shares of NME stock for every NMC share they owned. At the time, NMC's common stock price was about $13.50 and NME's price was around $21. Thus, the NMC premium was just about 50%, and the transaction valued NMC at about $350 million.

The boards of directors of both corporations were to meet on April 10, 1984 to consider and presumably approve the transaction. The NMC board met telephonically with Hampers in New York City. General Counsel Paul Brountas briefed the NMC board, questions were addressed by management and a brief discussion followed. Thereupon, the NMC board approved the deal. Hampers went about his business in New York, while Brountas monitored the NME board meeting which was held at 3 p.m. pacific (6 p.m. EST) time. While dining at the "21 Club" in New York a few hours later, Hampers received a call from Brountas, advising him that the NME board rejected the deal. He called Dick Eamer and determined from him that the board felt it was overpaying, since it viewed NMC's projections for future growth and earnings as speculative. Eamer, knowing that Hampers would never accept less than the proposed 0.95-for-one deal, didn't attempt to renegotiate the price.

This second close call had a very salutary effect, however. As a result of the hard, arm's length bargaining between the two companies over the value of NMC in 1984 with Hampers and his cohorts arguing as hard as possible for the highest possible value, an agreed price of $350 million had been established. A few weeks later Hampers and his management team switched roles and offered to purchased NMC from its public shareholders for approximately the same price. Without the NME episode the 1984 leveraged buyout of NMC by Hampers and W.R. Grace would have been at best obstructed by disabling lawsuits, and at worst, impossible. "What seemed like a disaster at the time turned out to be a blessing in disguise," Hampers concluded.

9

Measuring NMC's Performance

National Medical Care's performance as an investment within the capitalist system in which it operated, like any other enterprise that uses private capital to produce goods and services, was rated objectively and carefully by its bankers, institutional investors, pension fund managers, investment analysts, individual stockholders and the financial press. In a rough, but powerful way, these judgments were reflected by the price of a share of its common stock, which was publicly traded first "over-the-counter" and later on the New York Stock Exchange from December 1971 until December 1984 when it reverted to a private corporation. While the NMC stock price measured factors other than the company's return on the capital invested in the enterprise, such as fluctuations in interest rates, inflation, and the ever ephemeral "investor confidence," the daily rise and fall of the price of the last reported trade of a share of NMC common stock between a willing and informed buyer and seller provided constant feedback to NMC's management and to the public of the measure of NMC's performance relative to other, available alternative investments.

The criteria by which capitalists (and that includes virtually all Americans who have a savings account, enjoy a vested interest in a pension fund, or purchase shares of mutual funds, as well as trust fund millionaires and investment bankers) make these judgments about NMC or any company are harsh and unforgiving, but ultimately objective and rational. NMC's value to investors was not influenced by its management structure, or the political philosophy of its executives, or by the processes it used to seek and retrieve information, or even by the subjective feelings of its employees, patients, regulators, and competitors, unless and until these factors affected, or in the view of the investors might affect, its operations and financial performance. Ultimately, the stock price (or other comparable measures of investment value once its stock was no longer traded publicly) reflected NMC's output, not its structure or way of doing business. Moreover, the prejudice or misjudgment of any particular investor as to NMC's value as an investment would be corrected by any one of millions of other investors who would discount the errors of biased analyses. The market punishes prejudice by selling to the overly optimistic and buying from the irrationally negative.

The American healthcare system has no comparable mechanism for rationally measuring output that it considers desirable. As a result, National Medical Care and the End-Stage Renal Disease Program (as well as every other provider and program) have been rated poorly by analysts and politicians who fix their attention on personalities, structures, subjective assessments, tradition and processes. The failure of American healthcare to accurately measure the output of physicians, hospitals, health maintenance organizations, pharmacies and other providers has resulted in an enormous waste of resources in pursuit of illusive and irrational goals or of no goals at all. Illustrative is the vengeful pursuit of stripping Hampers and Hager of their academic appointments at Harvard Medical School because a series of newspaper articles suggested potential conflicts of interest that might have skewed their medical judgment. Despite their demonstrated skills as clinicians, teachers and researchers, and without any showing of actual harm, one of the country's most respected medical schools deprived its constituents of the services of Hampers and Hager. Similarly, politicians squeezed millions of dollars out of the ESRD Program because NMC, the Program's largest single provider was making profits, regardless of the fact that the unit cost of providing dialysis had declined continuously throughout the life of the Program, in stark contrast to the record of every other public and private healthcare program in the nation. Unlike the capitalist system that assesses output and directs resources to the most productive uses, the American healthcare system assesses structures and processes, rather than output, and thereby misdirects valuable assets into unproductive activities.

Every evaluation, whether in an academic, capitalist or health-care environment, consists of measuring results against goals or standards. This obviously requires the preliminary step of setting objective goals. NMC's managers knew that the capitalist system would evaluate their performance based on investment returns - the combination of earnings and appreciation on each dollar invested in the enterprise. By these criteria, NMC was a phenom-enal success. Unfortunately, the objectives of the healthcare sys-tem are not as well defined. In addition, the evaluation of NMC was too often based on criteria that were different from the artic-ulated agenda. This led Gus Hampers to comment on more than one occasion, "If you succeed, they throw stones; only when you fail do they erect a monument."

Regrettably, the healthcare sector has grown so accustomed to failing, particularly in terms of controlling costs, that failure itself is deemed honorable. Hospital administrators who produce results within their budgets are routinely accused of sacrificing quality with no justification.

Evaluating success in delivering any healthcare service from inoculating infants against childhood diseases to the provision of maintenance dialysis, should be measured against a standard that maximizes four essential elements: quality, cost, access and innovation. This chapter describes why these four elements are important, how trade offs among these elements are sometimes necessary, what these elements mean in terms of providing life-sustaining care for patients with end-stage renal disease, and how National Medical Care's performance measured up against these four criteria. In the case of each of these elements, a specific case study will illustrate the manner in which National Medical Care responded to circumstances that would have affected these ele-ments for thousands of patients. These are also the four criteria against which future reform efforts in the American healthcare system need to be judged, and as set forth in the final chapter, NMC's performance with respect to these four factors may suggest useful directions in reforming the system in general.

Unfortunately, for the past quarter century the public sector has focused almost exclusively on access and cost, without ever attempting to account for quality or encourage innovation. To a

Medicare bureaucrat one triple bypass procedure is the same as another. At the same time, many physicians and other healthcare providers have been single mindedly pursuing quality and innovation without regard to cost or access. Doctors order blood tests without knowing how much these tests cost or who will pay for them. These two equally critical segments of the healthcare system have collided, and they don't even speak the same language. NMC's contribution has been to translate.

Once stated, these four elements - quality, cost, access and innovation - are obvious, but these were not the criteria that were generally referenced in evaluating either NMC or the federal ESRD Program. Too often the for-profit structure of NMC, or the competitive (sometimes combative) process that NMC adopted in conducting its business, rather than outcomes measured by quality, cost, access and innovation standards, were cited in criticizing NMC's performance. And in fact, monuments of praise were heaped on providers that were "properly" structured as traditional charities and successful in the polite and sophisticated political and public relations process, despite their poor quality, high costs, lack of innovation and barriers to access. As a result, NMC managers and affiliated physicians became cynical about the fairness and objectivity of the evaluation of their efforts.

Over time, these NMC managers and affiliates predictably responded to the clear and objective criteria of the capitalist system more readily and favorably than they did to the shifting and illogical predilections of the healthcare community. There would be times when the goals of investors and patients would be in conflict during the short term, and it became increasingly difficult to disappoint investors when the healthcare constituencies - patients, doctors and insurers - never appreciated or commented positively on choices made to their benefit. A perfect illustration of this phenomenon occurred in 1986 within NMC's home care division, which had accumulated over $9 million in unpaid accounts receivable for intradialytic parenteral nutrition (IDPN) services it had provided to undernourished and "wasting" dialysis patients who were unable to digest food. Medicare had engaged the services of Blue Cross of South Carolina to evaluate, process and pay these claims, but for a variety of reasons, Blue Cross refused to pay NMC for these services. Financial considerations dictated that NMC stop providing these services until the controversy was eliminated and the accounts were paid. Dr. Hampers refused to cut off treatments to patients who were already being serviced by the home care division, despite the fact that this would incur even larger expenses without any clear chance that NMC would ever be paid. Hampers took his lumps from NMC's investors (at the time, W.R. Grace & Co. and affiliated shareholders) for this decision, but instead of receiving countervailing kudos for continuing the parenteral service, NMC was criticized by physicians and others for not offering the service to new patients. Terry Daniels recalled the incident vividly, "Gus was resolute about not terminating the IDPN service for the patients already on the therapy. My business brain told me this was irrational, but Gus was putting the patients ahead of profits and I admired him for that."

The inquiry then is whether National Medical Care did in fact provide high quality, low cost, accessible and innovative healthcare services, and if so, what was (and is) wrong with a healthcare system that failed to recognize and reward such successful outcomes.

10

Quality:
Empowering the Medical Directors

Healthcare is unique among all the products and services that Americans consume in not being offered ostensibly in varying quality grades. Everyone wants the best, and all providers claim to offer the best. In pursuit of economy consumers accept coach seats on airplanes and a bag of peanuts, while first class passengers nibble shrimp cocktail. Housewives seek out bargain cuts of lower quality meat. And no one mounts a protest over the fact that their five-year old Geo lacks the features of a new Audi. In fact, most people take a certain amount of pride in "cutting corners" and saving money as a result. However, when it comes to healthcare Americans express outrage that a millionaire might be able to purchase better care than his housekeeper. Wage earners, who consider a private school education for their child an unneeded luxury, brag about taking that same child to a "specialist" for her allergies. There is a universal sense of entitlement and egalitarianism with respect to healthcare. Even with respect to drugs, it is very difficult to convince consumers that generic substitutes are as safe and effective as brand name varieties.

In such an environment it becomes difficult to broach the subject of measuring quality of healthcare services. However, differences in outcomes do occur, and in the care of end-stage renal disease patients there are quantifiable measures of successful treatment. Comparing outcomes for patients who are similar in age, race, gender, cause of renal failure, and medical cofactors, such as diabetes or coronary artery disease, is an imperfect but helpful gauge of quality. It is imperfect because no two patients, let alone a sample large enough to justify sweeping conclusions, are alike, and we learn more everyday about the complicated interrelationships of genetics and environment that affect a person's health in general and his survival with ESRD in particular. It is also imperfect insofar as these measure do not account for subjective assessments that are influenced by each patient's family and socioeconomic situation, his relationship with his doctor and other care givers, and his own psychology and outlook on life in general. A patient who has been consistently underdialyzed, has experienced multiple problems with his access site, and has been hospitalized several times may believe he has received the best care in the world, while his statistical twin who has had a perfectly uneventful course of treatment may complain endlessly.

NMC itself began measuring outcomes at its own dialysis clinics well before academic and government funded studies examined these data. Tax and accounting considerations led NMC to evaluate its relationships with its patients as assets, that had to be depreciated over time. In collecting the data to determine patient survival, NMC discovered variations in mortality rates among its clinics. Delving further into these data, NMC found measurable differences in morbidity rates as well, as measured by the number of days NMC patients spent in the hospital during the course of a year or other span of time. NMC realized it had a wealth of data to examine, and began routinely collecting and analyzing not just mortality and morbidity rates, but certain indicators of quality care as well, such as hematocrits, serum albumin and levels of urea clearance. Long before HCFA required these measures, NMC was routinely testing and comparing these data precisely because this information helped reduce morbidity and mortality rates and thereby improved financial performance as well.

This was not just a scientific inquiry (although Dr. Lowrie who designed and implemented these studies was justly proud of the contribution these studies made to the store of knowledge about renal disease and dialysis) but in fact, suggested a way to increase revenues and profits, while simultaneously improving renal care at the NMC clinics. NMC was paid for each dialysis treatment its clinics provided. Losing patients to death or hospitalizations affected the bottom line directly. It was extremely expensive to "acquire" patients by purchasing other dialysis clinics or by building new facilities in outlying, underserved areas. Retaining patients by reducing hospitalizations and lengthening survival became far more profitable and important strategies for growth. Those clinics with the highest quality of care, i.e., the lowest rates of mortality and morbidity, were the same clinics that made more profits. Improving the performance of the poorer producing clinics and those with above average mortality and morbidity rates was in NMC's corporate interest. During the late 1980's and early 1990's NMC launched a concentrated effort to determine why outcomes varied, in order to improve quality and profits at the same time. One of the most important factors influencing these outcomes was the time spent by the physicians per month with each patient, particularly in personally observing the signs of potential underdialysis and preventing access problems before these led to hospitalization and surgical repair.

From its founding years NMC had been rigorous in recruiting the best nephrologists to direct its clinics. Many of these doctors held academic appointments at the top medical schools and affiliated hospitals in the country, and the pioneers of NMC largely came from a close knit circle of specialists who had undergone extensive fellowships with the leaders in the field. It was very easy and very informative for Dr. Hampers or Dr. Schupak to check the credentials of potential medical directors by calling their academic mentors, whom they knew on a first name basis around the country. "Gene and Ted and I agreed from the outset that the best antidote to criticism was to affiliate with the best kidney specialists who would insure us against any attacks on the quality of care issue," Hampers recalled. This was the advice they had received from John Merrill and George Schreiner, two of the most prominent earlier generation of nephrologists, and it was advice they always followed.

Even NMC's harshest critics admitted (but rarely emphasized) that the quality of care at NMC's dialysis centers was impeccable. In large measure, in the first decade of its existence, NMC set the standard for an efficient, high quality outpatient facility, incorporating the best technology with a well trained staff, supervised by excellent physicians who were empowered to make all decisions relating to medical care in their clinics without interference by

Hampers or anyone else at NMC headquarters. As confirmed by strong willed medical directors, such as Bill Cirksena in Washington, D.C., and Alan Hull in Dallas, Hampers, Schupak and Hager never dictated or second guessed their decisions when it came to quality of care issues.

Every year, usually in the autumn, NMC convened its medical directors at a resort location for three days, and provided a variety of meetings. In the mornings, seminars in the style of "grand rounds" offered the medical directors the results of the latest clinical and scientific research in transplantation and dialysis. The presentations, often made by one of the medical directors himself, included animated questions and debates, challenges and confirmations. During breaks the doctors huddled with friends from medical school or fellowship days, and queried each other on their various experiences with a new type of artificial kidney or the desirability of a certain blood test. At some point Dr Hampers and Dr Schupak, and in later years, Dr. Lowrie, would apprise the directors of the state of the company, which usually included some "recommendations" to improve performance and profitability, citing pilot programs that they urged the doctors to adopt. At these meetings there was no lack of challengers and "naysayers" who took the opportunity to contradict the corporate leaders and assert their independence. "Point and counterpoint" debates enlivened the gatherings, and in the end, each medical director was left to his or her own judgment about how to operate the clinic. One of the liveliest debates occurred at the 1978 meeting in Puerto Rico when Hampers and Schupak actively debated each other over the issue of reusing dialyzers, with Schupak opposed to the practice. No medical director was discouraged from speaking his mind, and they all did.

This interaction among the corporate executives and the medical directors continued throughout the year, with medical directors checking in with each other and sharing experiences among the NMC network of physicians. In this way each director was exposed to the practices and prejudices of his counterparts from other regions of the country. Generally, there are in nephrology, and in all areas of medicine, regional variations in standards of care and practice modalities. Doctors in Dallas and Boston will differ less among themselves than they will with the doctors in the distant city. The NMC national system encouraged an interchange of experiences and opinions that the clinicians would otherwise not encounter. Once the results of Dr. Lowrie's studies on quality of care were available in the late 1980's the medical directors naturally wanted to know where they ranked and try to understand why in order to improve the performance of their clinics.

Nonetheless, despite the quality of its medical directors and the praise of unbiased and knowledgeable observers in government, the media, and among patient groups, there was (and is) a hard core of antiproprietary zealots who never gave up the challenge to NMC's assertions of providing excellent dialysis care. In the years prior to hard data on dialysis outcomes, these critics relied on simplistic logical arguments and anecdotes. For an ardent cadre of largely academic purists the idea that profits and quality could be compatible and coexistent was anathema. They have consistently used poor logic and faulty research to support their bias against investor owned facilities, and their critiques have resonated with a suspicious and unrestrained media.

Their theoretical argument, to which they retreat whenever the data are ambiguous or show no difference between for-profit and not-for-profit clinics, is that profits are derived from skimping on care. It's a zero sum mentality that contends that every dollar paid to investors is a dollar that has been taken away from patient-care expenses. In the first instance, the argument ignores the capacity of managers to spend less, save more, and still maintain or even improve quality. Home makers on a fixed budget, for example, learn how to feed, clothe and shelter their families and still have some savings at the end of the week to put in the bank. Others never learn this skill, and no one has ever argued that mothers who spend less and save more are giving their families inferior meals, poor quality clothing or substandard housing. The traditional rural family physician generally did well financially compared to his farming and laboring neighbors, but no one has argued that his financial success was the result of cheating his patients. In metropolitan medical centers today there are surgeons who make a decent living and there are surgeons who become extremely wealthy, yet no one argues that the wealthy surgeon must be providing inferior care than his struggling counterpart. The fact is that some entrepreneurs and managers are good at economizing and some are not. There are good and poor money managers in both the for-profit and not-for-profit sector, but the for-profit sector generally weeds out the poor managers faster than the non-profit sector, although this is changing as non-profit board become more conscious of economic realities.

In addition, the argument takes no account of the cost of capital and the element of risk. Non-profits secure the capital necessary to build plant and equipment through foundation grants, corporate contributions and individual gifts. In addition, loans that non-profits borrow to provide capital are often financed at lower interest costs or subsidized or guaranteed by larger non-profit entities or by the government or some similar bonding authority. Investors supply the capital for proprietary entities with an expectation but no guarantee of a return in the form of profits, which either are paid as dividends to the investors or are reinvested in growing the enterprise. The profits then are a fair return for the risk taker. By eliminating profits, capital would have to come from donors or taxpayers, both highly unreliable and restricted pools of funding. In fact, this was exactly the situation that faced Hampers and Hager when they started NMC. The governmental and charitable sources to which they turned to supply capital had no capacity or interest in building dialysis centers. To the extent that investors supply capital with the expectation of profits, the charitable and governmental universe can spend its capital on other worthy projects. The doctors at Harvard Medical School who complained about NMC being operated as a for-profit corporation were the same doctors who would have howled in protest if Harvard had diverted funds from their labs and classrooms in order to build a non-profit clinic for Hampers and Hager.

Specifically, in the case of dialysis centers, the anti-proprietary logic implodes. If higher profits mean lower quality, because of dialyzer reuse, inferior equipment and supplies, less skilled staff, higher patient-to-staff ratios, and shortened dialysis treatments, then the clinics will experience higher morbidity and mortality rates with patients dying and leaving the for-profit clinic for hospital care. Revenues will fall and profits dry up. The logic is exactly backwards. Better care means higher revenues and larger profits for dialysis centers.

In the healthcare universe today, increasingly the line between non-profits and for-profits is blurring, as more and more non-profits learn better management techniques from their for-profit counterparts. Non-profits can no longer spend more than they receive in fees, and the best non-profits actually realize "surpluses" that can be used to retire debt or expand capacity. Both proprietary and charitable clinics compete for the same labor, and purchase equipment, supplies and pharmaceuticals from the same suppliers at the same prices. If the anti-profit purists are consistent in their logic, they should similarly condemn successful non-profit managers who are able to bank surpluses, by arguing that those surpluses are endangering patient care.

At the center of a medical service as sophisticated as dialysis is the physician. Patients don't walk into dialysis centers off the street and they don't stay in a particular clinic because they have no alternatives. In most areas of the United States today, physicians are able to choose the facilities to which they send their patients and at which they choose to practice. Who is better equipped to judge the quality of care and who is more invested in insuring quality of care for patients than their individual physician? If there were measurable differences in quality of care that favored non-profit clinics, the for-profit sector would be shrinking. In fact, the percentage of dialysis patients being treated at for-profit centers has steadily increased over time and today is close to 70%. This shift would not have occurred if the physicians believed that care at non-profit clinics was superior.

To accept the anti-profit argument, one has to ignore the logic and experience of capitalism's success in every area of the economy and in every region of the globe. Do strong General Motors profits mean that Buicks are inferior automobiles? Would anyone want to buy a car from a non-profit corporation? In years when Burroughs Wellcome makes larger profits, are its drugs less effective and safe? Does Federal Express offer an inferior service to the U.S. Postal Service, which is not investor owned? Why has Russia decided to allow Chevron to mine its oil fields rather than use a state monopoly? The critics will and do argue that healthcare is different from automobiles, or delivery services or drug manufacturing, and they are right. That is why healthcare facilities are licensed and heavily regulated. If services at any particular clinic or within a whole segment of the field are substandard, then the regulators are at least partially at fault. The public has a right to expect its regulators to close any dialysis clinic, nursing home, or other provider that fails to meet quality standards, irrespective of its status as a tax paying, for-profit enterprise, or a tax free, noprofit charity.

For many years the critics would amplify their poor logic with the argument that for-profit providers (dialysis clinics and others) "skimmed" the cream of the cases, i.e., the "easy" routine cases went to the for-profit facilities and the tough and expensive cases went to the non-profit centers, especially the hospitals. This argument was used to justify the dual rate reimbursement system that went into effect in August 1983. The data most recently accumulated, however, belie this assumption, and the argument was never proven by NMC's critics.

In April 1997 the National Institutes of Health (National Institute of Diabetes, Digestive and Kidney Diseases) published the U.S. Renal Data System's (USRDS) 1997 Annual Report. The USRDS 1997 Report analyzed data collected on 200,000 patients for the 1990-1993 period who were treated at free standing, for-profit centers, free standing, non-profit clinics, and hospital settings. After adjusting the data for age, race, gender and primary diagnosis, the study found that the standard mortality rate (SMR) varied only slightly among the three types of settings and concluded that the type of ownership did not influence the outcomes. The SMR was highest (1.04) in hospital units, lowest (0.94) in free standing, non-profit facilities, and somewhere in the middle (1.01) in free standing, for-profit clinics. The study noted that the differences could be accounted for by relative patient sickness among the three types of settings.

Moreover, in the decade 1987-1997, the crude, annual mortality rate in the U.S. among dialysis patients decreased from 25.8% to 21.8%, at the same time as the percentage of dialysis patients being treated at for-profit centers increased to over 65% (and the trend toward accepting older and sicker patients also continued to rise). If for-profit care is bad for the health of dialysis patients, why are patients living longer as more, and sicker, patients are treated at for-profit clinics?

Yet the critics were persistent. On the evening news programs on November 24, 1999, as Americans were preparing for the next day's Thanksgiving holiday, reports of an article to be published in the November 25, 1999 edition of The New England Journal of Medicine were broadcast to the effect that for-profit dialysis facilities experienced 20% higher rates of mortality than their non-profit counterparts. In addition, the study concluded that for-profit facilities had lower rates of placement on the waiting list for kidney transplants. In typical hyperbole, the news broadcasters cited the study as evidence that for-profit ownership of any and all healthcare facilities was dangerous for one's health. The critical chorus added an "I-told-you-so" refrain.

The most surprising feature of the study ("Effect of the Ownership of Dialysis Facilities on Patient's Survival and Referral for Transplantation," by Garg, et al.) is that it did not reference the earlier 1997 USRDS study and its contrary findings, even though the Garg study used the USRDS data. Most importantly, the Garg study looked at a mere 3,569 patients out of a data base of 220,000, and only 336 patients in the Garg study were from the free standing, non-profit universe. The expected, logical design would be to compare an equal number of patients from the two types of facilities. With one pool ten times larger than the comparative pool the effects of sampling errors and selection biases are accentuated. Other technical, statistical anomalies have been pointed out by the medical officers of the major for-profit dialysis corporations .

The most compelling critique of the Garg study, however, came from Dr. Norman Levinsky, a nephrologist and chairman of the department of medicine at the Boston University Medical Center in an editorial in the same issue of the NEJM. "The literature on the effect of ownership of dialysis facilities on the quality of care they provide and on the outcomes of long term dialysis is scanty," Levinsky wrote. He went on to note that "[A]ll providers have been under pressure to maintain the quality of dialysis treatments despite the progressive ratcheting down of reimbursement."

The charge that dialysis patients at for-profit facilities are less likely to be referred for transplantation is another canard, unsubstantiated by hard data. Here though, the logic is compelling, since "losing" a patient to transplantation reduces the dialysis census and would negatively affect revenues and profits of a clinic. An unscrupulous, profit chaser would have an incentive to keep patients away from the transplantation option, of course. The problem with this contention is that dialysis clinic operators have no control over whether patients are referred for transplantation, and they shouldn't have any control. The decision concerning which therapy to undertake and for how long and whether to switch therapies is up to the patient and his doctor. To prevent any undue influence a particular physician may have (and physicians like all human beings do develop preferences that sometimes harden into prejudices over time), all ESRD patients are routinely and periodically evaluated by a committee of specialists including transplant surgeons. In any event, the demand for transplantable kidneys far exceeds the supply, and adding more patients to transplant waiting lists should not be the ultimate goal. The issue public policy makers, academic researchers, and the anti-proprietary purists should be addressing is the supply of kidneys, not the relative difference between for-profit and not-for-profit dialysis clinics in putting their patients on endless waiting lists.

Allegations of poor quality have not adhered to diminish the reputation of NMC's clinics for excellent care. The key to NMC's excellence and leadership was affiliation with prominent physician medical directors who were then empowered to make the critical decisions without fear of veto from a corporate hierarchy. Healthcare quality is all about the skills of the people delivering the care, as kidney patient Rick Faber stated, "Quality is not dependent on ownership but on the competence and care of the clinic staff."

Tim McFeeley

11

Access:
Substituting Universality for Rationing

The combination of NMC's free enterprise model and the Medicare ESRD Program created universal access for patients with end-stage renal disease in record time. Of the four criteria for success in healthcare delivery - quality, access, cost and innovation - access has been NMC's and the ESRD Program's strongest suit. Where kidney dialysis had been a special service rationed for only the most "deserving" cases in the mid-sixties, within a decade dialysis was available to nearly every American, young and old, sick and healthy, rich and poor alike. It's fair to say that no other specialty care category in U.S. healthcare enjoys such universal access. In fact, some persistent critics of NMC and the ESRD Program have viewed this universal access as too successful.

Without the Medicare reimbursement system, NMC would have survived and prospered, because the demand for dialysis services was so strong, and over time private insurers would have been compelled to provide coverage. However, care would have been limited to patients of means and those with insurance. Poor and low income, uninsured working families would not have had access to dialysis except through Medicaid and other special state welfare programs. What Medicare's ESRD Program did almost overnight was to place all kidney patients on the same footing, regardless of wealth, region, age, sickness, race, or "connections." It created one, national, monopsonistic system, and it meant that middle class patients did not have to spend down to the poverty level and go on Medicaid and welfare because of their medical condition. Today, patients with similar chronic diseases that require expensive treatment, such as AIDS, and who don't have or have used up their insurance, are not as fortunate as ESRD patients in this regard.

Similarly, without the free enterprise model generally, or National Medical Care in particular, the ESRD Program would have been successful, but universal access would not have been attained as quickly. NMC supplied the capital that was a necessary and critical element in building low cost, efficient, free standing outpatient clinics based on the model created by Dr. Schupak at the Queens Artificial Kidney Center in 1970, three years before the ESRD Program was implemented. If NMC and its imitators had not been around in 1973, the ESRD Program would have gotten off to a slower start and would have taken a different course altogether in all likelihood. The free standing outpatient model, whether built with private capital or with donated funds in a nonprofit form, would not have evolved for many years. Instead, the hospitals would have started to expand their outpatient, in hospital facilities which were much more expensive, and less accessible for patients. There's no way to turn back the clock, but it is highly improbable that hospitals such as Massachusetts General in Boston or Elmhurst in New York or Cedars Sinai in Los Angeles would have had the capital to build these centers or would have devoted their scarce capital to dialysis rather than to other specialties. It's important to recall, that some states, such as Massachusetts, didn't have licensing laws at that time that even allowed free standing dialysis centers to be built. Eventually the ESRD Program would have stimulated other free market entrepreneurs as well as non-profit corporations to develop these clinics, but at its start date in July 1973, the ESRD Program had NMC available with an efficient model of dialysis delivery that had already been in operation for over three years.

To carry the "what if" speculation one step further, if NMC did not exist and if only the traditional hospital sector was available to provide dialysis under the ESRD Program, the costs might have been so enormous that the whole experiment might well have collapsed before economies-of-scale were available to make dialysis at $138/treatment even possible. In the mid-70's hospitals were paid on a cost based system, and competition was forbidden under the certification-of-need laws in most states. Hospital administrators would have naturally tried to convert the ESRD Program into a monopolistic, cost plus system (in fact, they never gave up this fight until the Reagan era). In the early 1970's the Brigham Hospital in Boston for example was charging over $300 per dialysis treatment.

Even if the ESRD Program survived without NMC and other for-profit providers, there would have been little if any incentive for hospitals and their non-profit, outpatient offspring to penetrate the country the way NMC did. The model would have been large outpatient centers in major cities to which patients would have had to commute. To use one of thousands of examples, ESRD patients on Cape Cod had to drive over 100 miles (200 miles roundtrip) three times a week to receive dialysis care in either Boston or Providence, R.I. NMC had an incentive to capture this market and therefore built a center on the Cape in 1978. It would not have been feasible for the city hospitals to erect an outpatient center, and it would have taken much longer for a non-profit entity to fill this need and demand for service. Another example was cited in Chapter 3 regarding the certificate of need laws, concerning Meharry/Hubbard Hospital in Nashville, where Vanderbilt University Medical Center had a monopoly on outpatient dialysis. The largely African American community of doctors practicing at Hubbard and the medical students at Meharry were not able to attend patients at Vanderbilt. Meharry/Hubbard did not have the capital to build its own outpatient dialysis unit and invited NMC to build a clinic on its campus. Thus, while the ESRD Program created "universal access" in terms of providing an entitlement for the patients, that access was virtual, and not actual, until NMC built clinics with private capital in locations where the patients could easily commute and could be followed by their own physicians.

In stark contrast to the universality of dialysis is the relative inaccessibility of transplantation services. The ESRD Program provided an entitlement not only for dialysis, but also for transplantation (although, unfairly, the ESRD Program pays for anti-rejection medications for a limited amount of time only). Despite the fact that transplantation is the preferred therapy for the majority of kidney patients and has become very successful in the past decade with newer and less debilitating anti-rejection drugs, the relative mix overwhelmingly favors dialysis. Largely, this is due to the lack of transplantable kidneys, but it may also be due to the fact that the free market hasn't been involved in the provision of transplantation services. Other countries have been more successful than the United States in developing resources for kidney transplantation. The ESRD Program alone with its admirable universal benefits, is not sufficient to assure access to all Americans who need this therapy, in part due to the fact that the healthcare system that delivers these services is still based on an urban, teaching hospital, non-profit model.

Some critics of NMC and the ESRD Program complained that there was "too much" access, and that therefore too many Medicare dollars were being spent on a single therapy. What these critics, like Dr. Arnold Relman, himself a nephrologist and the former editor of the prestigious New England Journal of Medicine, contended was that dialysis should not have been extended to the old and the very sick, people with major complicating conditions. They determined accurately that most other advanced countries in Europe did not extend dialysis to people over a certain age or to those with other severe illnesses. A diabetic, 70 year old was most unlikely to receive dialysis anywhere in the world other than in the United States. What happened to these people, say, in England? They died. These critics saw universal access as simply a blank check for companies like NMC to draw on, provided they could "round up" ESRD patients regardless of their age or diagnoses. Fortunately, their complaints carried no appeal for politicians, or the bureaucrats in the Department of Health and Human Services who were managing the ESRD Program.

The fact that there is such near universal access to dialysis in the United States means that dialysis outcomes appear poorer than in countries where access is limited to the younger and healthier patients. Dialysis patients in the United States have higher gross mortality and morbidity rates than their foreign counterparts precisely because the older and sicker patients in these countries are not part of the patient population. This is a clear example of how the pursuit and attainment of one goal in healthcare delivery can and will affect other objectives. The near perfect score that the United States has achieved in terms of ensuring access to dialysis for every ESRD patient tends to skew the measure of quality. In fact, quality and access are being achieved at very high levels in the United States, even though the measures of quality appear less than optimum. That is why the decline in gross mortality over the past decade while patients continue to grow older and sicker is encouraging.

National Medical Care's corporate objectives always aligned with the healthcare objective of universal access, and NMC was one of the principal factors in achieving near universal access to dialysis so quickly after the start of the ESRD Program. Obviously extending care to every possible patient was in NMC's best financial interest. The government could not have invented or commissioned a better agent than NMC and the other for-profit, investor-owned clinics in its quest for universal access. NMC found the patients by finding the doctors, and building and buying more and more clinics. This growth also increased profits as economies-of-scale contributed to reduced per unit costs as volume and revenues rose. In this regard what was good for America as prescribed by the ESRD statute and regulations, namely, universal access, was also good for NMC.

One specific policy that contributed to NMC's success in achieving such wide access for all patients was its "open staffing" policy. Traditionally, most teaching hospitals and specialty clinics have a "closed" staff. A physician who is not part of the group that has contracted with the hospital to provide the service, say, orthopedics or urology, cannot attend and care for patients admitted to the hospital. In these cases the patients are "referred" by their doctor to a member of the closed panel of specialists. The referring physician is shut out of collecting fees while the patient is under the care of the hospital contracted physician. NMC early on at both the Babcock Center and at the Queens Center allowed all physicians who were qualified to attend their patients at these clinics. They had to abide by the rules and policies established by the medical director, but they could come to the center, prescribe a regimen of care, see their patients, use the facilities and services of the kidney center, and most importantly, bill Medicare for their physician services to their patients. This was rare in the

1970's and some of NMC's medical directors objected to an "open staffing" policy. However, even the most recalcitrant medical directors quickly saw the advantages to their clinics and to NMC in opening the medical staff to all qualified nephrologists and internists. Again, what was good for patients in terms of assuring continuity of care was also good for NMC's finances, since the more doctors who were admitted to a clinic's staff, the higher the patient census, as well as revenues and profits. There were spats and tensions among these doctors, who were effectively colleagues but also competitors, in working under the same clinic roof. NMC executives including Drs. Hampers and Schupak were often called in to arbitrate these disputes, but it was worth their while, since having all the doctors working within NMC's clinics built goodwill, the census, and the bottom line.

Through an open staffing policy, aggressive challenges to certificate of need laws, which would have otherwise prevented NMC from establishing new clinics, and by other means, National Medical Care aligned itself firmly behind a policy of accepting all doctors and patients and thus helped the ESRD Program achieve its goal of universal access.

12

Cost:
Saving Expenses Saves Lives

The third criteria by which success is measured in healthcare delivery is "owned" by NMC. Even its harshest critics, in fact, especially its harshest critics acknowledge NMC's outstanding contribution in reducing the cost of delivering dialysis. While NMC's detractors characterize every dollar saved by NMC as a dollar that lessened the quality of patient care, in fact, NMC's ability to continually reduce the per unit cost of providing outpatient hemodialysis, can fairly be credited with saving the entire ESRD Program from collapse.

People within the healthcare system, especially physicians, have traditionally focused their attention on the elements of quality and access, while the issue of cost has been relegated, somewhat contemptuously, to the "administrators," the folks without medical or nursing degrees. The bias among healthcare "professionals," led by physicians, but also percolating down the command chain to the RN's, LPN's, PA's, and other hands on care givers, was that their sole job was to deliver quality care. The job of watching the costs was a less meaningful and valuable task that could be entrusted to the administrators and their assistants.

One of the profound contributions of NMC's founders was to change that attitude radically, and make the doctors and nurses responsible for expenses as well. This attitude change was born out of necessity, of course. Hampers, Schupak and Hager were essentially entrepreneurs when they began their clinics, and they had no money to spare, no endowment to fall back on, and no board of trustees willing to fund raise for them if they failed. Early on, whether they liked it or not, the founders had to spend part of their limited time looking over expenses and figuring out how to save every dollar they could. This began long before the Medicare ESRD Program went into effect. It was a responsibility that they accepted, perfected and never surrendered. As a result, the entire culture of NMC was influenced. If the three nephrologist-founders at the top of the corporation took an intense interest in saving money, then so did the clinic medical directors (who were originally motivated to do so as well through the profit sharing system), their nursing staff, and virtually all NMC employees. No function or department was exempt from this pervasive bias against wasting money. Some executives, who joined NMC in its later years from major U.S. corporations, were shocked by the founders' "obsession" with cost control.

Even into the mid-1980's, by which time NMC had become a prospering, multimillion dollar, international company, Hampers, Hager and Schupak still played by the entrepreneurial rules, "squeezing every dollar until Washington wept." From time to time Gene Schupak stood at the company entrance at 9 a.m, threatening to dock employees for "stealing" company time by arriving late for work, and in an intense labor dispute with a powerful New York City healthcare workers union, Schupak refused to budge, bringing in NMC nurses from all over the country to break the strike. When his secretary pointed out that the office walls were dirty and needed to be repainted, Hager rolled up his sleeves, filled a bucket full of hot, soapy water and scrubbed the walls clean to the amazement of his employees.

For his part, Hampers never fully released his control over spending money, requiring even senior executives to get his approval to purchase a file cabinet or attend a professional conference. Hampers was particularly keen on examining expense reports before reimbursing employees for their travel. "Some of these guys thought that a $50 difference between a moderate hotel room and an economy hotel room was no big deal," Hampers fumed. "But I remember when we didn't have $50 to spare for an autoclave in the clinic." Hampers put his personal secretary, Laura Baker, in charge of booking all office travel, and made her responsible for insuring the cheapest flights even to the point of reducing the per diem reimbursement if the employee was provided a free lunch on a cross country flight. One senior NMC staffer recalled an embarrasing incident when he was engaged in an important business conversation with Hampers and Dr. Joe Chazan, the medical director of the NMC clinic in Providence, as they waited in an airport for a flight to Boston. "As we got on the plane we had to suspend the conference, because I wasn't allowed to fly first class with Gus and Joe," he remembered. "Dr. Chazan laughed and teased Gus mercilessly, but Gus wouldn't relent." In the mid-80's Hampers made it a company policy that senior executives at NMC could have either a company leased automobile to use, or first class travel, but not both, and the employee's choice was irrevocable.

Hampers argued that the money was going somewhere and it was better for NMC's mission to provide high quality, low cost care to everyone who needed it that the money go to the investors or to expanding the network than for the money to go to vendors and others. "Why should I send money to Baxter or to United Airlines when I could use the money to pay my investors or to build a new clinic?" Hampers contended. No one ever claimed that NMC wasted ESRD Program money on high living expense accounts or luxury corporate offices. When W.R. Grace & Co. bought a controlling interest in NMC in late 1984, Grace executives were dumbfounded at the disparity in perquisites between themselves and their NMC counterparts. Terry Daniels, a former Grace executive recalled, "Gus never let the Grace culture influence his barebones style of spending at NMC, and as Gus became more powerful within Grace, the Grace guys got very nervous."

As NMC expanded and Hampers had to delegate some of these responsibilities to others, he chose people whom he could trust and who shared his passion for cost savings. Sam Saitz, Sam Scialabba, and Ernie Lowrie all came from humble backgrounds, like Dr. Hampers, and enforced the ban on excessive spending and waste. Saitz found all sorts of ways to economize, particularly in the early years when the company was building its first centers. Scialabba, who joined the company in early 1974, attacked the inventory control system and brought a seasoned accountant's and manager's eye to making the clinics adopt uniform purchasing policies. No one, however, could stretch a dollar at NMC better than Ernie Lowrie. When Mrs. Lowrie, an RN, who had been working with Gus Hampers since 1964, took over operational control of all of NMC's dialysis clinics in the late 70's, she took to her task like a duck to water, focusing especially on staffing patterns. She cut back on staff, initiated a program of using lower paid technicians to do the jobs formerly done by higher paid nurses, and she rearranged shifts in order to coincide with patient dialysis times. By changing clinical staff hours from eight hours per day, five days a week to ten hours a day, four days a week, Mrs. Lowrie was able to schedule two patient shifts (which normally took five hours each) for each clinical shift, thereby saving hundreds of thousands of dollars over the course of a year at every clinic. She drew the line, however, at any cost saving plans that she felt endangered patient care. Little did the ESRD Program bureaucrats or state regulators know it, but Ernie Lowrie acted as their "ombudsman" within NMC in advocating for patient health and safety. "Ernie was in many ways a diffident person, but she was aggressive as hell when she was fighting for her patients," Hampers recalled. "We had some intense verbal brawls over the years." As a nurse, who was more comfortable in a hectic, busy dialysis clinic than she was in a sedate, wood paneled, corporate boardroom, Ernie Lowrie knew the difference between patient needs and staff convenience. She never asked any of her nurses or corporate staff to work harder than she did, and she didn't expect less either. She brought her obsession for a clean work space that was so critical in the clinics to the casual confines of the office suite, and pity the poor employee who left a dirty coffee cup in Ernie Lowrie's sink!

There are essentially three, nearly equal cost components of providing dialysis, and in each of these areas, NMC was a leader in providing care for less expense. One is the fixed, capital cost of plant and equipment, including land acquisition expenses, or rent, and the depreciation of the building improvements and equipment, and other startup expenses, over the useful life of the facility. There are two general ways to reduce this cost; first, by spending less to begin with; and second, by extending the useful life of the facility by cost effective maintenance and spreading the annual fixed cost over a large number of units, or, in other words, maximizing the capacity. The clinic sites were selected with cost, rather than the convenience of the doctors in mind, and while located near the prominent teaching hospitals, they were rarely sited on the high cost medical campus itself, but in a storefront on a side street or around the corner. NMC bargained hard for low prices on its fixed equipment and furniture, and the larger NMC became, the more potent its bargaining power. One example is illustrative. When they first began an outpatient clinic in the late sixties, the NMC founders made a radical decision to put patients in reclining lounge chairs, rather than on beds, as was the norm in the hospital settings which was the only model they had. The decision was motivated by cost factors since recliners cost less than beds, but there were attendant benefits as well. First, the chairs required less floor space, allowing greater capacity. Second, the recliners permitted more flexibility for the staff in working around the patient which enhanced both efficiency and safety for the patient. In addition, patients were generally more cognizant and animated in a sitting as opposed to a lying position, and thus quicker to respond to anomalies or changes in the treatment by calling staff. In general, the recliners help lessen the passivity that often afflicts ESRD patients undergoing chronic dialysis.

Another third of the cost of providing care is personnel expenses. This was an area that Ernie Lowrie perfected in terms of efficiency, not just in the clinical arena, but in the administrative sector as well. Hampers and Mrs. Lowrie created the position of nurse-administrator in most NMC clinics. It was essentially modeled after the role Mrs. Lowrie assumed at the Babcock Artificial Kidney Center. The conversion required training the head nurses in basic financial and management skills, and this wasn't always easy, not because these skills were beyond the capacity of RN's, but because the nurses enjoyed spending their time in the hurly burly of the clinics. Mrs. Lowrie's gift was to show the head nurses that they could do both jobs, and that by acquiring these administrative skills, they would be better nurses and patient advocates as well, just as she had become. Over time, several clinics were grouped in miniregions with a business manager backing up the clinic's nurse administrators. The personnel savings from eliminating a full time administrator at every clinic were immense. Versatility was the key for Mrs. Lowrie's pursuit of efficiency. In the hide bound world of traditional healthcare, doctors did one set of tasks, nurses another, technicians a third, and so forth. Mrs. Lowrie saved millions of dollars for NMC and for the ESRD Program by challenging these traditional boundaries, seeing staff as capable of multiple tasks.

Expenses associated with the supplies used to provide dialysis comprise the third segment of clinic costs. This includes everything from swabs and bandages to the artificial kidney itself. In addition to cost savings that were attained through greater inventory control, bulk purchases and vertical integration, the major advance promoted by NMC was in reducing the cost of the artificial kidney through reuse. The battle over reuse was difficult both within NMC itself and between NMC and its patients and their advocates, including powerful U.S. Senators. Years later, the reuse of dialyzers has become the industry standard, not just out of necessity, since the government hasn't changed the reimbursement rate for over a decade, but because using an expensive artificial kidney just once is akin to throwing away one's toothbrush after every brushing. In fact, despite the boilerplate warnings against reuse that adorn artificial kidney labels, the kidney manufacturers today know that the kidneys will be cleaned and reused and have responded by improving the design to facilitate reuse. However, twenty years ago, NMC was considered a pariah for suggesting that artificial kidneys be reused. The usual pattern in the healthcare industry when faced with shrinking or static reimbursement and rising costs is to push in one direction - towards raising the service fee. NMC did this, of course, but also pushed in the opposite direction, by promoting reuse, demanding price concessions and insisting that part of the sacrifice come from the dialyzer manufacturers, as well as the service providers.

NMC was able to do this and thereby benefited itself, its competitors and the ESRD Program and therefore the U.S. taxpayers, because it was willing to make the dialyzers itself. From the earliest days at the Normandy House, Hager and Hampers only received price concessions by threatening to take the kidneys apart, clean them and reassemble them. In the 1970's under Gene Schupak's direction the Erika subsidiary transformed itself from a bulk purchasing agent into a manufacturer of dialysis supplies, including artificial kidneys. It's doubtful whether Schupak or Hampers ever really believed that Erika (later NMC's Medical Products Division) could produce an artificial kidney as well as and efficiently as Baxter, Gambro or Fresenius, but they knew that they had to try in order to keep supply prices in check. Without this kind of risk taking by NMC, the lion's share of ESRD Program dollars would have been diverted from the clinics to the suppliers.

Despite the efforts and spectacular results of cost cutting strategies at National Medical Care over two and a half decades, the achievement was turned on its head and criticized by patient advocates, academic commentators and government bureaucrats. In fact, NMC was often hoist on its own cost cutting petard. During the intense struggle to raise, or at least maintain, reimbursement rates during the 1980-82 period, ESRD Program administrators routinely argued that reimbursement should be cut, precisely because NMC was earning profits and expanding its network of clinics. Saving money and passing some of those savings on to investors in the form of dividends and reinvesting the rest in building more clinics justified reimbursement reductions in the eyes of NMC's critics. It's fair to say that without NMC's leadership and risk taking in the area of cutting costs, the ESRD Program would have been forced to raise the reimbursement rates across the board, and today's $13 billion program would either be costing U.S. taxpayers much more, or the program would have been scaled back to the detriment of ESRD patients and their families.

13

Innovation:
Encouraging Growth

Even a superior healthcare delivery system that provides top quality care at continually lower cost and provides access to that high quality, low cost care to everyone who needs it, still fails over time unless the system encourages, recognizes and implements innovation. Innovation guards against stasis, and patients and doctors should reasonably expect that those in charge of the system are willing to take risks by exploring new options. National Medical Care was not risk averse and maintained and increased its lead in the dialysis industry precisely because it was willing to innovate.

Much of the credit also goes to the original architects of Medicare's ESRD Program's reimbursement scheme, especially Dr. Ron Klar. Bucking the private (Blue Cross) and public (Medicare and Medicaid) cost based healthcare system in place in 1973, these bureaucrats called for an incentive reimbursement system that fixed a fair price (at the time) and allowed providers to retain the differences between their costs and the reimbursement rate. In hindsight many commentators claimed that the 1973 rate was set too high. However, whether by prescience or chance, the rate allowed enough surplus to fuel the growth that was necessary to make the program accessible to all ESRD patients in the United States very quickly. As costs of all sorts rose during the high inflation years of the 1970's, the incentive rate system forced providers to economize and innovate, both in terms of saving expenses, and also in terms of accommodating patient preferences and the demands of physicians. As a result, the delivery system was dynamic and avoided stasis at least during its first decade.

Moreover, during the Reagan era makeover of the entire Medicare system of payment, the cost based system was replaced by a prospective payment system which incorporated the essential elements of the ESRD incentive rate system that had by then been in operation for a decade.

Innovation is the essential element in the healthcare system that supports the other three critical elements. Only through innovation can providers and payers insure high quality and low cost and universal access over time.

All of the cost cutting measures already described were innovations, including the substitution of recliners for beds, the conversion of storefronts into clinics, the reuse of artificial kidneys, and the staffing innovations adopted by Mrs. Lowrie. Probably the single greatest innovation that NMC imposed system wide was making the physician medical director also the CEO of his clinic, and reorienting these clinicians toward economic stimuli. Unlike the recent HMO practice of threatening doctors and demanding that they produce a certain level of revenue and eliminate certain expensive tests and procedures, the NMC system provided incentives that engaged the creativity of its medical directors. NMC used carrots, not sticks to get doctors to learn how much supplies and personnel cost and why it was better to have an open staffing policy, for example.

NMC was at the forefront of instituting treatment advances in its clinics as well. The use of bicarbonate based dialysis solutions, the construction of central delivery systems and water purification equipment, the incorporation of polysulfone membranes in artificial kidneys, and the revolution in technology occasioned by hollow fiber kidneys and high flux dialysis are all leading examples where NMC flexed its system to accommodate change that helped patients and improved care. Aside from its cost savings aspects, even the reuse of dialyzers was a huge benefit to patients by eliminating the "first use syndrome" (the adverse reactions that some patients experience from using a brand new dialyzer) that affected some patients, and by forcing the manufacturers to create more efficient and stronger dialyzers. Patients and nurses who remember the days of ruptured coil dialyzers do not long for the "bad old days."

Being a risk taking, investor owned, for-profit corporation, NMC was challenged to be at the forefront of all these developments in order to maintain and extend its preeminence in the field. NMC's structure itself required deference and allegiance to innovative changes, and with the leading nephrologists serving as NMC's medical directors, the company was receptive to innovation and sensible risk taking. Changes that NMC instituted overnight were not adopted by hospital dialysis units for years. NMC executives realized that in providing a service so dependent on science and technology, it had to be on top of and leading these developments. As a result, the universe of ESRD care in America benefited from NMC's leadership.

Government-as-payer was not always a helpful or willing partner in encouraging innovation, however, even where government-as-researcher was helping create these innovations. Scientific and technological advances that could trace their origins to NIH sponsored research were sometimes then left unfunded by Medicare. One example where the government did pay for the advance in treatment was the administration of artificial erythropoietin (EPO) which replaced the natural substance produced by healthy kidneys and prevented anemia. Prior to the discovery and manufacture of artificial EPO, ESRD patients frequently underwent blood transfusions to counteract the anemic effects of ESRD. Over time, transfusions can present considerable health risks, as well as expense. When Amgen patented and produced artificial EPO, doctors quickly prescribed it for nearly all their kidney patients, giving these passive and run down people a new lease on life. To its credit and contrary to its usual method of ignoring innovations, the government agreed to pay for artificial EPO as an "add on" to the standard dialysis fee. Over time, HHS reduced this additional fee, thereby "squeezing" the clinics, which had no control over the Amgen price. What the government has failed to do in the area of funding artificial EPO is determining whether and to what extent the dosage and method of administering of the drug could be altered to save costs without affecting patient care. Studies indicate that administering a much smaller dosage subcutaneously at less frequent intervals has the same effect as intravenous administration of larger doses on a more frequent basis. As a general pattern, however, HHS tends to maintain the status quo reimbursement system and fails to recognize that funding innovations could improve patient care and save money at the same time.

More frequently, however, the government blocked attempts to provide newer therapies for patients. In one instance its refusal actually ended up costing the government more money. According to a study by the House Committee on Government Reform, approximately 89,000 ESRD patients use a calcium supplement to counteract the loss in bone density from the body's inability to absorb calcium, which is also a byproduct of ESRD. The drug in injectable form is paid for by Medicare, but Medicare has so far refused to pay for a capsule recently developed by Hoffman-LaRoche that has the same effect and is more convenient for the patient. Medicare pays for prescribed drugs that are administered intravenously, but does not pay for oral medications. Moreover, the difference in cost is over $1,500 per patient per year, or over $110 million dollars every year! Rather than change the policy and embrace this cost saving innovation, Medicare continues to require the less convenient, more expensive therapy.

NMC and other providers as well as the Renal Physicians Association and the National Kidney Foundation have asked the ESRD Program administrators to consider funding innovations in kidney care, or at least fund and study pilot projects to determine their feasibility, but the government is unwilling to encourage innovation in this manner. One such innovation was in the area of providing intradialytic parenteral nutrition (IDPN) for ESRD patients who also are afflicted with the inability to absorb nutrients. IDPN is a therapy of intravenous feeding while the patient is at the clinic undergoing dialysis. The ESRD Program was unwilling to pay for this service directly, thus forcing NMC and other providers to bill it as a home healthcare service, which led to charges of fraud and abuse against NMC. Other innovations so far rejected by Medicare include changes in the reimbursement system for paying kidney doctors for their services in order to encourage more frequent hands on examinations, which could lead to less frequent hospitalizations and lower morbidity. Many experts have also advised Medicare to explore the "Japanese" system of paying for dialysis on the basis of the amount of time on dialysis rather than the present system of paying the same amount regardless of the time on dialysis. These experts believe that paying on a time calculated basis would help eliminate the phenomenon of "under dialyzing" many ESRD patients, and again reduce morbidity and save on hospitalization costs. The ESRD bureaucrats see these as attempts to "milk" more money out of the system, and don't seem interested in whether or not these changes might improve the quality of care and the lives of ESRD patients on dialysis.

14

Adoption by W.R. Grace & Co.

When Paul Paganucci left Wall Street in 1971 to become a dean at the Amos Tuck School of Business at Dartmouth College, he was determined to expose students and faculty to real world personalities from the realm of business and finance. From time to time Mr. Paganucci would invite corporate leaders to address assemblies at the Tuck School, dine with faculty members and spend time on the campus in an attempt to enliven the case study for students and involve business leaders in the academy. None of these visitors was more enlivening and engaging than Peter Grace, the chief executive of W. R. Grace & Company, a business founded by Mr. Grace's grandfather and expanded by Peter Grace into a major conglomerate. "When Peter Grace came to Dartmouth with his entourage it was always a big show," Paganucci recalled. "He loved the lecture podium and the students were entertained."

Early in his career, Paul Paganucci, then an investment advisor, met Peter Grace in New York and they became close associates. When he established trusts for his nine children, Mr. Grace appointed Paganucci as trustee, a role he continued for many years, and Mr. Paganucci worked for the Grace Company for awhile before his Dartmouth tenure.

Another role Mr. Paganucci played at the Amos Tuck School was fund raising and maintaining goodwill among the alumni. At one of these alumni presentations in 1973, Paul met David Lubrano, a Tuck alumnus, and at that time treasurer and board member of National Medical Care. NMC had under Lubrano's guidance been through two public offerings, and its stock was being traded in an active over-the-counter market. As an experienced, former auditor of public corporations, Lubrano knew that NMC needed some additional, independent, non-employee members on its board of directors, and the dean of Dartmouth's business school looked like an ideal candidate to "dress-up" the board and to bring on a seasoned professional to advise management.

Mr. Lubrano arranged a meeting among himself, Paganucci, and Drs. Schupak, Hager, and Hampers at the Harvard Club in Boston's Back Bay in the spring of 1973, and as a result of that felicitous meeting, Paul Paganucci joined the NMC board that year and remained on the board for the next sixteen years, serving during most of that time as the chairman of the audit committee, and the acknowledged leader of the non-management directors group. He also became a close, personal friend and trusted advisor of Dr. Hampers, and enlisted Hampers in supporting Dartmouth College and its medical school. Gus Hampers, like Peter Grace, became one of Dean Paganucci's regular business speakers for his course on "entrepreneurship" and NMC became one of the business cases studied. However, unlike Mr. Grace, Dr. Hampers came to Dartmouth without entourage, gave his lecture, and left. "Gus was the only one of our visiting presenters who never stayed for dinner, let alone overnight," Paganucci remembered. His presentations were "unvarnished" and "awesome" in Paganucci's words. He could be counted on to shatter the stereotypes that many Dartmouth students and faculty members had about doctors in the role of business executive.

As an NMC director and an astute analyst of corporate finance, Mr. Paganucci was keenly aware of NMC's dilemma in the early 1980's and of its attempts to find solutions to the "fishbowl" problem, including its mixed results with diversification outside the field of chronic dialysis services and supplies. The aborted 1977 merger with Becton, Dickinson and Company was an unhappy memory for Paganucci and his independent colleagues on the NMC board, not merely because the company was rejected by the Becton Dickinson board, but because Hampers, Schupak and Hager conducted the negotiations without attention to the NMC board's needs to be informed, to exercise its own judgment, and to advise management on behalf of the company's shareholders. Later, during the combination negotiations with National Medical Enterprises in early 1984, Hampers kept the board well advised in Paganucci's opinion. "I remember that neither the NMC board or the NME board wanted to address the merger question first, but we went first, and in a telephone meeting approved the transaction," Paganucci recalled. "Then the NME board tried to get a better deal, and the whole thing collapsed," he added.

"As a public company, NMC was too visible and became a target for reimbursement cuts by Medicare," Paganucci concluded. Investors were chary, especially after the failure of the Becton Dickinson and NME negotiations. Whereas the NMC common stock had once traded at a multiple of 30 or 40 times annual per share earnings, by 1984 its price was stuck at a level of about 12 times the prior year's earnings. With the government's August 1983 dialysis reimbursement cut of $12 per treatment, the future prospects of maximizing stockholder value looked grim, even though the company was doing everything right in terms of economizing in order to maintain margins in the face of these reductions.

When Hampers called Paganucci in April 1984 to advise him of the NME debacle, Mr. Paganucci asked him whether he'd be willing to sell NMC for the same price (about $360 million, or $19.50 per share) to another, appropriate and reputable company. "He didn't hesitate to say that he would," Paganucci recalled. That week Paganucci wrote a letter to Walt Robbins, the director of acquisitions and mergers at W.R. Grace, suggesting that Grace take a look at a possible combination with NMC.

At precisely the same time in the spring of 1984, Terry Daniels, a senior vice president at Grace, was examining investment and combination prospects in the healthcare industry for Grace, which by then had become a conglomerate monster, expanding well beyond its core, specialty chemicals business into retail sporting goods stores, ethnic restaurants, and cattle breeding. "We knew the healthcare industry was huge and growing larger, and we were looking for opportunities where technology was a heavy component and might tie in to Grace's technology-based businesses," Daniels noted. What Daniels' team was looking at specifically was Delmed, another Massachusetts based company. Although Delmed had some dialysis services clinics, its capital was largely invested in developing a new plastic bag for delivering IV solutions, peritoneal dialysate and other medically prescribed, sterile fluids for infusion, which would directly compete with

Baxter and Abbott, the industry giants. In the course of learning about the dialysis industry, Daniels noted a familiar name in the NMC annual report, that of Paul Paganucci, whom Daniels had never met, but of whom he had heard a great deal from Peter Grace. Daniels, unaware that Paganucci had written Walt Robbins about Grace's interest in NMC, asked Robbins' assistant, Ben Handler, to call Paganucci about NMC.

Walt Robbins called Paul, and a meeting was arranged at the Union Club, facing the Boston Commons, on Thursday, May 3, 1984, less than a week before the annual - and as it was to turn out, the final - NMC stockholders meeting. Gus Hampers came with Paul Paganucci but without any lawyers or any one else from the company. They were joined by Terry Daniels and Ben Handler. Later Paganucci described the meeting as having "very good chemistry" with Daniels and Hampers quickly establishing an excellent rapport, mutual respect and trust. "Terry was very solicitous," Hampers recalled. Most of the executives Hampers had dealt with on the subject of acquisition or merger of NMC always began the conversation with a grim assessment of NMC's prospects in order to secure the company at the lowest price. "Terry wasn't like that at all," Hampers reflected. "He was selling Grace, trying to convince me that combining with Grace would be a smart move." At the end of the meeting Gus handed Terry a folder with NMC's projections and other inside information to support his oral presentation. Mr. Paganucci was surprised that Hampers would volunteer these data to someone he had met only two hours before without asking for a confidentiality agreement. As Hampers later noted, "I wanted Terry to know I trusted him and expected his trust in return; that's the only way this deal was going to work. Contracts drawn by high price lawyers were no substitute." As they concluded the meeting at the Union Club, Daniels assured Hampers that he'd find a way to structure the deal.

A second meeting with Terry Daniels followed on May 23rd at the Ritz Hotel in Boston, at which Hampers introduced Sam Scialabba and Ed Lowrie to Daniels. Again, the meeting was positive, with the parties eager to pursue some sort of merger. The issue was not whether, but how, to effect the combination. Grace's stock sold at a lower multiple of earnings than most conglomerates at the time, and much lower than NMC. Thus, a stock swap would result in significant dilution for Grace stockholders, including the Grace family and Grace Company executives.

In order to convince himself, Peter Grace, and the Grace board to acquire or invest in National Medical Care, Daniels had to hurdle three serious obstacles. First, the shear size of the acquisition - somewhere in the neighborhood of $360 million - was too massive for Grace to absorb in a stock-for-stock deal without further diluting the control of the Grace family and other company insiders. Second, taking the alternate route of buying NMC stock for cash presented substantial financing problems, causing the Grace balance sheet to be overburdened with debt, and also would result in enormous, non-depreciable goodwill on Grace's books, since the cash price far exceeded the value of the tangible assets. The third hurdle was the inexperience of Grace in running a healthcare company, combined with the independent, entrepreneurial character of Hampers and his cadre of medical directors, whose continued goodwill formed the foundation of future earnings for NMC. "We had painful experiences at Grace with acquisitions where the essential business managers took a walk after we bought their business," Daniels noted. "If Gus Hampers sold NMC to Grace and then walked away, we'd be in serious trouble."

Daniels was right. Despite some modest synergies in the technology of creating artificial membranes to be used in separating materials of varying molecular size, as in dialysis, Grace and NMC had virtually no overlapping functions. Unlike a merger with NME or even Becton Dickinson, a combination of NMC and Grace would not result in the elimination of much duplication or other economies of scale. This was a new business for Grace and its success depended on the continuing involvement of Hampers and his team. As Terry Daniels and his cohorts reviewed the NMC data, Daniels decided it was time to schedule a meeting among the top NMC executives and Mr. Grace. "I was curious to see how Gus and Peter got along," Daniels recalled. "After all, I don't think you could find two more dissimilar people than Peter Grace and Gus Hampers." Hampers, Lowrie and Scialabba flew to New York City on July 10, 1984 to meet the Grace CEO. "He kept us waiting," Hampers remembered. Daniels, Paganucci and Robbins joined the three NMC officers waiting for Mr. Grace's arrival. "He had some excuse about an important overseas telephone call," Hampers recalled. "But all I remember was that he was late and when I asked him some questions about problems Grace was having with its German operations, he basically dismissed me." Despite the largely ceremonial and unproductive meeting, a week later Daniels tracked Hampers down in Austin, Texas and got him on the telephone.

Daniels had gone to Peter Grace and laid out his plan to use a leveraged buy out ("LBO") technique for acquiring NMC from its public shareholders. In 1984 LBO's were just starting to be used to facilitate the takeover of public companies by a relatively small group of private investors, usually, but not always, led by the companies' top management. In a highly publicized and successful LBO less that a year before, former Treasury Secretary, Bill Simon, had used this technique to gain control of Gibson Greeting Cards. The funds to pay the purchase price to the public stockholders were borrowed, with the resulting balance sheet highly "leveraged," i.e., heavy on debt and short on equity. Corporate earnings would be used to pay off the debt, and, if successful, within a few years the small group of company executives and their private investors would own the corporation that had previously been owned by thousands of stockholders. The major risks involved rising interest rates, which could bankrupt a steeply leveraged company, and stockholder lawsuits that would accuse management of setting a low price and breaching its fiduciary duty to the public stockholders.

As Terry Daniels explained it to Mr. Grace, an LBO was the perfect vehicle for Grace's acquisition of NMC over a series of several years. First, Grace had to issue no stock. Second, Grace's cash contribution was limited to its investment in 49% of the common stock of the new holding company. Third, the new NMC balance sheet with its resulting huge debt and enormous goodwill would not be consolidated with that of W.R. Grace. Fourth, the debt would be without recourse to Grace, so that if the new NMC failed, Grace stood to lose only its initial investment. And fifth, and most importantly, the LBO with the Hampers led team holding 51% of the common stock provided a massive incentive for

Gus Hampers to continue to run the company. The deal would be structured so that over time, as the debt was paid off and earnings increased (and as Grace would gain experience and confidence in operating NMC), Grace would have the right to purchase control from Hampers and his inside team. "I told Peter that I didn't have the balls to recommend buying 100% of NMC," Daniels recalled. The question for Daniels and Grace was whether Hampers, who was then 51-years old and had watched his founding colleagues, Schupak and Hager, enjoy the fruits of their labor, would ever commit himself to such a long term, risky deal.

"Gus grasped the concept very quickly," Daniels recollected, referring to the July 17th telephone conversation. "He listened attentively and when I finished he said he had just one requirement - and that was that the price had to be fair to the public stockholders," Daniels continued.

Following that telephone conversation, things moved very quickly with Grace lawyers and analysts setting up a "war room" at Hale and Dorr, NMC's outside counsel. Only those few NMC executives whose assistance was necessary were briefed on the negotiations and regularly commuted from NMC's headquarters on Route 128 in Waltham (the company had moved out of the Hancock Tower in downtown Boston in 1981). Things were kept "underwraps" and there were no public announcements. While the Grace "due diligence" was proceeding, NMC began negotiations with Delmed concerning the possible acquisition of its dialysis centers, at the same time Grace continued discussions with Delmed regarding its product business, which had originally led Daniels to NMC earlier in the year.

As NMC's general counsel, Paul Brountas, a partner at Hale and Dorr, saw major legal pitfalls in the LBO mechanism, since the inside executives were essentially in a position of conflict of interest. Hampers and his colleagues owed a fiduciary obligation to NMC's stockholders, yet under the LBO structure these insiders were offering to buy stock from their investors at a price set by the executives. One thing Brountas was sure of - once the deal was announced publicly there would be one or more stockholder lawsuits challenging the fairness of the transaction and the bona fides of Hampers and his colleagues. Consequently, Brountas

anticipated the arguments and urged Hampers to adopt prophy-
lactic measures that would provide a solid defense to these lawsuits. The Grace lawyers supported Brountas fully in this regard.

Brountas insisted that the non-management NMC directors
exercise well informed and totally independent judgment concerning the transaction. The initial question was who among NMC's
seven directors could be fairly considered "independent." Dr.
Hampers and Dr. Lowrie certainly were not. Dr. Hager would continue to be part of the management investors' group and a director of the reorganized company, thus not sufficiently "disinterest-
ed." And Mr. Paganucci by virtue of his close dealings with Grace
and his role as broker of the transaction (for which he took no
compensation but did secure a $2,500,000 gift from NMC to
Dartmouth) could not be considered independent for the purposes of assessing the transaction on behalf of NMC's stockholders.
The remaining three independent directors - Frederick G. P.
Thorne, Jonathan Moore, and Carl H. Tiedemann - were empowered to hire their own law firm, Ropes & Gray, to advise them on
the transaction and negotiate on their behalf. In addition, this
committee of "outside" directors hired Dillon, Read & Co. Inc.,
investment advisors, to assess the terms of the deal and to opine
on the fairness of the transaction to the NMC stockholders.
Fortunately, the Dillon Read opinion could rest on the firm foundation of the aborted NME offer of $350 million, which NME had
abandoned as being too expensive. Any price at or above $350 mil-
lion would be, presumably, fair.

In fact, as the diligence was concluded during July 1984 and
the plan of merger drafted and the terms negotiated between NMC
and Grace, there was a significant difference between the price
Grace wanted to pay - $19.00 per share - and the price Hampers
sought for NMC shareholders - $19.50 per share - of over nine mil-
lion dollars. At the final substantive meeting on August 1, 1984,
the parties split the difference, and the price was set at $19.25 per
share, or about $354 million.

In order to buy the shares from the stockholders, pay out the
value of unexercised but valid employee options, and retire outstanding debt, the new company needed over $400 million. Where
would these funds come from? Grace would invest $60 million in

a 12% preferred stock issue, and an additional $5 million for stock that was convertible into 49.9% of the common stock of the new company. Hampers and the other 43 employee investors (who were handpicked by Hampers to participate in the lucrative opportunity) contributed about $2 million for 37.2% of the common stock, and 35 of NMC's medical directors (Hampers offered the opportunity to all the medical directors but just 35 opted to sign up) invested about $5 million for shares convertible into 12.8% of the common stock. The company itself would fund about $23 million out of cash and cash equivalents held in its treasury. All those sources combined amounted to less than $100 million. The remaining $315 million was to be borrowed from commercial lenders at commercial rates, the hallmark of a highly leveraged transaction. At that level of debt, a one percentage point increase in interest rates would cost the company an additional $3 million a year. The ultimate success of the combination for all concerned parties depended on a variety of factors, but none was as significant as the uncontrollable factor of interest rate movements. In that regard, it was a high stakes gamble.

The agreement incorporating this ambitious and risky deal was executed by the parties and publicly announced on Monday, August 6, 1984, causing NMC's stock price to jump from its previous (August 3, 1984) close of $13 to $16.75. As reported in the next day's papers, the common stockholders of National Medical Care would receive $19.25 per share in cash, and the public nature of the corporation, which was inaugurated with great fanfare in 1971 but had in recent years created the "fishbowl problem," would end. NMC would become a private corporation owned by W.R. Grace & Co. and less than 100 NMC employees and medical director affiliates.

The deal was subject to three substantive conditions: (1) raising the financing, including $315 million in borrowings; (2) a favorable opinion from Dillon Read; and (3) NMC stockholder approval. The vast majority of NMC stockholders (there were about 4,600 stockholders of record at the time, but this vastly understates the number of actual beneficial shareholders, since many investors hold their stock in their brokers, or socalled "nominee," names), including the large institutional investors in NMC stock, liked the deal. Not all NMC stockholders were happy, however. Some, like Henry Malkasian, who had been one of the original 1968 investors and had never sold a single share since then, acknowledged that the deal was fair in terms of value, but didn't like being excluded from the new deal. "I wish there was a way I could have continued as a stockholder," Malkasian later noted. Other stockholders saw the transaction as manipulated by management and as unfair. The first of two class action lawsuits was filed in Delaware on August 13, 1984, a week after the deal was announced, alleging "gross overreaching, self-dealing, and a breach of fiduciary duties." These lawsuits were subsequently settled and dismissed. In addition, a few NMC stockholders took advantage of their rights under Delaware corporation law to dissent from the merger terms and assert their appraisal rights. None of these stockholders received more than the $19.25 cash purchase price, however. As a whole, the NMC stockholders were pleased to receive a 48% gain (based on the preannouncement $13 price). Many key NMC employees, some of whom would also become stockholders in the new corporation, also made out very well, since the NMC board at Hampers' suggestion, accelerated the terms of their existing NMC stock options, thus permitting them to convert their options into cash once the merger had been consummated.

On October 15, 1984 Dillon Read & Co. Inc. delivered to the NMC Board its written opinion concerning the fairness of the terms to the NMC stockholders. The opinion was unequivocal in citing the $19.25 price as fair to the investors. In reaching this conclusion the most powerful evidence was the fact that in an arms length negotiation, the board of National Medical Enterprises had, just a few months prior, rejected a stock acquisition of NMC valued at between $18.41 and $19.50 per NMC share (the value would fluctuate as the price of NME's stock changed) as being too expensive. Moreover, after the NMC-Grace deal was publicly announced on August 6, 1984, no other potential acquirer had stepped forward and offered a higher price than the $19.25 per share that Grace and the Hampers group was offering. The Dillon Read opinion gave the NMC directors the comfort and protection they needed to recommend the deal to NMC's stockholders and provided nearly unassailable evidence for NMC and Grace lawyers to defend the transaction against any stockholder lawsuits.

Financing the deal was not so easy, however. W. R. Grace & Co. was investing a little more than $65 million, $60 million in preferred shares with an annual cumulative dividend of 12% and the right to elect one half the board of directors of NMC following the merger, and $5,012,000 for 3,580,000 shares of the so called "series A" stock at $1.40 per share, which was convertible into an equivalent number of common shares. The physicians were offered the opportunity to purchase shares of the "series B" stock, also convertible to common shares, at a price of $6.50 per share, and the 43 NMC key employees, including Drs. Hampers and Lowrie, would purchase the common stock at $1.09 per share. Some of the physicians objected to the terms, demanding that their price be the same as the lower, employee price, and as a result only 35 medical directors invested in the deal, and the portion allocated to the physician was undersubscribed. The price was eventually lowered to $5.12 per share, and the physicians held about 13% of the equity with the management holding the remaining 37%. Three years later the shares were valued at $35.

After the August 6th announcement Hampers and other NMC and Grace executives focused their energies on persuading the banks to lend the company $315 million. Since Grace was not willing to guarantee any portion of the debt, it was an uphill struggle. "To this day I still don't know why the banks agreed to do this," Hampers admitted many years later. At the start of the academic year in September 1984, as the deal was creeping toward completion and the banks were slowly signing up, Hampers went to Dartmouth at the urging of Paul Paganucci to meet Mr. Grace. This was to be their second meeting, and it didn't go much better than the first.

In the early 1980's President Reagan had persuaded Peter Grace to lead a special White House commission on waste and excessive spending by the federal government and its affiliated agencies. The commission soon became widely known as the "Grace Commission," and its final report became a blueprint for conservatives in their assault on government spending. President

Reagan admired Peter Grace, was amused by Grace's irreverent and often ribald comments on liberal government programs, and frequently cited and praised the Grace Commission Report. For his part, Peter Grace enjoyed press encounters and public lectures concerning the report. Mr. Grace had come to Dartmouth on his company's new, and presumably non-wasteful, Boeing 727 airplane to expound on the report's findings concerning the government's wasteful habits.

In their September meeting at Dartmouth, Peter Grace unloaded both barrels on Hampers. First, Grace told Hampers that contrary to the promises of Terry Daniels, Dr. Hampers would not have a seat on the Grace Company board of directors until a full year after the closing of the deal, or December 1985, at the earliest. This bothered Hampers, but it wasn't a deal breaker by any means. The second disturbing comment was far more serious. Peter Grace told Hampers that he assessed the chances of securing the necessary $315 million in loans a "long shot." "I was momentarily speechless," Hampers remembered. "The deal had been publicly disclosed for over a month, the proxy was about to be sent to our stockholders, and here was Grace's CEO calling it a longshot."

On September 20, 1984 NMC and Grace executives made a formal presentation to the nation's leading bankers to pitch the LBO. The presentations conducted in the Grace Company's cavernous boardroom at its 42nd Street headquarters were routine and unremarkable, except for a disarming presentation by Dr. Hampers. NMC's CEO exuded such confidence in his and NMC's ability to pay off the borrowings and still make money for Grace and the other stockholders that the Grace executives breathed a sigh of relief. Still, it was an uphill battle to secure such a large loan, and in the end, the banks required Grace to commit to pumping in an additional $40 million, over and above its $65 million investment, in the event that NMC was unable to pay back the borrowings on schedule. Thus, if events had turned out badly, Grace could have lost as much as $105 million on the deal. In addition, all the non-Grace stockholders, including Dr. Hampers, had to pledge their own NMC stock to the banks to secure the loan. When the proxy statement requesting approval of the LBO from NMC's public stockholders was distributed on October 17, 1984, the financing was still unconfirmed and the entire transaction was subject to completion of these loans. Finally, with a firm commitment from Marine Midland Bank for $25 million, the financing was secured in November and the deal proceeded to close on December 20, 1984, having been overwhelmingly approved by NMC's stockholders at the special meeting called for that purpose on November 15, 1984.

By the end of 1984 the Grace Company and the small group of roughly 80 employee stockholders and medical director stockholders had purchased NMC from the public shareholders at $19.25 per share. The first order of business was generating as much cash as possible to reduce the borrowings and expeditiously move to the next phase of the transaction. NMC continued to operate as an independent subsidiary of Grace with its own, new board of directors that included three Grace executives and Drs. Hampers, Hager, Christy Saller of Houston, and Mr. Paganucci.

For the individual stockholders, including Dr. Hampers, the major worry was the loss of any exit option, since there was no longer any public market for their NMC stock, and since they had pledged their NMC holdings to secure the bank borrowings. For many of the employee shareholders especially, their entire portfolios and hence their futures were tied up in an investment that could not be sold, and was difficult, if not impossible, to value. The agreement among the individual stockholders and W.R. Grace & Co. created an exit option for these employees and medical directors. As negotiated by Dr. Hampers, the plan set markers or goals that were expected to be met within the first five years, i.e., by the end of 1989. Once these objectives had been achieved, a majority of the individual stockholders had the right to sell their shares in an underwritten public offering. Since Hampers held a majority of the shares, his say so was obviously necessary and sufficient. At that point, Grace could step up and buy the shares at the price that an independent underwriter was willing to pay for these shares, or allow the other stockholders to sell their shares to the public, or, thirdly, join the individual stockholders in a public offering, thus taking the company public again. Everyone buckled down and pressed ahead, working hard to meet the 1989 goals.

However, by the third quarter of 1987 it was clear that the goals would be achieved by the end of that year, two years ahead of schedule. During the 1985-1987 period, NMC had increased its revenues, managed its cash, accounts receivables and inventory in a tight manner in order to reduce the loans and improve its balance sheet. In addition, interest rates were dropping, providing additional comfort for the company. During that initial three-year period Hampers and Terry Daniels jointly made all the important decisions concerning NMC. If Hampers had Daniels' support, the other Grace directors would not object. As Hampers had anticipated at their initial meeting in early 1984, the partnership could go smoothly or badly, all depending on his relationship with Daniels. Daniels also understood Hampers and his manner of operating. He didn't interfere, even when he might have made different assessments and judgments. The area of greatest sensitivity was in acquiring more dialysis providers. Since NMC had no cash to use to buy available facilities that were for sale and could not borrow funds for that purpose, while its huge LBO debt was still outstanding, these capital expenses had to be approved by, and be financed by, Grace. To his credit, Daniels saw the merit in continuing the acquisition and expansion program and was of a like mind with Hampers regarding NMC's growth, even while still saddled with huge debt. During the 1985 to 1987 period, NMC dialysis centers grew from 182 to 236.

By the end of the summer of 1987 Hampers assertively set the wheels in motion for a redemption of all or part of the individual shares. He asked the investment banking firm of Donaldson, Lufkin and Jenrette to evaluate the company, and the market for selling these shares and to offer a price at which DLJ would underwrite the sale of these shares to the public. The price DLJ established was $35 per share. Terry Daniels and the other Grace executives cleverly offered to meet that price, but also offered to a smaller group of key NMC executives, including Drs. Hampers and Lowrie, the right to defer part or all of the sale and enter into a second-phase agreement. Like the first phase the new agreement would give the stockholders the right to sell, or a "put," and would give Grace the right to purchase, or a "call" at an independently fixed price, once the goals had been achieved. The second "bite at

the apple" was not offered to the thirty-five medical director shareholders, but only a few complained, since they had done very well
under the 1985-1987 deal: the NMC stock which they had purchased for $5.12 was repurchased by Grace for $35 per share. The
typical director-shareholder had invested $150,000 and in three
years cashed out at over a million dollars.

The employee shareholders did even better. They had paid
$1.09 per share in December 1984 and sold their shares, or in
some cases part of their holdings, to Grace for $35 each. These
ranged from Dr. Hampers' 917,432 shares, valued in 1987 at over
$32 million, to several middle management, veteran NMC employ-
ees whose investments of $4,000 in 1987 generated about
$125,000 in capital gains three years later. In the aggregate,
Grace increased its NMC holdings from 49.9% to 82.8%, and at
that point (January 1988) began consolidating NMC's financial
results with its those of the larger conglomerate.

The objectives sought by Terry Daniels for the Grace Company
had largely been achieved. Within thirty-six months Grace's initial
investment of about $65 million had doubled in value with NMC
"bootstrapping" the acquisition with its own earnings. In addition,
the NMC debt was by then manageable, and the ever increasing
revenues and earnings of NMC were improving both the balance
sheet and the income statement of Grace. In one respect, however, the Daniels plan had not succeeded. Between the end of 1984
and the beginning of 1988, when Grace increased its holdings of
NMC from just under 50% to nearly 83%, Grace had not been able
to learn how to operate NMC or assert the control that would be
expected from a parent corporation over its subsidiary. Unlike
other Grace controlled companies, NMC maintained its own personnel policies, annual bonus and other benefits plans, an independent auditing firm, a separate law department, and its own
cadre of lobbyists and outside consultants. Except for Terry
Daniels, no Grace executives regularly required NMC officials to
respond to their inquiries or follow the normal corporate, hierarchical protocols, and even Daniels worked solely through
Hampers. This "special treatment" obviously annoyed many executives at Grace, and it also nurtured an independent and somewhat cocky attitude among the NMC management team toward

THE PRICE OF ACCESS

the Grace establishment. This dynamic would later explode after Daniels departed the scene and Hampers spent less time on NMC day-to-day management. The goal of using a step-by-step approach in acquiring NMC in order to lessen Grace's dependency on Hampers and his chief lieutenants had not been met. As a result, when it came to negotiating the second phase for the post-1987 period, Hampers still had sufficient leverage to exact a high, but fair, price. Thus, Hampers agreed to a new, two-year deal for 1988 and 1989.

In a repeat of the experience with the first incentive plan, the NMC team met the goals for the second phase at the end of 1988, a full year ahead of schedule. Those employee shareholders who had decided not to sell all of their shares at the end of 1987, including most prominently, Dr. Hampers and Dr. Lowrie, were handsomely rewarded. In late 1988 DLJ and Merrill Lynch were engaged to evaluate the NMC investment. The price thus independently established was $55 per share, a 57% increase in twelve months. Grace saw this price as excessive and trimmed its offer to $45 per share. At first Hampers adamantly refused to budge off the $55 price, but ultimately settled at $50 per share. "When I insisted on $55 the people at Grace started to pout," Hampers reflected. "I was willing to deduct 5%, or about $2.75, as equivalent to the underwriters' commission that we would save if Grace purchased the stock. They still weren't happy and I figured I could make even more money down the road if I didn't push them to the point of being disgruntled." As a result, at the $50 price, several senior and middle management NMC employees were millionaires. In January 1989 Grace bought nearly all the remaining NMC shares from these employee-stockholders at $50, increasing its holdings in NMC from 82.8% to 97.5%. Only Drs. Hampers and Lowrie retained the remaining two and one half percent of NMC common stock. Following 1988 NMC continued a generous incentive plan for its managers (49 individuals selected by Hampers) using a "phantom" stock concept, i.e., virtual, not actual, ownership. And once again, the results for the three-year period, 1989 to 1991, were spectacular.

In addition to lower interest rates, one major reason NMC was able to reduce its large bank debt, and thereby achieve its goals ahead of schedule during the 1985-1989, five-year period, was by amortizing a large portion of its goodwill, thus reducing its taxable income and holding onto the cash that would otherwise have gone to the U.S. treasury in the form of taxes. The theory was that a substantial, intangible, but nonetheless depleting and depreciating, asset of NMC was its relationships with its dialysis patients. These relationships were valuable, but, like a piece of equipment or an oil reserve, they were not enduring, since patients eventually expired or left dialysis after successful transplants. Based on years of experience with thousands of patients with every conceivable "comorbidity" or complication (such as diabetes), NMC was able to calculate the expected, remaining life of these relationships (and in most cases this was also the statistical equivalent of the remaining life of the patient himself) with its patients, and thus amortize those over time. This amortization expense lowered taxable income and tax payments, leaving more cash with which to pay off the bank borrowings.

The idea of allocating part of the goodwill to a depreciable asset account called "patient relationships" and amortizing this asset over five years for tax purposes and over sixteen years for general accounting purposes was the brainchild of John Spellman, the chief financial officer of W.R. Grace & Co., and a member of the NMC board of directors from 1985 until 1989. (Mr. Spellman in his typically modest fashion credited the notion to Brian Smith, the Grace controller at that time.) "John Spellman was the smartest financial officer I've ever met," Dr. Hampers later recalled. "And on top of that, he was one of the nicest people at Grace as well." Hampers' esteem for Spellman was enhanced, when Spellman, alone among Hampers' advisors and colleagues, withdrew all his assets from the equity markets about two weeks before the calamitous "Black Monday" in October 1987. In addition, Spellman was a singular workaholic. A major stroke had confined him in 1988 to a wheelchair, but did not affect his output. At a particular NMC review session at Grace, Spellman experienced an embarrassing and very messy nosebleed. Watching blood gushing onto the conference table, Peter Grace and the other officers became queasy and panicked. Dr. Lowrie quickly and calmly attended to Spellman, as Dr. Hampers continued to answer the

questions Mr. Grace had asked. "I think Peter Grace had a different measure of trust and respect for Gus and me, after we took
care of John that afternoon," Lowrie later recalled. Hampers' level
of respect for Spellman couldn't have been higher. "Spellman gets
all the credit," Gus explained. "The amortization practice saved us
nearly $180 million in taxes over five years, and really made the
early buyout possible."

No one believed that the Internal Revenue Service would readily acquiesce in this bold accounting maneuver by NMC, and the
IRS did in fact disallow the practice on its initial review. Grace and
NMC had anticipated a challenge by the government and had
carefully documented the length of time dialysis patients of varying demographic classifications could be expected to survive. In
addition, at Spellman's request, American Appraising, an independent firm skilled in the appraisal of unusual assets, was hired
to review the assessments and support the NMC-Grace position.
Finally, in early 1990, the IRS acquiesced and allowed NMC to
deduct $172 million of the $176 million, or about 98%, of the
depreciation expense that NMC had claimed for tax purposes.

This accounting practice was risky, but logical. If a farmer
purchased a cow for $500, but the cow's capacity to produce milk,
from which the farmer derives his income, will end in five years,
he would persuasively argue that he should be allowed to deduct
$100 from his income over each of the next five years in order to
replace the cow at the end of that period. The cow's ability to produce income decreases over time. Similarly, caring for a dialysis
patient will produce income only so long as that patient is both
alive and is not able to leave dialysis, NMC contended. Even if logical from a tax accounting point of view, the exposition of this
practice appears ghoulish and inhumane. Comparing dialysis
patients to milk cows, or any other depreciable asset would invite
trouble. It turned out, however, that the practice instituted by
NMC to save taxes actually resulted in great benefits to its dialysis patients.

By calculating "remaining lives" for a broad range of patients,
which varied according to diagnosis, age, sex, race, and other relevant factors, NMC was establishing standards by which it could
then compare the predicted results to the actual outcomes. This

allowed the company to spot and investigate statistical anomalies, which were useful in raising the quality of care. Particular dialysis facilities and physicians that surpassed the expected results in terms of morbidity and mortality were studied to determine why they exceeded expectations with the intent of adopting their superior methods and practices system wide. Conversely, NMC officials scrutinized the practices of any NMC dialysis center, which fell below the predicted standards, in order to get these centers back in line with the norm. Only NMC with its huge base of dialysis patients could effect such a system of data collection, analysis, and reform. Thus, for instance, NMC officials could compare the effects of longer dialysis times (say, five hours vs. four hours), or the use of particular medications, or the substitution of a new, higher flux artificial kidney, or a change in diet regimens, on the morbidity and mortality of patients. Morbidity statistics (the number of days per year that a dialysis patient was hospitalized and thus not being treated at the NMC center) were just as important as mortality and transplantation statistics, because hospitalized patients generated no income for NMC. It was always in NMC's financial interest to keep patients alive and well. Critics of NMC's profit making orientation often missed this point. Cutting corners that could result in poor quality would eventually raise the morbidity factor, thus reducing the company's revenue and profit. Across the board, better health for NMC's dialysis patients meant a healthier financial statement for NMC.

The system of evaluating patients as "depreciable assets," which NMC adopted for tax savings reasons and had very important benefits for their quality of care, also provided a new and useful paradigm in analyzing healthcare reform strategies. Instead of viewing patients as liabilities that need to be controlled by doing as little as possible and as cheaply as possible, the NMC medical directors saw their patients as assets that would be wasted unless properly maintained. The difference in attitude and approach were as significant as the difference in a patient's attitude about his own healthcare. Patients who understand "healthcare" as a regimen of sensible diet and hygiene, exercise, reducing risk factors, preventive practices, regular check-ups, and following their doctor's prescriptions and advice, as part of a program of maintaining their health asset, are going to be in far better shape than similar patients who view "healthcare" as episodic trips to the doctor to combat manifest disease or injury.

Unfortunately, for the most part, the U.S. healthcare financing system is based on the "patient-as-liability" model. Providers - doctors, pharmacies, clinics and hospitals - are paid for services and products delivered to combat disease and injury. They aren't paid for keeping patients healthy. Health maintenance organizations were organized to institute a new approach, which was more in line with the "patient-as-asset" model by securing a monthly fee for each patient, which is paid by the patient or his employer regardless of whether services are rendered or not. The HMO model assumes that preventive care will reduce costs in the long run. The third party, fee-for-service model produced overuse, whereas the HMO approach encourages the provider to under-prescribe and ration care. In both systems the patient presents an actual or potential liability and providing care is a burden and a drain on resources.

In providing chronic, maintenance dialysis NMC viewed the sick patient as a liability, but the healthy, well maintained patient was an asset for the company, thus aligning the company's financial interest with the patient's health. In a sense, NMC was paid only when the patients were healthy, not when they were unhealthy. With thousands of patients, even marginal advances in measurable outcomes, such as higher clearances of wastes from the blood; clean, uninfected access sites; and less anemia, meant less morbidity, lower potential mortality, and more income for NMC. The value of these dialysis patients as assets was reflected in the fact that NMC was willing to pay a price considerably higher than the value of fixed assets in acquiring facilities from other dialysis operators. When Hampers and Grace teamed up to buy NMC from the public shareholders, they were equally willing to pay a huge premium for these patient relationships.

What NMC's experience suggests in the larger world of healthcare delivery and finance is that tying quality and positive outcomes to payments creates a system that values the patient as an asset and aligns the financial interest of the provider with the health of the patient. Substituting a system that measures and rewards results, rather than pays a fee for therapeutic services or that encourages underutilization via the HMO model, should be the goal of healthcare reform. For the most part, this approach is counter intuitive to the logic of government, insurance company, and HMO bureaucrats, who generally equate quality with expense, not with savings. The NMC model should encourage the adoption of broader and longer term perspectives, and the elimination of the micromanagement of cases, cures and costs. The devolution of responsibility to the actor in the system most likely to control the outcome with rewards and penalties allocated based on results is the proper prescription for healthcare reform that aligns patient health with fiscal accountability.

The combination of National Medical Care and W.R. Grace & Co. that started in 1984 after NMC had been spurned by other suitors and undervalued by both Wall Street experts and government bureaucrats, worked well for all constituents. NMC was without question the most successful investment Grace ever made. NMC gained a partner in Grace that could shield the company from the "fishbowl" of public disclosure that transformed financial success into potential cutbacks. In addition, NMC undoubtedly benefited from strong, sophisticated management support in areas such as tax accounting, human resource management, and public relations. NMC's key employees and medical directors shared in the successes of their labor and loyalty, and the patient base was also advantaged by the system of medical information and resulting efforts at improving outcomes. The ESRD System and the government received a very good deal as well. After cutting the dialysis reimbursement rate by $12 in late 1983, services continued to expand and rationing and political pressure were avoided, largely due to the leadership of NMC in cutting costs and improving quality of care. These rate cuts were, and remain, unprecedented in Medicare's history.

Essentially the Grace-NMC combination was successful at so many levels, because it allowed Hampers and his managers a longer period of time and broader measures of achievement in which to perform. Instead of having to worry about, and therefore anticipate and correct for, three month revenue and earnings reports that would often be misinterpreted by shareholders and their advisors, NMC's executives could involve Grace as its major investor in the process, explain the company's plans and receive back Grace's support, capital and leeway to perfect those plans. NMC's public stockholders made no commitment to the long-term, and if disappointed with the results of a particular calendar quarter, could simply sell their shares on the market. Obviously, if enough investors shared that opinion, the price of NMC's stock would fall, even if the disappointing results were necessary in the short term to capture greater gains over the longer term. Grace, on the other hand, had made a substantial financial commitment and a moral pledge to stand by NMC through the longer term and was therefore more likely to approve short term disappointments in order to realize long term success. No where was this more true than in the area of expansion and acquisition. With some rare exceptions, Grace was ready, willing, and able to supply capital to NMC in order to fund a promising purchase. Naturally, Grace had other capital requirements, and NMC had to compete with other Grace subsidiaries and projects for funding. None matched the "ROI" - return on investment - that NMC produced for its parent corporation. For his part, Hampers never over promised and swiftly gained the trust of the Grace officers and directors through outstanding results. In short, the formula for success that worked for Hampers and Daniels, as the key liaison with the Grace Corporation, was composed of equal measures of trust and non-interference as well as a longer time horizon.

The Grace-NMC combination, brokered by Paul Paganucci in early 1984, worked so well that it reintroduced Paganucci into the Grace corporate hierarchy. In November 1985, about a year after the LBO, and about the same time that Hampers was appointed to the Grace board of directors, Mr. Paganucci re-joined W.R. Grace & Co., leaving Dartmouth after 14 years in Hanover. A few months later, Peter Grace, then the chairman of the board and CEO of Grace, created three coequal vice chairman positions with the intention that one of the three would become his successor as CEO. Two of the three vice chairmen - Terry Daniels and Paul Paganucci - were close associates of Hampers and owed their vice chairmanships, at least in part, to the success of the NMC deal. The third vice chairman was J.P. Bolduc, a relative newcomer to

Grace, who had served as the chief of staff to the Grace Commission in the early 1980's. Hampers own stature on the Grace board expanded as NMC's performance outpaced all expectations and as Daniels and Paganucci assumed more prominent roles in the corporation.

The smooth course of events between NMC and Grace suffered initial fractures in 1989, however. One was a literal fracture - that of Peter Grace's hip. Always a robust athlete since his school days, Mr. Grace kicked a football and landed in the hospital with a serious hip fracture at the age of 76. The fracture precipitated a steady, gradual decline in Mr. Grace's health that he disguised for several months, but clearly influenced his demeanor, judgement, and timing. Because the break was so slow to heal, requiring a long hospital stay, transfusions and chemotherapy, Hampers correctly concluded that this was no routine fracture. It was later determined that the bone tissue was infiltrated with tumor.

The second break that had a negative impact on the course of events was the departure of Terry Daniels from the Grace Company and consequently his role as chief liaison to Hampers and NMC. By March 1989 Daniels, his wife and four children had moved to rural Virginia from which Daniels commuted to Grace offices in New York. Over the Easter weekend Daniels received a call from an agitated Peter Grace, upset over a major $100 million overrun in the cost of constructing a Grace chemical plant outside Brussels, which was under Daniels' control. Mr. Grace demanded that Daniels' fly at once to Belgium to gather the facts to present to Mr. Grace the following week. Daniels uncharacteristically refused to leave his family over the holiday, and a period of estrangement between Peter Grace and Terry Daniels began. It ended six months later with Daniels' departure in September. As a reward for his outstanding work in effecting the 1984 merger with NMC and as an inducement to making the combination succeed, Mr. Grace and the Grace board had granted Daniels 100,000 shares of NMC common stock which he could sell back to Grace at their fair market value. Daniels left Grace with a five and a half million dollar parachute, but continued his close association with Gus Hampers. "Things were never the same for Gus and NMC after Terry left," Mr. Paganucci explained. Hampers agreed, and smilingly noted, "What bugged me was that the NMC shares were worth $55 in 1989, but I accepted $50 to make Terry look good, but when Terry left, he demanded the full $55 a share."

15

A Difficult Accommodation

On April 14, 1993 the world of finance and investment centered around Wall Street in lower Manhattan discovered what only a few senior executives at W.R. Grace & Co. had known since the end of the prior calendar year. The news, first released in Grace's proxy statement for the upcoming election of directors to its board, and then published in the financial press, surprised many of those same Grace director nominees and all but the top echelons at both Grace and its National Medical Care subsidiary.

Under the rules of full and fair disclosure enforced by the Securities and Exchange Commission, when the management of a corporation whose stock is publicly traded, like Grace, solicits the proxies of its shareholders, it must provide the stockholders and the public with all the information that a reasonably prudent investor might deem relevant in his decision to grant or withhold his proxy to the company's management. In this case, the Grace management was engaged in the annual, routine request for shareholders' proxies that would allow management to elect its nominees to the board of directors at its stockholders meeting in May. Compliance with the SEC rules of relevant disclosure required Grace to report all the details of each director's remuneration and benefits derived from Grace, whether those particular directors were nominated for reelection or not. Although the investors were the owners of the corporation, they could do nothing to change the compensation that had been paid or promised to these directors, but they might decide to withhold their proxies and hence not vote for the election of these directors in the future.

While investors rely on the independent and unbiased judgment of the board of directors, they lack the ability to eliminate conflicts of interest that will inevitably arise when these directors are handsomely rewarded with annual stipends, per diem reimbursements for every board and committee meeting they attend, stock options, travel and other perquisites, and generous consulting contracts. Most often the shareholders can vote only "yes" or "no," because they are not presented with alternate nominees for these directorships. Ultimately, if a stockholder doesn't like the way a company is being managed, he can simply sell his shares and invest his capital in those enterprises which meet his standards. Public disclosure is the antidote to abuse, and many corporate lawyers create lucrative careers centered on their expertise in advising management whether and how to disclose important information to the capitalist community.

As an employee and "inside" director, Gus Hampers' compensation would naturally be disclosed in the Grace proxy statement. This didn't bother Hampers. Since he had been CEO of National Medical Care when it was a public company and subject to these same proxy rules, he was well aware of the law and accustomed to the annual disclosure ritual. Besides, Hampers wasn't embarrassed that his compensation, which was largely based on NMC's performance, was too high. Lower compensation would have indicated smaller profits and a lower return on capital from NMC to its Grace parent, and that would have been cause for embarrassment. Still, even in the world of multimillion dollar salaries, the revelation that Grace had paid Hampers $27.5 million dollars in 1993 was worthy of prominent articles in the financial press.

The $27.5 million compensation represented Hampers' share of the earnings that NMC had contributed to the Grace treasury during the prior three years. His right to share in these profits was established in a contract between Grace and the cadre of NMC executives and managers headed by Dr. Hampers for the 1990-1992 period. For J.P. Bolduc, who had taken over the CEO position at Grace in late December, 1992, it was personally irritating, even though he defended the incentive package for the NMC executives publicly to his board of directors and to the community of financial analysts. Bolduc had no choice, since he had negotiated the terms of the NMC incentive contract on behalf of Grace three years before. In defending the unusually large payment to Hampers, Bolduc was defending his own judgment and skill as a negotiator and businessman. Nonetheless, Bolduc knew that Hampers had gotten the best of him, and now the world knew as well.

The events that led up to the April 1993 disclosure began in early 1990, precipitated by a telephone call to Hampers from J. Peter Grace, the veteran CEO and Chairman of W..R. Grace & Co., a company controlled by Peter Grace since 1945. Although NMC had been a Grace subsidiary since late 1984 and Gus Hampers was a member of Mr. Grace's hand picked board of directors, the call came as a surprise to Hampers. "Peter never called me before," Hampers reflected. "He tracked me down in St. Louis and asked me to meet him as soon as possible."

They met the next day aboard Mr. Grace's jet at the airport in Baltimore. J.P. Bolduc was with the Grace chairman. To all interested observers Bolduc seemed to be ahead in the race to succeed Peter Grace, who at that time was already 76 years old. Bolduc was then 50 and had been employed by W.R. Grace & Co. for only seven years. A native of Lewiston, Maine with a degree in business administration from St. Cloud State University, J.P. Bolduc's background could not have been further removed from the privileged environment of Peter Grace, a graduate of Yale, a member of the Knights of Malta, and the director of several major U.S. corporations and charities, including Citicorp and the University of Notre Dame.

Bolduc had been at the U.S. Department of Agriculture in the mid-1970's during the Nixon-Ford administrations, ending his career there as Assistant Secretary of Agriculture in 1977, when he became affiliated with the management consulting firm of Booz, Allen & Hamilton. When Mr. Grace accepted President Reagan's invitation to chair a citizens' panel to investigate government waste, later known as "The Grace Commission" after its illustrious and colorful leader, Peter Grace hired Bolduc as the commission's chief of staff. Once the commission's work had ended in 1983, Peter Grace created a position (director of special projects) for Bolduc at Grace headquarters in New York City.

Reluctantly anticipating his eventual retirement, Peter Grace, a fierce competitor who had been a national equestrian champion and a semiprofessional hockey player, established a contest in the spring of 1986 among the leading inhouse contenders for his office. Like Caesar dividing Gaul, Grace created three positions of vice chairman, each with his own responsibilities and with the overt understanding that his successor would be the man that performed best. One vice chairman was Terry Daniels, who had engineered the purchase of National Medical Care by Grace and had forged a close, effective working relationship with Gus Hampers and other top executives at NMC. Another vice chairman was Paul Paganucci, a man who had worked at Grace for several years and had become a close personal advisor to Mr. Grace and other members of the Grace family. In 1971 Mr. Paganucci left to become dean of the Amos Tuck School of Business at Dartmouth University, and had returned to Grace in late 1985, following his successful, informal role brokering the marriage between NMC, where he had served on the board of directors since 1973, and Grace. The third vice chairman slot was awarded to J.P. Bolduc.

Since the Grace-NMC combination in 1984 and through the period of the three vice chairmen that began in 1986, Gus Hampers reported to Terry Daniels. In fact, Hampers and Daniels operated as partners, each understanding and respecting the needs and goals of the other. Daniels was especially adept at allowing Hampers to "run his own shop," and insulating him from interference from Peter Grace or from the Grace bureaucracy. Daniels fought for NMC's independence from the corporate straight jacket, and Gus was granted exemptions from Grace procedures. All that mattered was the bottom line. Terry Daniels recalled one illuminating example. Peter Grace required all top executives who worked for him to submit detailed work schedules with Mr. Grace's office so he would know where each of his officers was at any moment, day or night. Hampers laughed when requested to comply, and Daniels persuaded Grace to exempt Gus from his rule. For his part, Gus Hampers delivered the results which he had committed NMC to produce, and he kept Daniels well informed. Hampers knew that the worst outcome in corporate America, especially at a white shoe firm like Grace, was a surprise. Hampers never surprised Daniels. As a result, they formed a close friendship as well as a trusting business partnership. In addition, because of his extraordinary efforts in bringing NMC to

Grace, Daniels was rewarded with the grant of 100,000 shares of NMC common stock. The value of these shares was tied to NMC's profitability, so Daniels had a major incentive in seeing Hampers and NMC succeed.

The "era of good feeling" ended abruptly at the end of 1989 upon the resignation of Terry Daniels from Grace, creating a "sea change" in the words of Gus Hampers. Daniels chafed under the tight, often irrational, control of his mentor, Peter Grace, and resented the increasingly large sacrifice the "race to succeed Peter" was exacting from his family and personal life. His departure ended the productive five-year partnership that he and Hampers had created. For Peter Grace the problem was straight forward – Hampers would simply have to form a new working and reporting relationship with one of the remaining top executives at Grace, and Peter Grace was going to make it easy for Hampers, allowing the NMC head to make his own choice. That was the subject of the meeting on the tarmac at the Baltimore airport in early 1990.

Dr. Hampers was not by training or temperament comfortable with accepting choices that were restricted by circumstance or the dictates of others, whether his superiors or his staff. If he were so inclined, Hampers would still be running the dialysis unit at the Brigham Hospital, rationing care among the "most deserving," and seeing the charges for that care escalate beyond the means of insurers or the government to finance. Peter Grace offered Hampers three alternatives – he could report directly to Peter, or to Paul Paganucci, or to Bolduc. Hampers' response was that he didn't want to report to Mr. Grace or to Mr. Paganucci, and that he'd meet with Bolduc to see whether they could work together. Peter Grace, relieved at Hampers' choice of Bolduc (as Hampers knew Grace would be) figured the problem was solved, or at least that it was now Bolduc's problem to solve. His task of effecting a hand off from Daniels to Bolduc had been completed. Gus Hampers had other ideas.

About a week later in early 1990, Bolduc and Hampers met privately in New York. Bolduc, gleeful that his principal rival, Terry Daniels, was now out of the picture, and that NMC, the strongest asset in the Grace corporate arsenal, was now part of his fiefdom, began to tell Hampers that they could, in Hampers' words, "make beautiful music together." Hampers listened attentively to Bolduc's sales pitch, but he had grave misgivings. Although he didn't know Bolduc very well, certainly not as well as he knew Terry Daniels or Paul Paganucci, Hampers knew that Bolduc was not an "operating guy." He had spent his career as an accountant and consultant, calculating other people's money and mistakes, but never actually running a business. He was a staff, not a field, officer. In addition, Hampers knew Bolduc was intensely competitive, and Hampers always felt more secure negotiating with a tough competitor, rather than with a "nice" guy. The competition whetted Hampers' negotiating edge, and he didn't feel bad or guilty when he trumped a tough opponent.

When Bolduc finished his overture, Hampers told him he didn't think it would work and he wanted to buy NMC back from Grace. He put Bolduc on the defensive by telling him that he was wary of working for a man who had never run a company and didn't understand the entrepreneur mentality. Hampers presented Bolduc and W.R. Grace & Co. with an alternative that Peter Grace hadn't even considered, namely, ending the relationship in 1990. Bolduc rose to the Hampers bait, giving Hampers everything he sought and putting it in a written contract - independence and a major share in NMC's earnings over the ensuing three-year period. Rather than be blamed with losing Grace's stellar subsidiary and thereby shrinking in comparison with Daniels and Paganucci, Bolduc deferred the inevitable confrontation for three years and accepted the contractual terms that Hampers required. Perhaps Bolduc even thought that he could domesticate Hampers and make him a "team player" before the contract ended in 1993.

In 1993 when the bill came due on the arrangement that he had agreed to in 1990, Bolduc had no choice but to defend it, including the $27.5 million paid to Hampers, as a good deal for Grace and Grace's shareholders. In the meantime, Bolduc had consolidated his power at Grace without any resistance from Hampers. Hampers looked to all the world as Bolduc's strongest ally, and in fact, Hampers supported many of the strategic plans Bolduc effected as he took on more and more responsibilities at Grace. Three men stood between Bolduc and the chairmanship of Grace. Charles H. Erhart, Jr., the president of Grace and a long time member of its board of directors, was part of the Grace family, both literally as a relative of Peter Grace, and figuratively, as a long time Grace employee. He had reached retirement age and was eased out as president. Bolduc took over as president and chief operating officer in August of 1990. Paul Paganucci was a tougher obstacle. Smart, loyal and extremely popular, Paganucci had close, personal links with Peter Grace, Gus Hampers, members of the Grace family and virtually every member of the Grace board of directors. Bolduc knew that Peter Grace would never fire Paganucci and that as long as Paul was around, Bolduc would have a harder time climbing to the top. Bolduc enlisted Hampers' support to get rid of Paganucci. Gus refused to be part of Bolduc's plan, and in fact warned Paganucci and advised him to negotiate a good contract for himself, so that when the time came, Paul could walk away from Grace financially secure. It took only a few months. Paul Paganucci left in March of 1991.

With Hampers busy making money for the corporation and Erhart and Paganucci eliminated, Bolduc had only one hurdle left. But the 78-year old (in 1991) chairman was still not ready to retire from the company that his grandfather, a two term mayor of New York City, had started in 1854, and that Peter's father, Joseph, had subsequently controlled as a private corporation. Peter Grace began working at the company as a mail room attendant in 1936, and after World War II stepped into the shoes of his ailing father. He presided over the corporation after its shares became publicly traded in 1954 and led it in an era of diversification, turning W.R. Grace & Co. into one of the 100 largest corporations in the United States. As president and COO, J.P. Bolduc was restrained by Peter Grace who still held the title of Chief Executive Officer and held sway as chairman over a 22-member board entirely of his creation. Bolduc's goal was to steer Grace through a period of streamlining and divestiture, and these plans, while approved by the Wall Street community, often met Peter Grace's resistance. It was said that Peter Grace never met an acquisition he didn't like, and Bolduc's strategy of discarding businesses that had been acquired by the chairman became increasingly difficult to effect. Nonetheless, Bolduc persisted. As The Wall Street Journal later reported, "[Bolduc] jettisoned pet subsidiaries of Mr. Grace, who had led the company into fields as diverse as ethnic restaurants, energy, cattle breeding and sports stores."

Gus Hampers liked Bolduc's strategy of focusing the corporation on its core, successful businesses and shedding the myriad enterprises that were not producing adequate returns on capital. One effect of selling off these unrelated, diverse business was to free up capital which was then available for investment in NMC's expansion. Bolduc fed Hampers' need for capital, and Hampers' support on the board of directors made Bolduc's task of overcoming Peter Grace's opposition much easier. As Bolduc later commented, "Gus Hampers wanted to acquire the world if we were to give him enough money."

Although by 1992 Mr. Grace's health was failing, he was not ready to retire and lie down. His work gave him a purpose and focus in life that may well have extended it beyond the diagnosis of cancer that he had received in July, 1992. In December 1992 at the insistence of Bolduc, Peter Grace relinquished the title of CEO to Bolduc, thereby ceding control of the corporation's daily operations as well as its strategic direction to his protege. Peter Grace remained chairman of the board of directors, accepting a retirement bonus of $5 million, an annual pension of one million dollars and a consulting contract of $50,000 per month. Bolduc severely reduced Peter Grace's staff from ten to four and confiscated his Gulfstream IV jet. In 1995, Business Week noted, "After Bolduc took over as CEO in 1993, J. Peter Grace simmered bitterly for 2 1/2 years."

Bolduc simultaneously sweetened the pot for the Grace directors, hoping to win their loyalty as well as their obvious respect for his business acumen. In 1993 shortly after Bolduc took over as CEO, Grace directors received a "raise" to $24,000 per annum, plus $2,000 per board meeting (there were ten such meetings a year) and $1,000 for every committee meeting. In total, conscientious directors were paid close to $50,000 per year each for sitting on the Grace board. In addition, five of the outside, non-employee directors received substantial consulting contracts. With favorable reviews from Wall Street analysts and Grace's institutional investor base, strong strategic support from Hampers, and a chairman whose health was declining rapidly, all Bolduc had to do was wait. But Bolduc was not a patient man. "He [Peter Grace] never really retired...he had his cronies in at the board...because I was quote unquote destroying his company," Bolduc later complained.

Bolduc's strategy of selling Grace's fringe enterprises was good for NMC. His plan to transform Grace from a holding company into a management company by centralizing control over critical, overlapping functions such as personnel, payroll, accounting, collections and management information systems was not perceived sanguinely by NMC's management, however. Conflicts became routine and intense as Bolduc and his top lieutenants at Grace tightened their control of NMC. In many ways Dr. Hampers was the last to recognize the importance of these changes on NMC. With his focus on acquisitions, worldwide expansion, and long-term strategies in the delivery of healthcare, and long divorced from the day-to-day operations, Hampers initially saw these conflicts as small skirmishes in the inevitable tug-of-war of ego's in the corporate world. In addition, prosaic matters involving personnel policies, accounting deadlines and computer interface had always been unimportant to Hampers, even when NMC was an independent company. However, each concession on small matters led to larger demands in the consolidation push by Bolduc's staff, until these invaded the areas of real concern to Hampers.

For his part, Bolduc resented NMC's independence. He viewed Hampers and the other NMC doctors as arrogant and uncooperative. They weren't team players, and following the 1993 payment of millions of dollars to Hampers and his managers, Bolduc's urge to domesticate the NMC cadre became an obsession. He was going to make the NMC goose lay the golden egg precisely as he commanded. Bolduc recalled, "When we first acquired NMC, there were all sorts of agreements, some in writing and some verbal [sic] and I was not involved. NMC wanted to retain quote and unquote its entrepreneurial independence...I moved to create a management company at the Grace level not a holding company, which would integrate all of the operating units within W.R. Grace, and my single biggest challenge at that time was NMC."

Dr. Hampers began to see the negative effects on NMC. "I felt [Bolduc] was impinging on the health of this company, that he was wasting an enormous amount of time trying to put round pegs in square holes. I have the philosophy that Grace should be a holding company. But Bolduc was clearly moving towards being an operating company. And the pain started to get high here. I started spending 20 to 30% of my time defending us from decisions that I didn't believe in. And I got tired of arguing with him," Hampers was quoted in a 1995 article in The Boston Globe.

The cultural differences between the two companies had always been large, but they were easily ignored so long as Grace maintained a "hands off" attitude toward its subsidiary. The balance that Terry Daniels and Gus Hampers had worked out for five years and that Hampers had required during the 1990 to 1993 period began to topple. The pent-up resentment exploded. Alex Pham reported in The Boston Globe: "National Medical, with its spartan second hand desks and chairs, is a stark contrast to Grace's lavish Florida offices. 'There was a culture gap that became a chasm', said Geoff Swett, an National Medical senior vice president. 'We were literally laughed at by others at Grace because of our attitudes toward money.'"

The people that Hampers had hired over the years to run NMC were selected for their ability to think independently, to craft solutions, and to create opportunities for NMC. Allegiance to tradition and compliance with regulation by bureaucrats far removed from the dialysis clinic were not qualities prized by Hampers or his top executives like Ed and Ernie Lowrie, who had been with Hampers when he started NMC in 1968. And the Lowrie's became increasingly vocal both within and outside the walls of NMC about their dissatisfaction. "Let's face it. Grace [the company] was fat, dumb and happy - not lean and mean like NMC," Ernie Lowrie argued. "Gus was always lucky to have good people around him. He picked self-motivated people." Ed Lowrie, as NMC's president and chief operating officer, was increasingly upset and combative. Squeezed between the Grace hierarchy on the one side and the medical directors of the clinics on the other, Lowrie tried to hold the line, but without Hampers personal involvement the struggle was futile.

By the end of 1994 when Grace tried to consolidate the accounting for and collection of accounts receivable, Lowrie persuaded Hampers to get involved. Dr. Lowrie understood synergies in corporate consolidations, but to him collecting delinquent accounts for medical services and products supplied to thousands of individual patients with hundreds of third-party insurers and government programs, each with its own set of guidelines and traditions, was distinct from operating a routine collection effort for sales of chemicals and packaging to multinational businesses. Hampers agreed, and forced a show down. Bolduc backed off, but was furious. Hampers also bucked the corporate culture of Grace by refusing to allow NMC managers to attend Grace seminars and training sessions. "They had these touchy feely, three and four day seances and administered personality profile tests. After a while all my senior people were away from the day-to-day business of running the clinics," Hampers recalled.

Whether he won or lost these battles, Bolduc grew more and more upset that he had opposition to his plans to consolidate from NMC alone. "The big mistake Grace made early on in '84 was to buy the company with an understanding that he [Hampers] would remain an independent entrepreneur," Bolduc opined later, ignoring the fact that as an independent operation NMC was providing nearly half of the operating profits of W.R. Grace & Co. "We're dealing with an unusual ego here. If he [Hampers] and Lowrie walked into this room the walls would move out. That's why they were called doctors. If you worked for Dr. Hampers you either said yes or somebody else would replace you," Bolduc said several months later.

As these internecine struggles were occurring in late 1993 and throughout 1994, Bolduc was consolidating his power within the corporation, placing his people in prime slots, and effecting a very successful public relations strategy. He had favorably impressed the institutions that held large blocks of Grace stock, as well as the financial press and Wall Street analysts. For years people who followed Grace's stock felt it was undervalued and the company poorly managed. "This company [W.R. Grace & Co.] was always run as a private fiefdom, and the directors were of the men's club mentality," Neil Eigen, a director of equities at Bear Stearns Asset Management, a large Grace stockholder, told The Wall Street Journal. They liked the results that Bolduc had produced during his tenure first as president and more lately as CEO. "Long a lackluster per-former, the company's [Grace] stock climbed from $35.25 in early December [1994] to $45.375 in early March [1995], partly thanks to Mr. Bolduc's efforts to focus the company on its core business-es," declared The New York Times.

By late 1994 Bolduc, impatient with Peter Grace's refusal to step down as chairman, and confident of his self-promoting efforts inside and outside the company, made a bold decision to take on Peter Grace and the Grace "cronies," as he called them, directly.

16

Disintegration

Patrick P. Grace was puzzled when he received an urgent call from Mr. Bolduc on November 8, 1994. Although Patrick had worked for the Grace company in a variety of roles since 1977 and had been the general manager of Grace Logistic Services in Greenville, South Carolina since 1991, he did not report directly to the CEO and had only infrequent contact with Bolduc. He was also suspicious. Having watched Bolduc's moves over the past several months, Patrick did not have a high regard for his father's presumptive successor. J.P. Bolduc told Patrick Grace in their 45-minute "election day" conversation that Patrick's older brother, J. Peter Grace III had inappropriately diverted hundreds of thousand of dollars of Grace company funds from a Grace subsidiary managed by Peter Grace III to an unrelated corporation which Peter Grace III controlled. Mr. Bolduc stated that he wanted to "protect" the elder Mr. Grace by keeping him "out of the loop" and thus Bolduc's need to communicate with the Grace family through Patrick.

Bolduc stressed to Patrick that Peter Grace III's conduct would probably result in criminal proceedings and would have to be disclosed in the company's next proxy statement because it involved a member of Mr. Grace's family. Patrick knew that W.R. Grace & Co. planned to sell its subsidiary, Grace Hotel Services Corp. to HSC Holding Co., a corporation which his brother, Peter, had formed for that purpose. He asked Bolduc for more details and Bolduc promised to furnish Patrick with a copy of the internal memorandum that explained how transactions between Grace Hotel Services Corp. and HSC were to be handled. Bolduc asserted that Peter Grace III had violated those procedures in a blatant and criminal manner. In essence, Bolduc was calling Peter Grace's

son and namesake a thief and threatening to have him prosecut-
ed and embarrass the Grace family by airing the matter publicly
in Grace's 1995 proxy materials. In Bolduc's view, of course, he
had no alternatives. As he later stated, "...his [Mr. Grace's] son
embezzled money in the company and I didn't hesitate but to fire
him..."

The next day, November 9, Grace's executive vice president, J.
P. Neeves and its general counsel, R.H. Beber, confronted Peter
Grace III, gave him less than an hour to consult an attorney, and
forced his resignation. Patrick Grace, at Mr. Bolduc's request, met
with Mr. Beber, Grace chief inhouse lawyer at Grace headquarters
in Boca Raton, Florida. Patrick again asked for the internal memorandum which Peter Grace III was alleged to have violated and
other relevant documents, and about a week later, Peter Grace
demanded the documents, which had still not been produced as
promised, from Mr. Beber. In response, Beber and Bolduc arrived
in Mr. Grace's office in Boca Raton and told the chairman of the
board that since the matter involved his son, he could not see the
documents. This was necessary, they argued, for his own protection. Although weakened by advancing cancer, Mr. Grace dismissed their patronizing advice and sought counsel from his long
time friend and fellow Grace board member, Bob Macauley, who
acted as an intermediary between Bolduc and Mr. Grace. It was
clear to Macauley that what Bolduc was after was Mr. Grace's
immediate resignation from the board of directors.

The Monday after Thanksgiving, the audit committee of the
Grace board of directors met in New York and reviewed matters
presented by Mr. Bolduc concerning the diversion of funds by
Peter Grace III and other unspecified matters relating to the board
chairman. Mr. Grace was not invited to attend, and was not copied
on the materials given to the committee, and had previously been
advised by Bolduc through Mr. Macauley not to retain a lawyer,
because it "would just escalate matters." The following day,
November 29th, Bolduc and Harold A. Eckmann, the chairman of
the audit committee, met with Bob Macauley and laid out the
committee's conclusions, which Macauley relayed to Mr. Grace
later that afternoon. The committee demanded that Mr. Grace pay
$1.5 million to the company by 5 p.m. the next day, thereby

restoring the money supposedly diverted by his son to HCS Holding Co., and resign from the board by the end of 1994. If Mr. Grace complied, the company would not be forced to disclose the embarrassing and potentially criminal conduct of Peter Grace III in its proxy materials, and it would grant Mr. Grace an extension of his $50,000 per month consulting contract for two additional years, ending in 1997. Bolduc called a special meeting of the board of directors for December 7, 1994 to announce Peter Grace's resignation.

With the clock ticking on the 5 p.m deadline on November 30, 1994, Mr. Grace met with his son Patrick and Paul Paganucci. Peter Grace was still ignorant of the precise terms of the agreement that his son, Peter III, was alleged to have violated. No one inside the company could help for fear of alienating Bolduc. It took several hours for Paganucci and Patrick Grace to persuade Peter not to surrender. Finally, they decided to retain counsel, and around 5:30 that afternoon Larry Lederman and Toni Lichstein of the prestigious firm of Milbank, Tweed, Hadley and McCloy joined the meeting. The deadline passed, and the Milbank lawyers went to work, interviewing and collecting files from Peter III, conducting research and running the scenario past the U.S. attorney's office for an informal review of any alleged criminal conduct. By the end of the week, Lederman had reached his conclusion and advised Peter Grace that his son's activities in using Grace funds to advance working capital to HSC were not remotely criminal, and that, if the funds were restored to Grace by year end, the transaction would not be reportable in the company's proxy statement. They could see no reason for Peter Grace to resign from the board of directors. On that basis Mr. Grace refused to resign, and Peter Grace III paid $1,000,000 to the company and placed an additional $381,000 in escrow for disbursement to Grace depending on the outcome of an audit of the Grace Hotel Services - HSC transactions by an independent accounting firm. Bolduc cancelled the scheduled Pearl Harbor Day board meeting.

Although not directly involved in these machinations, Gus Hampers was aware of them. During the Thanksgiving weekend, Bolduc had called Hampers and told him that he and Peter Grace had had a major confrontation, and that Peter had to go. Bolduc explained that Peter did not want the company to disclose in its next proxy certain benefits and perquisites paid to Mr. Grace. He also told Hampers that Peter Grace III had been caught with "his hand in the till," and this had to be disclosed as well. In his typical unemotional manner, Hampers advised Bolduc to do whatever the lawyers advised, disclose the perquisites in the proxy and ignore Mr. Grace. In Hampers mind, Bolduc held all the cards and could simply comply with company counsel's opinion regarding proxy disclosure. If Mr. Grace chose not to resign, Hampers told Bolduc, let it go. The chairman was dying of cancer, and it made no sense to fight Mr. Grace, if he decided to remain on the board. Bolduc had the authority to fire Peter Grace III and to disclose whatever he felt he had to in the proxy statement. Why bother trying to use these as leverage to secure the elder Peter Grace's resignation?

Soon, Hampers had what he considered several far more important issues to discuss with J.P. Bolduc. The consolidation and centralization issues were coming to a head. Ed and Ernie Lowrie had lined up the top NMC executives to demand that Gus support their position. They were prepared to resign, if he didn't. In addition, in late December after the NMC bonus awards for 1994 had already been announced, Bolduc called Hampers and informed him that he couldn't accept the preliminary earnings estimates for that year, and was shaving $450,000 off the aggregate bonus pool to be distributed among NMC executives. Not only did Hampers believe that Bolduc's numbers were wrong, but Bolduc's decision would undermine Hampers by reducing the year end bonuses that Hampers had awarded over a week before. Hampers argued, but Bolduc wouldn't back down. Hampers countered that he wanted $450,000 taken from the amount that he was to receive personally in order to make up the difference. If Bolduc stood firm on reducing the pool by $450,000, then Hampers insisted that he alone would bear the reduction. Neither would back off and the matter went unresolved.

As 1994 drew to a close, Hampers was convinced that he would be leaving NMC and Grace during the next year, and that Bolduc's management style would likely result in the resignation of NMC's top deputies as well. Most of the senior NMC managers were financially secure and approaching retirement age. If staying at NMC meant continually fighting with Grace management, Hampers knew that he and most of the others who had been with him for the past twenty or twenty-five years would leave. The only other alternative was to buy NMC back from Grace. In Hampers mind, the marriage was over.

During the remainder of December the warfare between Peter Grace and J.P. Bolduc went underground. Bolduc had the company retain the law firm of Proskauer Rose Goetz & Mendelsohn to review the opposing opinions of Grace's general counsel and the Milbank lawyers on the necessity of disclosing the transactions involving Peter Grace III. Revived to his normally feisty state, Peter Grace attended the annual banquet of the Knights of Malta, a group of Catholic lay leaders selected by the Pope, primarily for their generosity to the Church and its various charities. Mr. Grace was officially the president of the American Association of the Sovereign Military Order of Malta and a member of its board of councilors. At the event, surrounded by friends and admirers, including Bob Macauley, Peter Grace denounced Bolduc's treachery to anyone who would listen and bragged that he was about to fire him, until Macauley took Peter aside and upbraided him. "I told him he was being an asshole," the ever blunt Macauley remembered. "He called me the next morning and apologized. He really was sorry about it," Macauley stated.

The resolution of the proxy disclosure issue came before the Grace board of directors on January 5, 1995, its first meeting of the new year, a year that would turn out to be the most traumatic in the 140-year history of W.R. Grace & Co. and transformative for National Medical Care. None of the directors was happy. The dispute between Peter Grace and Bolduc was distressing, forcing reluctant directors to take sides. In the opinion of most directors even those loyal to Mr. Grace, Bolduc was doing a great job, unlocking value for the shareholders, but he had became mired in this petty dispute with the chairman. Peter Grace's health was failing, and for many members of the board who had known the irrepressible, vivacious Peter Grace for decades, seeing him devastated by cancer was upsetting. And Dr. Hampers, the head of the company's most profitable unit, had privately expressed his dissatisfaction to Bolduc and a few other close associates on the board.

At the conclusion of the normal proceedings the matter of resolving the disclosure question came before the board and both Peter Grace and J.P. Bolduc were excused from the meeting. Without the leadership of either the chairman or the chief executive officer, the board was unable to reach consensus regarding the conflicting opinions of the Proskauer firm, which not surprisingly supported Bolduc's position, and the Milbank lawyers retained by Mr. Grace. To resolve the conflict among these expert attorneys, the board decided to hire more expert attorneys. Judge Harold R. Tyler, Jr. of Patterson, Belknap, Webb and Tyler, another outstanding and expensive New York law firm, was retained to advise the board.

Judge Tyler immediately sought the written opinions of both the Proskauer firm and the Milbank attorneys. The Proskauer group delivered its memorandum on January 17, 1995, in which it substantially shifted the focus away from the diversion of funds issue involving Peter Grace III, and toward the benefits and perquisites awarded to the senior Mr. Grace from the time of his withdrawal as CEO in December 1992 through 1994. These were separate and distinct from the alleged misuse of funds and which, according to the Milbank lawyers, had been cured by the repayment during December, 1994. In turn, the Milbank firm reviewed these new issues concerning reimbursement for Mr. Grace's expenses and submitted its supplementary brief to Judge Tyler on January 27, 1995. Four days later Judge Tyler delivered his advice. Essentially he agreed with the Milbank firm and the Grace family with respect to the disclosure of the so called diversion of funds, concluding that the matter did not require disclosure.

Concerning the expenses that the company had paid for Mr. Grace, Tyler opined that non-disclosure of some of these benefits would amount to a very "aggressive position." The benefits were not insubstantial. The company was picking up the tab for Mr. Grace's nursing care which was not covered by the company's health insurance, roughly at a level of $165,000 per year. In addition, the company continued to pay $200,000 annually for security guards. Expenses to maintain the company's apartment in

New York City, which was used exclusively by Mr. Grace and his family, were about $75,000 per year. Judge Tyler's opinion on these matters was that it would be safer to disclose them in the proxy statement that would have to be mailed to Grace stockholders no later than 30 days before the May 10, 1995 annual meeting. He didn't go so far as saying that non-disclosure would be illegal, but that it would be risky.

Judge Tyler as well as the directors realized that these same benefits had not been previously disclosed in prior years and that inconsistency in disclosure policy could be problematic. The touchstone was always whether a prudent investor would consider such information relevant in deciding whether to grant or withhold his proxy. On the question of relevance, prudent investors and the attorneys advising company management could obviously disagree. In its February 2nd meeting the board adopted Judge Tyler's advice and deferred the final disposition on disclosure language until it could review a draft of the proxy statement itself in early April prior to its publication and mailing to stockholders. The Grace board of directors had investigated and resolved the matter, or so they thought. Within a few weeks the entire issue, which had consumed the energies of three outside law firms would become moot.

As the "Groundhog Day meeting," which was conducted via telephone conference call, was about to conclude, one of the directors, Gordon Humphrey, the former U.S. Senator from New Hampshire, expressed his concern that the relationship between the chairman, Mr. Grace, and Bolduc had deteriorated and posed a threat to the company's welfare. Fellow director, Roger Milliken, the 79-year old CEO of Milliken & Co., suggested that the board create and empower a committee to investigate and attempt to resolve differences between the chairman and the CEO. The committee, explained Mr. Milliken, who took himself very seriously and in Gus Hampers' recollection, "thought of himself as royalty," would continue to use the services and advice of Judge Tyler's law firm in trying to settle the "feud" between J.P. Bolduc and Peter Grace.

Several directors disagreed with Milliken's characterization and resisted the creation of the committee and the use of Judge

Tyler. Mr. Macauley, who had known Peter Grace for decades, and who also thought Bolduc "was doing a hell of a job," could see no good coming of spending even more money on lawyers to make the judgments that the directors were responsible for making. The board had done its job in resolving the proxy disclosure issue, Macauley and others argued, and having a committee investigate the so called feud would only exacerbate the situation and threaten and upset the company's senior staff. Mr. Grace had been asked not to attend the February board meeting, so his advice was neither given or sought. Nonetheless, Milliken prevailed, and a six member committee with Mr. Eckmann as its chairman was created. During the month of February, 1995 the committee and lawyers from Patterson, Belknap, Webb & Tyler started digging. What they uncovered did nothing to suppress the "feud" and threw the company into turmoil.

The board opened up a process which encouraged anyone at Grace who had a grudge against either Mr. Grace or Mr. Bolduc to bring the matter to the attention of Judge Tyler. The committee and its independent attorneys insured the confidentiality of these sources, and the subjects, namely Bolduc and Grace, weren't permitted to cross examine the complainants, or respond to charges in any meaningful way. One accusation or complaint led the investigators to others. Because he had brought a great deal of change and was at the top of the hierarchy, the allegations were directed at J.P. Bolduc. Mr. Grace was no longer a factor in the lives of Grace employees and there was a general respect for Peter Grace and great sorrow regarding his illness. In short order the "feud investigation" became an accumulation of grievances against the CEO.

Many would say Bolduc had made the porridge he was forced to eat. He was perceived as arrogant and untrustworthy. At the same time, any CEO that pursues a course of selling and closing divisions and cutting expenses is not likely to win popularity contests, except, of course with the stockholders who stood to benefit from these changes. By the end of February, the board committee and Judge Tyler had amassed a long indictment against Bolduc. Several key operating executives at Grace units registered their lack of confidence in Bolduc's management. Bolduc's ownership interests in non-Grace businesses bothered the committee. There were specific but unproven charges of conflicts of interest. However, the issue that truly galvanized the committee's attention was a pattern of alleged sexual harassment by Bolduc.

Five women told the Tyler committee that they had been physically harassed by J.P. Bolduc. None of these women had filed a grievance or formal complaint and none of them intended to. They were assured by the committee that their identities would not be revealed. Nonetheless, the volume of incidents (some women complained of multiple incidents) and the credibility of these employees impressed the committee. Subsequently two of the five women were interviewed by reporters for Time magazine on an anonymous basis, and in its April 17, 1995 issue Time published their allegations as well as Bolduc's vehement denial. One woman reportedly told Judge Tyler that when she bent over to put his coffee cup on a table, he reached over and ran his hand up her leg. Another Grace female employee recounted an incident when she and Bolduc were in an elevator together and he reached over and put his hand on her derriere. This same woman recalled watching Bolduc stick his tongue successively into the ears of two women as he was leaving a business meeting. Later, one board member found the "tongue story" bizarre. "Either she was leaning very close to J.P., or he has the longest tongue in the world," the director observed.

On Mardi Gras, February 28, 1995, the board of directors met in executive session at Tyler's office to hear the report from the committee and Judge Tyler. Mr. Grace was asked to absent himself from the meeting again, but Mr. Bolduc was invited to address the directors on the pending matters. Bolduc refused and asked to be represented at the meeting by his lawyer, a request the board denied. The special committee recommended on a vote of five to one to seek Bolduc's resignation as CEO. Judge Tyler and his associates agreed with the majority, and the board of directors adopted a resolution to sever the relationship between the company and J.P. Bolduc. The board appointed a three man committee to negotiate the terms of a severance agreement with Bolduc, and adjourned until Thursday morning, March 2, 1995, when the board would reconvene in its regular session at the Boca Raton headquarters.

In its Mardi Gras resolution, the Grace board did not terminate Bolduc for cause. The directors were bound to respect the privacy of the complainants, yet by denying Bolduc the right to know who had accused him so that he could defend himself, the directors failed to substantiate just cause for the termination. If they ignored the allegations and the recommendations of the committee and a retired federal judge who had interviewed the accusers, they could be inviting a lawsuit from the alleged victims and be exposing the company to massive litigation in the future should Bolduc continue in his alleged offensive behavior. Conversely, if they fired the well respected CEO without cause, they'd have a messy lawsuit on their hands from Bolduc and many unhappy and perplexed shareholders. The Mardi Gras resolution essentially empowered the committee of three to buy Bolduc off. No one was confident that Bolduc would take a settlement and withdraw quietly. The board had no strategy to counter Bolduc's demands or the inevitable inquiries of the large institutional investors and Wall Street analysts.

Bolduc was smart. If he played his hand smartly, he could have it both ways. He'd temporarily retreat with a large severance award, quietly marshall his supporters in the investment community to force Mr. Grace and "his cronies" off the board, and return to the CEO position at Grace with a new board of directors and a vengeance.

As the March 2nd meeting convened, the tension in the board room in Boca Raton was palpable. The last thing the board wanted was a continuation and escalation of the hostilities that had dominated the company's business for the last three months. So there was a collective, long sigh of genuine relief when the three man special committee composed of George C. Dacey, Roger Milliken, and John A. Puelicher (the one member of the "feud investigation committee" who had opposed the Mardi Gras resolution) proudly reported to the board that they had secured a written termination agreement from J.P. Bolduc during a late night negotiating session that had ended just a few hours before. They did not explain why the negotiation took so long, since they had capitulated in every respect to Bolduc's demands. They asked the board to endorse the terms, which it readily did with only one dissenting vote.

The company would pay Mr. Bolduc $5 million to terminate his employment contract. This was virtually unavoidable, since Bolduc had secured a contract, which Peter Grace had executed for the company, that required Grace to continue to pay Bolduc, even if he had been terminated for cause, so long as the validity of that cause was being litigated and appealed. In addition, Grace would repurchase his 270,000 shares of Grace common stock, valued at about $12 million. Bolduc was also granted an additional $1.3 million in incentive compensation and $1.5 million in deferred compensation. On top of this immediate $19.8 million buyout, Bolduc would be entitled to receive his pension valued at $848,000 per year (plus healthcare insurance then valued at $3,312 per year) for the rest of his life (he was then 55 years old and the immediate value of this pension based on actuarial tables was $22.8 million). In exchange, Mr. Bolduc waived any legal rights he might have against the company. No further services were required. Finally and significantly, the company agreed that the termination would be characterized as a mutually satisfactory separation without cause, and Bolduc would have the right to approve the company's press release on the subject. In fact, he and his lawyer reportedly wrote the press release, which stated that the company accepted the CEO's resignation "with regret" and that it resulted from "differences in style and philosophy." The board members were cautioned about not commenting about Bolduc's departure beyond the press release, and the directors agreed to keep matters quiet.

The lone dissenter was Bob Macauley, who refused to endorse paying Bolduc a bonus for leaving. He also privately denounced the subterfuge of mischaracterizing the reasons for the termination. Three weeks after the March 2nd meeting in a private letter to a few selected Grace directors, which was later disclosed by an anonymous source to, and published by, The New York Times, Macauley stated, "Never in my recollection has there been an 'extra' given to an individual who was being discharged for cause...It would appear to me (and many others) that we are living a lie when we do not come forward with the truth...we do not even know how long we are supposed to perpetuate this lie."

As the events unfolded on March 2, Dr. Hampers was already thinking ahead. Bolduc's fate had been decided a few days before. The important question now was what would happen to National Medical Care. His interest in buying NMC back from Grace was already known by several directors and certainly by Bolduc and his top lieutenants on the company's staff. With the assistance of Terry Daniels, who, after leaving Grace, had started Quad-C, a successful investment company in Charlottesville, Virginia, Hampers was assembling financial commitments to repurchase NMC if that became necessary. Now, however, an easier route opened up. For the first time Hampers saw that with Bolduc's departure he could assume control of Grace and its NMC subsidiary without risking a dime. He decided to be a candidate to replace Bolduc as CEO. As he said in an interview later, "Knowing what I know about the company and where it can go and the value we can unlock, I decided I want to do it. I certainly don't need the money."

Hampers tossed these ideas around in his head as Peter Grace returned to his seat as chairman of the Grace board toward the conclusion of the March 2nd meeting, welcomed back with a standing ovation from the 22-member board, which he had hand-picked, but from which Mr. Grace had been sequestered for the past three months, while the board grappled with the resolution of the "feud" between himself and Mr. Bolduc. Peter Grace thanked the board for its fair resolution and diligence and then offered his regrets for having chosen and promoted J.P. Bolduc as his successor. The board voted to appoint the 71-year old Thomas A. Holmes, one of the members of the board and the retired CEO of Ingersoll Rand Co., to serve as "acting president and CEO." Mr. Grace retained his position as chairman of the board of directors. None of the directors failed to observe Mr. Grace's weakened condition. The cancer and the emotional turmoil were clearly taking their toll. Hamper's physician's eye, however, told him that Mr. Grace was in extreme danger. He had to be hospitalized as soon as possible.

Hampers left the meeting and called his administrative assistant at NMC headquarters in Massachusetts. Laura Baker had been an employee of NMC since 1980 and had been Dr. Hampers' administrative assistant for over a decade. She was responsible for arranging the complicated logistics involved in making sure Dr. Hampers' jet and its crew were ready, wherever and whenever he was. She was also accustomed to making sudden and frequent changes in these arrangements and following Hampers' instructions without comment or delay. Hampers told her that he needed to use Mr. Bolduc's Gulfstream IV jet, which was considerably larger and better equipped than Hampers' plane, to get the ailing Mr. Grace back to New York City and St. Vincent's Hospital, as soon as the board meeting was over. He told her that "Mr. Bolduc won't be needing it anymore," and instructed her to have Bolduc's pilot prepare the plane at the West Palm Beach airport for Dr. Hampers and Mr. Grace and to secure the necessary clearances for the trip back to New York.

Before the meeting ended, director Roger Milliken took a telephone call from J. P. Bolduc of all people. He returned to the board room enraged and accused Hampers of breaking the board's pledge not to leak the news of Bolduc's resignation. Once the word that Bolduc "didn't need the CEO's plane" bounced from Hampers to Laura Baker to Bolduc's pilot, it took only a few minutes to filter back to employees loyal to Mr. Bolduc. Bolduc later said, "Dr. Hampers broke out of that board meeting to call Brian McGowan's office to make sure that my plane...was started up and cooled off for him, because he knew that I was going to be out and he wanted his quote unquote plane ready to go...I called one of the senior directors and told him what had just taken place." Hampers was non-plussed, and felt no need to defend himself for acting out of concern for Peter's health. He wasn't in the habit of explaining his medical judgment to a group of laymen, nor was he comfortable discussing someone's medical condition in public with or without the patient present. Virginia Kamsky, a Grace director who was present at the meeting and who hitched a ride on the Gulfstream IV back to New York with Mr. Grace and Dr. Hampers after the session, believed that Hampers gave no thought to the appearance his "confiscating" Bolduc's airplane would have to the other directors. "Gus could not understand what these guys were so upset about," she recalled. It was not an auspicious beginning for

Hampers' CEO candidacy, but it did endear him to Mr. Grace and his family.

The board decided to issue the press release concerning Bolduc's departure after the stock market closed in New York on Thursday, March 2, 1995. The news was not well received. It didn't take long for the institutional investors to air their complaints publicly, to disregard the euphemisms in the press release about "regrets" and "differences of style and philosophy," and to blame the severance on J. Peter Grace. Reading between the lines with some tutoring from Bolduc and his loyalists, these investors and analysts initially believed that Mr. Grace had cowed his aging and subservient board to purge Bolduc for irrational and personal reasons. What else could "differences of style and philosophy" mean? And for their part, these investors liked Bolduc's style and philosophy, since it had increased shareholder value. Acting CEO Holmes and the Grace press operation would not elaborate or explain the reasons beyond the press release. An information vacuum was created, and the vacuum was filled in short order by accounts favorable to J. P. Bolduc and hostile to Mr. Grace and the Grace board. On every side lawyers were poised, ready to pounce at the slightest provocation or sign of weakness.

In its March 3rd report on the Bolduc departure, The Wall Street Journal characterized the resignation in the first paragraph as "abrupt," and in the next sentence stated, "Though the company didn't say so, that [differences with Grace leadership] would appear to refer to J. Peter Grace, 81 years old, the company's high profile chairman..." This first report of the Grace transition, which would soon be referred to increasingly by the press as a "turmoil," went on to say that the company would form a committee of directors to search for a permanent CEO "both inside and outside the company." Within a few days Kenneth N. Gilpin, writing for The New York Times reported that the College Retirement Equities Fund ("CREF"), which then owned about 8.4% of the Grace common stock (approximately 7.9 million shares, valued at $356 million), had expressed its concern over Bolduc's resignation and the dearth of information regarding his departure to Mr. Holmes in a letter dated March 3, 1995, and in that letter had requested a meeting with Mr. Holmes, who personally did not have a major stockholding in the company, and Mr. Grace. In the first sentence of his report, Gilpin also describes the resignation as "abrupt," and ends the article with a forecast of a proxy fight: "But analysts who have talked to the biggest shareholders said they would not be surprised if a new slate of directors, a group including Mr. Bolduc, might be proposed to replace the retiring group at the company's annual meeting on May 10."

At that time the Grace board consisted of 22 directors and their terms on the board were staggered, in order to ensure some measure of continuity, much like the U.S. Senate, so that each year the stockholders were entitled to elect a slate of seven or eight directors. In 1995 there were eight directors whose terms were expiring and who would either be reelected or replaced. It was this group of eight directors that Gilpin incorrectly characterized in the article as "retiring,." They weren't "retiring" in the sense of being shy, or of being old (although six of the eight were over 70), or of not seeking reelection. Pursuant to its bylaws, the Grace annual meeting would be held on the second Wednesday in May, which in 1995 fell on May 10.

Under the rules of the Securities and Exchange Commission that governed companies with publicly traded stock, a non-management, stockholder proposal that would solicit shareholders' proxies for the May 10 election had to be filed with the company and the SEC no later than sixty days prior to the meeting, or by March 11, 1995 (effectively, March 10, since March 11 was a Saturday), a date that was fast approaching following the Bolduc announcement. The company could then decide whether to include the proposal in its proxy materials to be sent a month later to the stockholders, or to allow the challengers to mail it to the stockholders directly by giving them the stockholder list. Only the management of the company had control over the stockholder list and hence the exclusive means to communicate with the owners of the company who would vote in the annual election. If it were not already aware of the possibility of a competing slate of director nominees being filed by unhappy investors, Grace management certainly took note of the shot fired across its bow in The New York Times article of March 6, 1995.

The Grace board hastily convened a telephonic conference

on Thursday, March 9, a week after it had approved the Bolduc severance terms. The Bolduc resignation had been a public relations disaster, and the company's institutional investors were besieging Grace officers directly and through the media for an explanation beyond "differences in style and philosophy." This was a new phenomenon for the Grace board which had always been insulated by its chairman and former CEO from scrutiny and criticism. In former times the affable, self-assured J. Peter Grace would have been able to handle the major stockholders, the press and the Wall Street analysts in an afternoon. Hospitalized immediately after the March 2nd meeting, Mr. Grace was too ill to contend with the controversy, and the acting CEO, Tom Holmes, was unsure of his authority and afraid to act without a cadre of lawyers pointing the way. The reporters and portfolio managers smelled a story and would not be shut out. Holmes did meet with a group of angry institutional stockholders, who collectively held about 35% of Grace common stock, on Wednesday, March 8, but they were not reassured. In the telephone conference with other board members the following day, Holmes sought their approval of his decision to engage the law firm of Wachtell Lipton Rosen & Katz and the services of Martin Lipton and his partner Bernie Nussbaum (the former chief White House lawyer). As The Wall Street Journal commented a few days later, "Wachtell's Martin Lipton is sometimes brought in by beseiged [sic] management." Shareholders were threatening lawsuits as well as demanding the resignations of Peter Grace and a majority of the Grace board. Several insisted that Bolduc be reinstated immediately.

While Holmes, Lipton and Nussbaum were conferring with the directors, Tom Burton, a reporter from The Wall Street Journal, called Grace headquarters and advised Holmes and the others that the Journal would run a front page story the next morning, Friday, March 10, 1995, stating that Bolduc had resigned from Grace as a result of irreconcilable differences with Mr. Grace over disclosure of his perks and his son's use of company assets. Burton, who also indicated to Holmes that he had heard from a Grace director that Bolduc had been accused of sexual harassment, was seeking comment from Holmes and other board members on the story. Management declined to participate, despite the fact that it was clear that the version of the story that would be on page one that next morning would be most favorable to Bolduc and would embarrass the Grace family and put the Grace directors even more clearly on the defensive. These were precisely the matters that the board had decided not to disclose after months of consultation with three separate, costly law firms. Rather than have the disclosure tucked away in a fine print footnote to a remuneration table in the company's proxy statement, it would now be on page one of The Wall Street Journal. Bolduc had trumped them.

The March 10th article in The Wall Street Journal, written by Tom Burton, James Miller and Randall Smith, blew up the bunker in which the Grace directors had hidden during the week after Bolduc's resignation. Except for a comment by Charles Erhart, Jr., the company's former president and a member of its then-current board, concerning allegations of sexual harassment against Bolduc - a comment which Erhart later denied making - the article could not have been more favorable to J.P. Bolduc if he had written it himself. It began by referencing the Grace Commission's assault on wasteful spending by the federal government and followed with "Some say J. Peter Grace's company could use the same advice." The authors cited "[d]ocuments obtained by The Wall Street Journal indicate that Mr. Grace...and his son, J. Peter Grace III, have been the personal beneficiaries of hundreds of thousands of dollars in company expenditures and perquisites that the company didn't disclose." In retrospect the company's refusal to tell its side of the story to Burton seems astonishing and reckless.

The Journal article of March 10th led the reader through the events of the previous fall and winter and portrayed J. P. Bolduc as a noble martyr. The story laid bare all the facts of the transactions that had resulted in the resignation of Peter Grace III in November 1994 and his repayment of approximately $1.3 million to the company. It then went on to describe the benefits and perks awarded to the senior Peter Grace and his adamant refusal to have these disclosed in the company's SEC filings, stating:

Those perks and the younger Mr. Grace's business dealings recently helped spark a heated internal debate pitting the elder Mr. Grace against the company's president and CEO, J. P. Bolduc. It culminated suddenly a week ago in Mr. Bolduc's resignation, attributed by the company to 'differences of style and philosophy.'

The report quoted a former Grace executive, Jack Shelton, "The very things the Grace Commission said about the government were true within Grace. The corporate culture had gotten mired down, lazy and fat," and characterized the Grace directors as acolytes of the senior Mr. Grace "Many of Grace's board members are retired executives who are longtime associates of the chairman.." and printed a sidebar containing the names, ages, and occupations of the 22-member board. Fourteen directors were over 70 years of age.

Charles Erhart, Jr., who later complained that he was tricked by the reporters into making his negative comments about Mr. Bolduc, attempted to assert the company's position, and made it much worse. He was reported to have told the journalists that the board had learned of allegations of sexual harassment against Bolduc and that, although these women did not want their identities revealed, the board "overwhelmingly decided the allegations were significant enough to warrant asking for Mr. Bolduc's resignation." Through his lawyer, Gerald Walpin, Mr. Bolduc refused to comment on these allegations for the Journal story. What was not reported, presumably because Erhart did not reveal the fact, was that the allegations had been investigated by Judge Tyler and found by him to be credible and that Tyler and his associates agreed that these allegations warranted Bolduc's departure. That fact would have been significant if reported in the March 10th article, because throughout the article the reporters approvingly cite the independent conclusions of Judge Tyler with respect to the benefit disclosure issues.

Erhart's tentative and abbreviated version of the sexual harassment charges made them appear as convenient and libelous excuses. An unnamed "person close to Mr. Bolduc" described the allegations in the article as "an attempt to sling mud on him [Bolduc]." Mr. Erhart later said that he had never spoken with a Journal reporter, and that denial was parenthetically noted in the article: "(When Mr. Erhart was called again later at the same home phone number, he denied having ever spoken to a Wall Street

Journal reporter.)" The lack of any company statement, the unspecified allegations against Bolduc and the denial by Erhart that he had even spoken to a reporter, all lent credence to the Bolduc version. An objective observer reading the March 10th Journal article would have had to conclude that Mr. Grace caused his subservient board to fire Bolduc because the CEO wanted to reveal Mr. Grace's perks and the use of Grace funds by his son. Even the disclosure of Bolduc's $20 million "exit package" implied that the board was willing to use company assets to purchase Bolduc's silence. It wasn't even slightly credible that a board would pay $20 million to a man who had sexually harassed company employees.

Bolduc's image had been buffed to a sheen just shy of sainthood. Like Archibald Cox's defiance of President Nixon, J.P. Bolduc was standing on the principled pedestal of full public disclosure and accountability, and, like Cox, he had paid for his principles by losing his job. What the board clearly needed was a public relations expert to get the company's story out in an expedited, convincing and sympathetic manner. Instead, what it chose to do was hire more lawyers. The lawyers from the Wachtell firm representing Grace negotiated with attorneys from the firm of Debevoise & Plimpton who had been retained by CREF. A group of institutional investors had assembled a slate of nominees to run against the board approved slate of nominees for election to the eight directorships that would be filled at the May 10, 1995 annual stockholders meeting. The leader of that group of potential nominees was J.P. Bolduc. With support from these major shareholders, Bolduc planned to get himself and seven others elected to the board. The deadline on filing the proposed slate would expire at the end of business on Friday, March 10, 1995.

Dr. Hampers learned of Bolduc's plans to lead a dissident slate of director nominees from Patrick Grace who had called him on March 10th after failing to connect with acting CEO Holmes. A former Grace employee, who had been asked to run for election to the board on the Bolduc slate and who had declined, had relayed this information to Patrick Grace. Through Hampers' intercession with Mr Holmes, Patrick relayed this news to the Wachtell lawyers on the afternoon of March 10.

Nothing happened. The deadline passed, and no alternate

slate of director nominees was filed or proposed. It's hard to imagine that the Bolduc investor group let the deadline pass voluntarily or without concessions from Grace. It would take only a few days for the public to learn what the company had surrendered to forestall the competition.

On Monday, March 13th, The Wall Street Journal broke the next installment of the saga in reporting that "according to people familiar with the situation" Grace was prepared to change its corporate bylaws to reduce the size of its board of directors and to bar anyone over the age of 70 from serving on its board. The effect would be to eliminate Mr. Grace and thirteen of his "cronies," as Bolduc has described these directors. If the report were accurate, it would indicate that Grace management capitulated on the issue of governance. The power of this unconfirmed rumor was strong enough to send the price of the Grace common stock soaring to new highs. The price rose 15% during the week of March 5-10 to a 52-week high of $48.50 per share. The speculation was fueled by a belief that change in the form of new management, the ouster of Mr. Grace, or even the break up or sale of Grace would all result in increased stockholder value. For CREF, one of the largest institutional investors, this 15% increase in the Grace stock price translated into roughly a $50 million rise in its portfolio value in a week. The comments of Andrea L. Schaefer, an analyst for UBS Securities, in the "Heard on the Street" column in The Wall Street Journal were typical: "the situation has gone so far that the current board and management leadership cannot continue."

These investors and analysts were particularly bullish about the increased value that would accompany the break-up of Grace, particularly the sale or spin off of National Medical Care, its most profitable subsidiary. Bloomberg Business News reported that once the bylaws were changed and the Grace loyalists removed, the institutional investors would insist that the company spin off National Medical Care. "If the right people gain control of the board, I think that's a likely possibility," Jeffrey Cianci, an analyst with Bear Stearns & Co. was quoted in the Fort Lauderdale Sunday Sentinel, the hometown newspaper of Grace headquarters in Florida. In the same article an "analyst who asked not to [sic] identified" stated, "The only way I think the stock could fall is if the Old Guard gets in control."

There was no question who "the Old Guard" referred to. It not only included Mr. Grace and his hand picked buddies on the Grace board, but Gus Hampers and his supporters, like Gordon Humphrey and Virginia Kamsky as well. If Dr. Hampers gained control, he would not be tempted to sell or spin off NMC, since that was his creation and his power base. Given the run up in value of the Grace stock on the speculation that NMC would be alienated by Grace, it was clearly in the financial interests of these investors, as they perceived them at least in the short term, to prevent Mr. Grace from retaining control, or Gus Hampers from assuming control, of the corporation.

In the negotiations with acting CEO Holmes and the Grace lawyers, the big investor group had clearly set their priorities. Dr. Hampers, a man who had aggressively supported Bolduc's divestiture strategies even when these conflicted with Mr. Grace, and an entrepreneur whose ability to unlock value for shareholders through vigorous cost cutting and focusing capital on its most productive uses, was mischaracterized as part of the "Old Guard." As events unfolded during the month of March 1995, Hampers became a stalking horse for the Grace family in the minds of Wall Street observers. Mr. Bolduc's former ally was transformed into Bolduc's archrival, even though Hampers had advised Bolduc the previous November to disclose the Grace family perks without so much as a "by your leave" from Peter Grace. Without any supporting evidence (except Hampers' confiscation of the CEO's plane on March 2 in order to transport Peter Grace to St Vincent's Hospital as quickly and painlessly as possible) Hampers became known as "Peter Grace's man." As Terry Daniels, who knew all the players better than anyone, later said, "He [Hampers] is less of a Peter man than Bolduc is, by a massive margin. He is probably the least of the Peter men on that board of directors. He is nobody's man. He never tried to be part of the 'club.' " Still, the goal of the institutional investors and portfolio managers was clear. Business Week quoted an unnamed "institutional shareholder" as stating, "Our primary objective is that Gus Hampers not get the job [as CEO]."

On St. Patrick's Day, March 17, 1995, just two weeks after

Bolduc's resignation was announced and a week after the devastating Wall Street Journal article, the Grace board convened a special meeting in New York, and on a divided vote with only nine directors in favor, six opposed and six directors either abstaining or absent (by that date the board had 21 active members, since the 22nd seat, formerly held by J.P. Bolduc, was then vacant), the board accepted the bylaw changes which Martin Lipton and his Wachtell partners and associates had negotiated with the institutional investors. These changes included a reduction in the size of the board from 22 to 12 members, and the disqualification of all Grace family members, including Peter Grace, from serving on the board of directors. The directors also agreed that the new CEO would have the right to replace up to six of the remaining twelve directors. Peter Grace's tenure on the board would thereby end at the May 10th annual meeting and the new 12-member board would consist of six directors hand picked by the new CEO. In The Wall Street Journal article of March 20, 1997 which reported these changes, the institutional investors again made it clear whom they did not want as that new CEO. Representatives of David J. Greene & Co., one such major stockholder, urged the board to consider separting NMC from Grace immediately, as it "would greatly clarify and simplify" the selection of the next CEO, that is, it would rule Hampers out. As Randall Smith and James Miller wrote in that same article, with Peter Grace forced out, the board could either appoint an outsider as CEO or "seriously consider two possibilities already on the scene"- Bolduc or Hampers.

Whether wittingly or not, Bolduc and his stockholder supporters had attained two of their three goals. First, they had cast Bolduc as the victim of Peter Grace's egomania and, as such, the champion of Grace shareholders, and second, they had removed Mr. Grace and ensured that the next CEO would control the board. And if they hadn't yet attained their third objective - the invalidation of Gus Hampers from consideration as the next CEO - they were within striking distance. Some would argue that the board leadership had already agreed with the institutional investors by the time of the St. Patrick's Day meeting that Hampers was not a viable candidate, but the evidence of such an understanding is purely circumstantial. Certainly no board leader was contradicting the criticism of Hampers, even though he had consistently out produced every other Grace executive year in and year out. And Board leaders assured Hampers that he was a viable candidate for the CEO position and should not rock the boat.

During this period, Paul Paganucci, who knew that the institutional investors' opposition to Hampers was based on misconceptions and unfamiliarity with his record of achievement and experiences, advised Hampers to ask acting CEO Holmes to arrange a meeting between Hampers and these major stockholders. Holmes refused, saying it would be an unusual procedure and unhelpful. Hampers acquiesced, although it seemed in hindsight that such a meeting could not have made matters worse for Hampers than they already were. Later, Dr. Hampers would wonder why Holmes did not want him to meet with these shareholders. On March 17 the "smart money" would have wagered not only that Hampers would not be selected as the next CEO of Grace, but that J.P. Bolduc would succeed himself as CEO after a break of a few weeks, and this time without a board of "Grace cronies."

It wasn't clear what the Grace board and its management had received in return for changing the bylaws, ousting Mr. Grace, concealing the reasons for Bolduc's departure, and retiring at least ten, and possibly sixteen, members of the 22-member board. They hadn't bought peace with the institutional investors who were now demanding a breakup of the 140-year old company. They had invited further interference from Wall Street in their CEO selection process. They certainly had not stabilized the environment for Grace employees who were still split between the Bolduc and anti-Bolduc forces. They hadn't secured the blessings of the SEC, which had started an investigation, and they hadn't even forestalled stockholder lawsuits. Derivative actions were already being prepared which would challenge both the legitimacy of the perks paid to Mr. Grace and the severance award granted to Mr. Bolduc. As the result of hiring three major outside law firms - four, if one counted the Milbank firm hired by Mr. Grace - Grace management found itself in a far worse predicament on St Patrick's Day than anyone had ever imagined on the prior Thanksgiving when all the furor began.

17

The End Game

J.P. Bolduc's plans for a McArthur like return to the CEO suite in Boca Raton was sabotaged by a front page story in the business section of The New York Times on March 30, 1995. Written by Diana B. Henriques and based on a leaked copy of the draft of the company's preliminary proxy statement, which had not yet been approved by the board of directors, and a similarly leaked letter from director Bob Macauley to acting CEO Holmes, the Times article revealed the facts behind the resignation of Bolduc on March 2, 1995, including Judge Tyler's report to the board, finding that "grounds existed to find that Mr. Bolduc had sexually harassed certain employees of the company." This, now, was the third reason advanced publicly for Bolduc's departure. The first reason, mutually announced on March 2, was "differences in style and philosophy;" the second, instigated by Bolduc and published first in The Wall Street Journal on March 10, was revenge by Mr. Grace's sycophantic board for Bolduc's insistence on disclosing Grace's perks; and this third version, "absolutely, categorically, unequivocally and vehemently" denied by Bolduc, set forth in Grace's preliminary proxy, was sexual harassment of several female employees. Mr. Bolduc and his lawyer not only denied that Bolduc had engaged in sexual misconduct, but that such allegations were the reason that he resigned from the company. Yet, Gus Hampers has stated, "There's no question that the board would never have demanded Bolduc's resignation except for the sexual harassment charges."

The third installment transformed the Bolduc-Grace story from one that mainly interested the financial community to one that also involved the larger social and political community, drawing comments from the National Organization for Women and other women's civil rights groups. As Ms. Henriques wrote in the March 30th story, "The case appears to be the first time that a major American corporation has cited sexual harassment complaints as the explanation for a chief executive's resignation..." Still, by paying Bolduc $20 million and initially obfuscating the sexual misconduct charges as the cause of his termination, the Grace company failed to win over its natural allies in the feminist community. Thus, Kim Gandy of NOW was quoted in Newsweek magazine, "Sexual harassment may have occurred, but the motivation for action against [Bolduc] clearly came from elsewhere."

In addition, when the company finally acknowledged that sexual harassment charges forced the CEO's resignation, the company was essentially admitting that its bogus press release of March 2, 1995 was "inoperative," to use a word popularized by President Nixon's press secretary, as successive waves of disclosure invalidated prior explanations. There's no convincing rationale for having told the public on March 2, 1995 that Bolduc's resignation was over "differences," and less than a month later admitting that it was because of allegations of sexual harassment. One possible rationale, and the rationale cited by Bolduc and his attorney, was that it was the company's attempt to punish Bolduc for having fostered the story that he was forced out because he "blew the whistle" on Peter Grace. Gerald Walpin, Bolduc's attorney, was quoted in Time magazine, "After Mr. Bolduc responsibly acted as a corporate officer [in reference to his attempt to enforce the proxy disclosure rules], suddenly charges were made, when there had never been a complaint [of harassment] before."

Under this asserted theory, the company would never have published the sexual harassment charges in its proxy if the public had accepted the simple "differences" explanation. Such an explanation is convincing only if the proxy rules would not have required disclosure of Bolduc's resignation. On the other hand, if the proxy rules required disclosure of the allegations that lay behind Bolduc's forced resignation, then Bolduc's subsequent conduct and the press speculations were irrelevant. Both Bolduc and the Grace board had experienced, knowledgeable corporate lawyers advising them on March 2, yet they seemed to ignore the proxy disclosure problem. The rules certainly didn't change between March 2 and March 30, yet in agreeing to advise the public that Bolduc's resignation was about "differences," both sides were denying that the sexual harassment charges would ever see the light of day.

In a twist of irony, the SEC proxy disclosure requirements, which J.P. Bolduc had tried to use as a weapon to remove Peter Grace from the board of directors, had revealed unsavory allegations about the former CEO and essentially prevented him from reasserting his claim to once again take over the leadership of Grace. Despite Bolduc's high regard among the large Grace stockholders and financial analysts, after the March 30th revelations, none of them continued to promote his return to the position of CEO, and his chances of running any other major corporation in the future became minute. By the mid-1990's allegations of sexual misconduct in the workplace, even if strongly denied and never proven, tainted the prospects of businessmen like J. P. Bolduc from ever again entering the executive suites of public companies.

The March 30th article in The New York Times did not, however, end the rampant speculation, largely repeated in The Wall Street Journal, that the Grace board was trying to cover up the perks that had been paid to the retiring chairman, and that Bolduc was dismissed because he fought to disclose these benefits. One board member, Gordon Humphrey, the former U.S. Senator from New Hampshire, stated in the Times story, "there has been no discord on the board" regarding the disclosure of the perks, and that the Grace board adopted Judge Tyler's opinion, "without a single dissenting voice." Yet, a week later, on April 4, the Journal, in an article that focused on the stale news that the U.S. Food and Drug Administration was pressuring National Medical Care to resolve quality control problems at its manufacturing plants, still reported that "Mr. Bolduc resigned after clashing with J. Peter Grace, the company's longtime chairman, over what would be disclosed to shareholders about certain rich perquisites that Mr. Grace was receiving. Mr. Grace was later forced to step down as chairman." Thus, the "Bolduc version" of events surrounding his departure from Grace still had credibility with many observers. That credibility was supported by the inept manner in which the company had handled the issue and the fact that the board had paid Bolduc

$20 million in severance.

At the Grace board meeting of Thursday, April 6, 1995 in New York City, the directors ratified the bylaw changes, which had been prepared by Martin Lipton and approved by nine of the 21 directors on St. Patrick's Day, thereby reducing the board to 12 members (six of whom would be named by the future CEO), forcing all directors over the age of 70 off the board, and barring members of the Grace family from serving on the board of directors, regardless of age. In an emotional valedictory address to the board, the ailing and angry chairman assailed these changes, which he described as "offensive." Mr. Grace also took the opportunity to denounce Bolduc and his "effort...to mislead you [the directors] and attempt to embarrass me and my family, and to pressure me from retiring from the board." Peter Grace could not complete his statement, but sat down silently while his wife, Margaret, continued to read it for him. The board also approved the proxy statement draft that had been leaked to the Times and would be sent to stockholders and filed with the SEC on the following Monday, April 10, a month before the Grace annual meeting. The proxy statement disclosed the perks that had been paid to Mr. Grace since his 1992 withdrawal as CEO, and the allegations of sexual misconduct against Bolduc, which constituted grounds for seeking Mr. Bolduc's resignation, as well as including Bolduc's strong denial of these allegations.

At the suggestion of Bob Macauley, before it adjourned its April 6th meeting, the board also addressed the subject of finding a new chief executive officer. Macauley, along with others, including Peter Grace and Gordon Humphrey, was convinced that Gus Hampers deserved the position based on his experience with Grace and his proven track record at NMC. Hampers excused himself from the meeting, while Macauley and Peter Grace made the case for Hampers. Virginia Kamsky, one of the directors who participated in the discussion, was convinced that Hampers had the necessary votes for appointment at the April meeting, despite the protests of Roger Milliken, who favored the continuation of the circumspect, objective search process that had already begun to find a new CEO. As the board was moving close to ending the discussion and calling the question, Gordon Humphrey left the room to consult with Hampers, advising him that in his opinion, Hampers could win the contest if it came to a vote. Mr. Grace's support, following his moving valedictory, was having an effect on many directors, as were the logical testimonials from Macauley and other Hampers allies on the board. Dr. Hampers, too, was certain that he'd prevail if a vote were held that day, but he was concerned that, if the board abandoned the search process it had announced in early March, the unrest with the company's institutional investors would escalate, making the job of running Grace difficult, if not impossible, for Hampers. The legitimacy of his selection would become the next installment in the events at Grace which many commentators had already begun calling a "soap opera."

Hampers made a hasty, and as it turned out, an ill-considered, decision to ask the board to defer the vote and follow the selection process to its conclusion. He did so in order to legitimize his eventual appointment. He calculated no risk, only delay, and he trusted Tom Holmes and the process he had instituted, just as he had in the past trusted Terry Daniels and Mr. Grace. With the clear support of Peter Grace and a majority of the directors, Hampers had no doubt that he would be the next CEO. He just wanted his appointment to be effected according to the prescribed process.

Hampers and Humphrey returned to the board room, and Hampers asked the board to defer the vote and continue the search process. Virginia Kamsky, for one, was stunned. "Gordon Humphrey knew how to count votes. Gus had it won. I was stupefied [by his demurral]." she later recalled. Hampers had snatched delay from the jaws of victory and gave his enemies more time to organize against him.

On Patriot's Day, April 19, 1995, a few hours after the tragic bombing of the federal building in Oklahoma City, J. Peter Grace died at St. Vincent's Hospital in New York City, a fortnight after his last Grace board meeting, and five weeks short of his 82nd birthday. Mr. Grace was survived by his wife, nine children, and twenty grandchildren. He had been chairman of the Grace board continuously since 1945; death intervened to spare him the embarrassment of having to turn the chairman's gavel over to a successor. With his passing, the leadership vacuum at W.R. Grace & Co. was acute. Tom Holmes, as acting president and CEO, was barely holding things together, and the staff lacked strategic direction and day-to-day accountability. Without a strong chairman and with eight of its members headed for a quick retirement, the board of directors was beginning to fragment into factions, and this fragmentation naturally centered around the selection of Grace's next CEO.

There are three basic constituencies in every corporation that compete for attention and resources. The people who work for the corporation, its employees, consultants, and contractors, comprise one constituency. This group has all the day-to-day power and the ability to effect immediate change or not. For decades the management/employee group had become ascendant at Grace, as evidenced by the rich compensation packages, perquisites, executive airplanes, unparalleled benefit packages and consulting retainers for members of the board of directors.

Another vital constituency is ownership, comprised in the case of a publicly traded corporation like Grace of the stockholders and their proxies, the financial analysts and portfolio managers. In the Grace situation this constituency and its board champions had successfully challenged the old order, "cleansed" the board, and were trying to influence the selection of the next CEO. These owners wanted Bolduc returned, or if not Bolduc, someone who would follow his strategic plan of focusing on Grace's core businesses and returning capital to the owners in the form of stock in spun-off subsidiaries, which these owners could then sell, or by paying off corporate debt and thereby increasing stockholder equity. The consequences of these sales and spin offs on the employees and the customers of the relatively unproductive businesses were not of concern to the capitalist constituency. In their view, they had indulged Peter Grace and his megalomania and empire building long enough, and they were very happy with Bolduc's record over the past two years.

The third constituency is comprised of the people who buy the corporation's products and services, without whose loyalty and goodwill the company would fold. Often this constituency goes unrepresented at the highest levels of decision making, both in the executive suite and in the board room. In the struggle to control the appointment of a new CEO and define his or her agenda, the interests of Grace's customers had no advocate. For Grace's most productive subsidiary, National Medical Care, these "customers" were the patients and their physicians and by extension their Medicare and private insurers, who all wanted NMC to deliver high quality care at the lowest possible price. It was this unrepresented constituency that motivated Gus Hampers, already 62 years old and independently wealthy, to enter the fray. He saw a danger to NMC's patients if a strategy of tight, centralized control, similar to that attempted by Bolduc and resisted by Hampers and his NMC lieutenants, were adopted by a new CEO at Grace. He wasn't eager to spend the next several years educating a new Grace executive in the necessity of maintaining a delicate balance between quality and efficiency in the NMC clinics. Conversely, there was an even greater danger to patients, Hampers felt, if the next Grace CEO followed the stockholder demands to either spin off NMC or sell the subsidiary to the highest bidder. Nearly thirty years of experience in operating the NMC clinics taught Hampers that they had to be run as partnerships with the local medical directors, who had a "lock" on patient loyalty and referral patterns. A sale of NMC might be good for Grace stockholders, but in the long run it would be disastrous for NMC clinics, their patients and the end-stage renal disease program, whose success was largely dependent on NMC's leadership in providing quality care at low cost.

Hampers and his colleagues did not form NMC in 1968 for the benefit of the stockholders who provided the capital or of the employees and executives, who provided the labor and management, although both of these constituencies had done very well in association with NMC. Hampers had formed NMC to provide quality medical services for patients at prices that they, and their insurers could afford.

Hampers found himself without vocal and aggressive supporters for his CEO candidacy. There were no patient or physician representatives on the board of directors or its search committee. The Grace staff, particularly the executives at Grace headquarters for the most part feared Hampers. They had seen or heard about his tight fisted, penny pinching management style. His high expectations from his staff and his penchant for a "barebones" operation made these Grace executives very nervous. Nor was Gus Hampers the candidate favored by the stockholders, at least the large, vocal, portfolio managers, and they had made their opposition to Hampers public. In their minds Hampers became identified with Peter Grace and the policies of the past, but largely, their opposition was based on the fact that his appointment would clearly mean that NMC would not be sold or spun off, and hence the stock price would fall, at least in the short term.

Dr. Hampers had not analyzed his candidacy in these structural terms and then planned a strategy to win over the management and stockholder constituencies and to empower his natural constituency among the patients and the medical directors. He never campaigned for the job, made no telephone calls to board members on the subject, sought no advice or counsel from public relations experts, took no one to lunch, nor requested the aid of others who might have helped him lobby for the CEO position. Where others more skilled in political strategies, like Gordon Humphrey, would have seized the opening to advance their candidacy at the end of the April 6th Grace Board meeting while Peter Grace was ready to bless his election, Hampers failed to strike. Subsequently, trusting in the bona fides of Tom Holmes and the other Board leaders and in the obvious fact that he was the most worthy candidate based on his record of achievement, Hampers disdained campaigning for the job. Instead, Dr. Hampers viewed the opposition to his candidacy in conspiratorial terms, and adopted a flawed, clandestine approach that contributed to his defeat.

Jules Kroll was hired by Gus Hampers on March 20, 1995, after Bolduc's termination and about the time that unflattering and hostile comments were being offered about Hampers in the financial and popular press. Kroll Associates, Inc. was engaged in helping corporations investigate internal problems, such as leaks of confidential information to competitors and the press, and external threats to corporate security and goodwill. Most corporations don't regularly employ people with the skills to find the sources of security breaches, interrogate suspected miscreants, or design systems to ensure confidentiality of proprietary data. From time to time companies require these services, and Kroll was highly regarded in the field. Board member Bob Macauley first suggested in February that Grace use Kroll in its investigation of the dispute between J. P.Bolduc and J. P. Grace, but this suggestion was rejected in favor of Judge Tyler's law firm.

Hampers engaged Kroll to find out who was orchestrating the negative comments about him in the press. According to Hampers, Kroll never discovered anything concrete, and Hampers ended the engagement within three weeks, around the time of the April board meeting in New York. It's not clear why Hampers wanted to know the identity of those who were opposed to his candidacy, since any subsequent attempt on his part to discredit these hostile sources, who were presumably people within and outside Grace who were loyal to Bolduc, would appear defensive, predictable and self-serving. Hiring Kroll didn't help polish Hampers' image, especially with the septuagenarian gentlemen on the Grace board who would decide his fate. They viewed such tactics as "dirty pool." Oddly enough, Hampers himself unabashedly disclosed the story of his hiring Kroll, when called about the rumor by a Business Week writer. Not only did he see no reason to hide this fact, but Hampers handed the telephone to Jules Kroll to talk to the reporter directly, since by coincidence Kroll was with Hampers when he took the journalist's call. Once the fact that Hampers had hired Kroll became public, it quickly transformed into the false and damaging account that Hampers used Kroll to dig up all the sexual misconduct charges against Bolduc, when, in fact, Bolduc was terminated pursuant to Judge Tyler's report long before Hampers even spoke to Kroll.

By engaging Kroll, however, Gus Hampers unwittingly assisted his detractors in their attempt to portray him as a sinister conniver, who preferred back stabbing his opponents rather than openly confronting them. Even the photographs of Hampers favored by the print media certainly conveyed that impression. The one most frequently chosen by editors was credited to Sherman Zent of The Palm Beach Post, in which Hampers appeared unsmiling, with a disdainful smirk on his lips, staring with narrowed eyes defiantly and directly into the camera, with the left side of his thin, long face in shadows, looking like a sleepy, evil Boris Karloff in the role of Iago. With hundreds of photographs of Hampers available from years of annual reports and earlier publications, and with their own staff photographers ready to capture his image, the editors of Business Week and The New York Times were very deliberate in their choice of the obscure and obscuring Palm Beach Post photograph.

Stories about the Grace "turmoil" and Hampers' role in it began including references to an incident that occurred in 1988 when Hampers was charged with violating the Endangered Species Law by smuggling the pelts of rare Mexican ocelots and jaguars into the United States, charges which were later reduced (Hampers maintained that he had been told that the necessary import permits had been secured) in a plea bargain in 1990 that required Hampers to pay an $180,000 fine by way of a donation to a wildlife preservation fund. It was never clear from any of these stories what that misdemeanor had to do with Hampers' intelligence, ability to lead a major U.S. corporation or moral character.

Press reports routinely described Hampers unfavorably. "Hampers is a complex character," reported Business Week. "Dr. Hampers...would be a controversial choice," The Wall Street Journal stated. And Kenneth N. Gilpin wrote in a New York Times story of Hampers' "appetite for more confrontation and intrigue," and quoted an unnamed "healthcare company executive" as describing Gus Hampers as "very much a Machiavellian." The Kroll story, the stale, seven-year old saga of hunting rare felines, and the re-airing of the FDA complaints concerning NMC's lax sterilization processes at its artificial kidney and blood line manufacturing plants were used to hurt Hampers' chances of becoming CEO of Grace.

At about the same time in early April, Dr. Hampers and Terry Daniels and his associates at Quad-C, Inc., many of whom had worked with Daniels at Grace and knew the company very well, were forming a syndicate to purchase W. R. Grace & Co. ("the whole ball of wax") out from under the Grace board of directors. While this story never became public during the relevant time period, the rumors of an attempted takeover of the $5 billion company by Hampers and Daniels were flying, and were noticed by several Grace directors. This further annoyed the board members. The Wall Street Journal reported on April 26, 1995: "The company maintains that it hasn't been contacted by any would be acquirer, though Wall Street has been rampant with rumors about the possible purchase of all or part of Grace."

The idea of purchasing Grace was first suggested by Terry Daniels in a telephone conversation with Hampers during a break in the April, 1995 board meeting. Daniels started investigating the capital markets for equity and credit to purchase the 140-year old corporate behemoth.

A couple weeks later, right after Peter Grace's funeral on April 22nd, Hampers was interviewed by the search committee, and had the distinct impression that they asked all the prescribed and predictable questions, but that they simply were not listening. As a physician who often talked with patients and their families, and as a medical school instructor lecturing young doctors, Hampers had a sixth sense of knowing when his audience was not fully engaged. "Holmes just wasn't paying attention to what I said," Hampers recalled concerning the acting CEO and the head of the search committee. One explanation was that the interview was a mere formality and that Hampers' election was a foregone conclusion. Still, nagging doubts plagued Hampers, and he continued to encourage Daniels to pursue the Grace buyout strategy. If the Grace board decided not to make him CEO, he would have a backup plan to head a group of investors and lenders who would acquire the corporation on his behalf.

On Sunday evening, April 30, 1995, Gus Hampers met acting CEO Tom Holmes and fellow search committee member, Ed Duffy, for dinner at the Plaza Hotel in New York. The Grace board was slated to meet the next day in New York to bring the search to a close and elect a new CEO and chairman. The annual stockholders meeting would be held May 10th in Boca Raton, and the board wanted to give the new CEO a week to meet with top staff members, key board members and representatives of the large institutional stockholders as well as the financial press, prior to the annual meeting. The agenda of the dinner meeting was no surprise for any of the three directors. It was Holmes' unpleasant duty to tell Hampers that he would not be selected, and it was

Hampers' equally unpleasant responsibility to accept this bad news graciously. Duffy, who had an instinct for self-preservation and a reputation for rigidity, was there to make sure Holmes didn't waiver and to be able to corroborate Holmes' version of the encounter should it take a bad turn. It didn't. There was nothing to be negotiated after the entrees were selected.

Until two days before the Plaza dinner, Hampers still believed the position would be his, based largely on the informal count taken by Gordon Humphrey, Bob Macauley and others at the April 6th board meeting, which was the last time the board had assembled formally, apart from Mr. Grace's funeral a week before Hampers' dinner with Holmes. But by the time he got to New York, Hampers knew the outcome. George Dacey, another member of the search committee, had called Hampers two days before while Hampers and his wife were flying to Boca Raton. "I could see something was terribly wrong as soon as Gus took the call from Dacey," Joyce Hampers recalled, "They waited until the last minute to tell him, but it turned out it was wired, and everyone, except Gus, knew the outcome."

Later that Sunday evening Hampers met in his hotel suite at the Four Seasons in New York City with Bob Macauley, Virginia Kamsky and Gordon Humphrey to decide what to do the next day at the board meeting. It was already too late. There were twenty directors, and Hampers could count on the support of six, perhaps seven, members. The institutional stockholders and the press were clamoring for an outsider to take charge of the tattered corporation, and Peter Grace, who could have provided an emotional appeal for Hampers, as well as another vote, was dead. So were Hampers' chances, it appeared. The meeting itself on May 1, 1995 was anti-climatic. Holmes reported that the search committee recommended Albert J. Costello and called the question. There was no discussion. The directors seemed to want to get the election and the past behind them as quickly as possible. The vote was thirteen in favor of appointing Costello president and CEO, six opposed, and one abstention.

The announcement of Costello's appointment was accompanied by carping from the same portfolio managers that had over the past eight weeks criticized Peter Grace, ridiculed the Grace board and blocked Hampers' chances of becoming CEO. The price of Grace stock closed on May 1, 1995 at 52 1/4, down 1 3/8, on the news. In the May 2nd account in The Boston Globe, Nicholas J. Kovich, a partner with Miller, Anderson & Sherrer, a money management firm in West Conshohocken, Pennsylvania, that then "controlled" about one million Grace shares, complained that "Mr. Costello.... should not be considered as a viable CEO candidate...Mr. Costello does not fit the CEO criteria..." A week before in The Wall Street Journal, Mr. Kovich emphasized that "[o]ur clients' interests are best served by having an outsider come in and clean up the situation...," and went on to argue that Dr. Hampers would be a bad choice. Another anonymous Grace shareholder was quoted in the Globe story, "This [Grace] board has not done a bona fide search."

Mr. Costello, then 59 years old, and a chemist by training and experience, had been employed by American Cyanamid Co. for 37 years, his entire adult life, rising to the position of CEO in 1993. Less than two years later, in December 1994, American Home Products purchased Cyanamid and "retired" Mr. Costello before his strategic direction for the chemical giant had taken hold. For the most part, his brief tenure as CEO at Cyanamid was marked by a restructuring effort that included divesting some of its chemical enterprises and expanding into foreign markets. He told The Wall Street Journal that his mandate from the Grace board was to "increase shareholder value." The constituency of Grace stockholders could find comfort in Costello's experience and ability to sell businesses and spin off subsidiaries to put more money in the pockets of shareholders. Those at National Medical Care, including Gus Hampers, were less sanguine about his ability to lead a service company that would look to the needs of the patient-consumers. In the May 2nd Globe article, Dr. Lowrie, NMC's president, was quoted: "There's been a great disaffection with Grace as a parent in the past couple of years. If [Costello] can't heal that very quickly, I certainly won't put up with this."

Dr. Hampers did not intend to lick his wounds and become a passive observer to see how Costello operated. By the time the reports of Costello's appointment hit Wall Street on Tuesday, May 2, 1995, Gus Hampers was already well on his way toward recapturing and controlling NMC, and putting Costello on the defensive before he cashed his first Grace paycheck.

18

A Raid or a Rescue?

Three days after his appointment as chief executive officer of Grace, Albert Costello met Gus Hampers at company headquarters in Boca Raton, Florida. Hampers didn't waste the new CEO's time with idle chit chat, but forthrightly presented him with an offer to purchase National Medical Care from Grace for $3.5 billion. Three billion dollars of the purchase price would be paid in cash. As a serious and credible offer to acquire the most profitable Grace subsidiary, Hampers' bid was publicly disclosed to the investment community by Grace management, and the news hit Wall Street on May 5, 1995. The proposal came less than a week before the annual Grace stockholders meeting, insuring that Costello would be questioned about it at the May 10th gathering. The headline on the front page of the business section of The New York Times of Monday, May 8, 1995 telegraphed the prevalent Wall Street view: "A Raider Removes His Sheep's Clothing. Grace Didn't Want Constantine Hampers, But He Still Wants Grace." Next to the article by Kenneth N. Gilpin was the Sherman Zent photograph of a sinister Hampers that indeed made him look like a wolf in corporate disguise.

From Hampers' point of view, he was trying to prevent a raid of National Medical Care, which he considered inevitable in the context of the history of the preceding five months and resulting investor expectations. Many large investors had bought or held Grace stock over the past few months based largely on the prevailing view that Grace would either sell NMC or spin it off, thereby increasing shareholder value. If the new management of Grace indicated a commitment to retain NMC, the price of Grace stock would fall, and this was not what any new CEO wanted to experience during his first month on the job. In addition, Costello's brief experience as a CEO was that of restructuring, trimming, selling and shaving, not of building and expanding. Hampers was giving Costello a chance to make a bold move early in his tenure that would please stockholders and fit his own instincts. Moreover, morale among managers and executives at NMC was at an all time low, and without the continuing energetic involvement of NMC personnel, the record setting pace of revenues and profits would drop, making NMC a less valuable investment for Grace. Hampers himself was not interested in continuing to direct NMC as a subsidiary of either Grace or any other large corporation, and he didn't see any of his top associates eager to assume that role. Ernie Lowrie had already resigned and Ed Lowrie had publicly stated his strong reservations.

Given these obvious factors, Hampers was convinced that Costello would have to sell NMC or spin it off to Grace shareholders as an independent entity. He saw the $3.5 billion offer as a genuine "win win" strategy for all parties, and anything other than a corporate "raid." Costello's responsibility was to ensure that the Hampers' proposal was backed up with credible financing, and to satisfy himself and the Grace board that there were no better deals possible from other, equally credible buyers. There were no more than three or four potential purchasers, they were all manufacturers of dialysis supplies and equipment, and, in Hampers' view, they all represented a serious threat to the standards of high quality care that NMC continued to provide its patients.

In many respects, Hampers' bid to restructure NMC as an independent corporation under his direction could be seen as a step backward to the pre-Grace past, with an entity largely dependent on a single, government financed program, with a great deal of upside potential over the long-term, but also with a huge amount of debt. In addition, by 1995 Gus Hampers was 62-years old, his loyalists at NMC, like Ernie Lowrie who had been with him for thirty years, were starting to retire, and his colleagues in the medical community were approaching emeritus status, and no longer had the same ambitions and plans that Hampers had been able to harness for the prior three decades. But Hampers' vision wasn't misted with nostalgia or fixed on the rear view of history; he saw exciting, new challenges for the future that he was confident he and NMC could meet. He was motivated both positively and negatively to take the risk and push himself to continue the long hours of work and an exhausting travel schedule for a few more years.

On the positive side, Hampers saw a great deal of potential in foreign countries. While the dialysis programs in many countries in Asia, Africa and South America were twenty-five years behind the United States, they could reach parity very quickly, and Hampers felt much more comfortable working in foreign contexts than he had a decade earlier. Also, on the positive side, Hampers envisioned potential value by combining the manufacturing and marketing expertise of successful suppliers with the service reputation and experience of the NMC clinics. Foreign expansion and innovative joint ventures that linked products and services together to provide better and cheaper clinical outcomes encompassed a vision and furnished objectives large enough to motivate Hampers from a positive perspective.

There was a negative perspective as well. Hampers wanted to forestall a takeover of National Medical Care by any of the large, well capitalized, well managed and aggressive product manufacturers and suppliers who were the only likely contenders to meet Grace's financial demands. Shifting control of the clinic operations from physicians and caregivers to product manufacturers was to be avoided in Hampers' view, and even without the positive reasons for undertaking the $3.5 billion venture, provided sufficient negative motivation for Hampers and his investor group. It was a struggle in which Hampers had thirty years experience.

When Gus Hampers and Ted Hager started an outpatient dialysis operation in a spare room at the Normandy House in 1966 and then began National Medical Care to deliver dialysis services around the country, they quickly discovered that the cost of supplies, specifically the cost of disposable supplies, would hold the key to financial success. The ability of a single clinic, whether operated by a charitable hospital or a chain of proprietary healthcare providers, to deliver dialysis services at the price fixed by Medicare and to generate profits was almost exclusively dependent on what it paid for disposable supplies - syringes, blood lines, sterile gloves, dialysate, disinfectants, drugs and, most importantly, the artificial kidney itself. Conversely, the profits derived by the corporations that manufactured and distributed these consumable products were inversely related to the clinics' profit margins.

Controlling the "profit see saw" between the dialysis clinics and the product manufacturers, in which the rise on one side was reflected in the decline on the other, has marked the thirty-year history of National Medical Care. So long as dialysis services were provided exclusively by large, multifaceted urban teaching hospitals, as they were in the 60's and still are in some parts of the United States and in most parts of the rest of the world, the manufacturers controlled the see saw. Hospital purchases were so massive that the cost of relatively few supplies in a small unit like an outpatient dialysis clinic would be overlooked, and, in the case of hospitals operated outside the capitalist system, i.e., "charitable" hospitals where capital is donated and taxes are non-existent, simply ignored. When Hampers and Hager started operating the first NMC clinics, and similarly when Dr. Schupak began his dialysis center in New York, they couldn't overlook or ignore the cost of supplies. The cost of an artificial kidney was a major issue, and their lenders and investors were not inclined to let them ignore supply costs because they were Harvard trained, skilled practitioners of the "healing arts."

In 1966 Travenol, then a division of Baxter International, Inc., the dominant U.S. based manufacturer of artificial kidneys, which held the patents derived from the work of Drs. Kolff and Walters, charged $59 for its coil dialyzer, which was used once and then thrown away. Hospitals, like the Brigham, didn't notice or care, and they consequently justified a charge of $360 for every dialysis treatment, which the patients' insurers - or later, the government - paid as a matter of course. It certainly didn't bother the nephrologists, if they were even aware of the cost. Once Hampers, Hager and Schupak started their own clinics, it did bother them - a lot. When they complained about the high price, Travenol reluctantly lowered it by four dollars to $55 per dialyzer. They were successful in forcing Travenol into reducing its price to $30 and conceding some of its profit margin, only by threatening to deconstruct, sterilize and reassemble the coils and teaching other clinic operators how to use the artificial kidneys more than once. When hollow fibre dialyzers were later introduced, reuse became more than a threat, and its perfection by NMC had kept supply costs in check for a dozen years.

The intricate "dance" between dialysis clinic operators, led by NMC, and the dialysis supply companies, typified by Baxter, had taken many twists and turns since the introduction in the early 60's of chronic, maintenance hemodialysis as the standard therapy for a growing population of ESRD patients. Both as Baxter's largest single customer and its most serious rival, National Medical Care created headaches for the leadership at Baxter and at other comparable companies. After 1972 this rivalry was often played out in the public arena in conspicuous debates regarding reimbursement policies and the best way to administer Medicare's end-stage renal disease program. The two sides fought over the services of highly skilled engineers, salesmen, managers and other personnel, the merits and authenticity of patents and proprietary information, the goodwill of the country's leading nephrologists, and the favor of Medicare bureaucrats and influential politicians. In the end, the result of these multifaceted contests was a balance of power that checked and counter checked each other, kept both sides honest, and benefitted the ESRD Program and the patients with better and less expensive services and products.

Early in NMC's history its leaders quickly realized that they could not become dependent on the manufacturers of dialyzers and other critical dialysis products. For the health and safety of their patients they had to line up alternative sources of supply, and be able to direct concerted pressure on the suppliers in order to force improvements in product design and performance, distribution reliability, and prices. They formed Erika, a subsidiary, to handle product supply for the growing network of NMC clinics.

As Erika expanded, it naturally began to recruit personnel from Baxter. There were only a handful of people in the country that were conversant with the product technology and the needs and expectations of the clinicians. The relationships between the salesmen and the clinic directors and head nurses were very valuable assets for their employers. Virtually all of Erika's original team of managers and sales force came from Baxter Travenol, including Dave Donlan, Howard Janneck, and Jesus Martinez.

These men transferred their knowledge, skills and relationships to Erika, and executives at Baxter were understandably upset. The third strike came once Erika and NMC leaders decided to engage in manufacturing, essentially attempting to integrate vertically and eliminate the product manufacturers from making any profit from the NMC clinics. Despite the fact that NMC was by then Baxter's largest dialysis product purchaser, it could not sit idly by and allow NMC to pick off its best people and replicate its products in the marketplace. What followed was a series of legal threats and counter threats over patents, "stealing" each other's personnel, and interfering with contractual relationships with each other's customers, leavened by the practical realization that the two corporations had become interdependent. Neither was dominant and neither was completely happy about the arrangement.

After that series of hostile exchanges subsided in the early 1970's, the corporations eased into a "cold war" of suspicion and mutual hostility, glossed over by a veneer of civility that reflected the fact that both NMC and Baxter were doing very well financially from the growth of the ESRD Program. Every year or two, executives of these two companies would get together and smooth over their differences, negotiate another supply agreement and try to find a permanent solution to their rivalries.

While NMC pursued a strategy of vertical integration and became actively engaged in the business of manufacturing artificial kidneys, bloodlines, and dialysate solutions, and of bulk purchasing, warehousing and distribution of every conceivable product used in dialysis clinics and in the home setting, Baxter steadfastly refused to pursue the converse strategy of directly operating its own chain of dialysis clinics or of managing the dialysis clinics owned by hospitals. There were no legal barriers to prevent Baxter from creating a service subsidiary, and more than one industry expert had urged Baxter to enter the dialysis service market. The first, ironically, was Gene Schupak. Before he struck a deal with Hampers and Hager to join National Medical Care in the late 60's, Dr. Schupak invited Baxter to help him start the first out-of-hospital dialysis clinic in New York. Desperate for funding to outfit his new clinic and faced with rejection from potential private, charitable and government sources, Dr. Schupak sought capital from

Baxter Travenol in 1969, and offered the company a 50% interest in the clinic for an investment of $250,000, which is what Schupak calculated was needed to build and equip the clinic. Baxter turned him down. Instead, Schupak sold 50% of his newly formed dialysis company, Bio-Medical Applications, to NMC, which supplied Schupak with the needed capital to start the New York clinic.

Peter Phildius, who had directed the dialysis division at Baxter from 1960 to 1978, when he became NMC's president, also urged Baxter's CEO, Bill Graham, in 1977 to purchase NMC and operate its dialysis clinics directly. Graham again refused to get involved in operating dialysis clinics, citing the potential conflicts that would arise between the Baxter-NMC clinics and the dialysis units owned by other corporations, independent physicians and hospitals. Phildius recalled that Graham wanted Baxter to stay on the best terms with all its customers, and invading the service arena traditionally reserved for hospitals and doctors would jeopardize the goodwill Baxter had carefully nurtured with its clients for decades. Graham subscribed to the theory that a bright line should divide drug and medical product manufacturers and suppliers from healthcare service providers. In his view, Baxter's job was to manufacture the best artificial kidneys in the world and to sell more of them than anyone else. Phildius understood, and later directed, the NMC strategic plan to shift profits to NMC from its product suppliers, but he was unable to persuade his Baxter superiors to eliminate this threat. Years later, after Graham retired, Baxter would, for a brief period of time, ignore the bright line divider and enter the home care service industry with the acquisition of Caremark.

In late 1981, when Baxter and NMC were engaged in fierce lobbying over changes in the manner of reimbursing dialysis clinics under the ESRD Program, Baxter publicly offered to operate the 60 dialysis clinics that NMC threatened to close if the federal government went forward with the reduced, "composite rate" reimbursement plan proposed by HHS Secretary Schweicker. Baxter never offered to purchase the clinics from NMC (Hampers said NMC would be willing to sell them to Baxter for $100 million.), but made the grand, dramatic gesture in order to try to embarrass

NMC, which had threatened to close the 60 clinics because their costs would exceed the proposed ESRD reimbursement rate, and to ingratiate Baxter with Schweicker and congressional leaders in their attempt to force more patients to leave the clinics and dialyze in their homes. Baxter made much more money from supplying individual home patients than from bulk sales to NMC clinics. Baxter's officials knew their offer would be spurned by Hampers and the company was in no danger of actually having to operate these marginal clinics.

Other manufacturers were less constricted than Baxter during the 70's and 80's, and explored and perfected tactics to challenge NMC on its own turf and operate dialysis clinics directly, and by 1995 Hampers saw these manufacturers as a direct threat to the independence of NMC and its medical directors, and in his view, an equally direct and dire threat to the quality of patient care. As perceived by Hampers, the prospect of having product manufacturers in a dominant role as owners and operators of dialysis clinics made the theoretical qualms of medical moralists in the academy insignificant by comparison. The discomfort that anti-NMC commentators like Dr. Relman and others felt about doctors running corporations that provided healthcare services paled in light of the trauma they should experience once these clinics were operated by manufacturing executives, trained not in medicine, but in product engineering and sales. By May 1995 one product manufacturer had invested in owning dialysis clinics, and other manufacturers, including Baxter, were ready to take the plunge. For Hampers, the challenge was to accommodate the inevitable merger of manufacturing and healthcare delivery with the doctor in the dominant, not the subservient, position.

Fresenius AG, a German manufacturer of high quality, hollow fibre kidneys, with whom NMC and Hampers had had a long and mutually productive relationship, was very serious about operating dialysis clinics in the United States. Gambro A.B., a Swedish dialyzer manufacturer, had already entered the American dialysis service market with its purchase of a 49% interest in REN, another kidney service corporation. These two companies, in addition to Baxter, could marshall the resources and expertise to acquire NMC from Grace. The one thing they couldn't acquire, and the one thing Grace could not deliver, was Gus Hampers. And Hampers was determined to maintain NMC's independence, even if it meant that he would have to stay on as its chief executive for several more years.

The problem for Hampers was not in exploiting the synergies that clearly existed between the manufacturer of artificial kidneys and other medical products and the service providing clinics. In fact, Hampers and his NMC partners had been the first to realize these advantages by creating NMC's Erika subsidiary, entering into long term symbiotic supply contracts with Baxter, Abbott Labs, Fresenius and others, and from time to time exploring mergers with these and other product manufacturers. The difficulty lay in retaining control in the hands of the physician, and insuring that the manufacturing goals didn't obscure, confuse, or dominate the goal of quality patient care.

Hampers had plenty of experience in adjudicating disputes between the "product guys" and the dialysis clinic directors within NMC itself. The lessons learned from the kidney reuse debate between himself and Gene Schupak were the most memorable. Hampers had a history of squeezing the corporate synergies to yield the highest profit, but always stopped short of demanding compliance from NMC's medical directors. As Bill Cirksena, the medical director of several NMC clinics in the Washington, D.C. area recalled, "Gus never told me that I had to do anything that I didn't think was best for my patients." At the end of the day, if Hampers could not persuade reluctant doctors to use the less costly alternative or accept a more efficient product or procedure, he would relent, not because he felt he was wrong, but because he would not tell another doctor how to practice medicine. In Hampers' view, no one ever managed the product division of NMC better than Gene Schupak, because Schupak also shared the same philosophy and values concerning the primacy of the patient-doctor relationship. His wider business experience from his years at Grace convinced Hampers that most manufacturing CEO's would not surrender a penny of profit in order to accommodate a physician's perceived folly, and that conviction required Hampers to stay in the arena for the next round of battles.

Too many physicians, in Hampers' view, had abandoned the

field of healthcare delivery and left its control in the hands of insurance company and health maintenance organization executives, and their counterparts in the Medicare and Medicaid bureaucracies. Hampers did not want to join the ranks of these deserting doctors, whose sole solution was to return to the bygone days of doctor controlled, community based, charitable hospitals and fee-for-service medicine. It was clear to Hampers that those nostalgic nostrums were simply not feasible, and that healthcare in the twenty first century would require the infusion of private capital, business acumen, advanced technology, information exchange, economies of scale and cost consciousness. The nineteenth century model of hospitals built and equipped with the "free capital" of philanthropy and taxes and physician offices that exchanged medical care for a few dollars or a dozen eggs was as relevant in 1995 as a transportation system based on the horse or a communication system centered on the telegraph. The assets required to build a modern healthcare delivery system could only come from the private capital markets which would necessarily demand a profit. The troubling issue was who would run these corporations, and Hampers strongly believed that only physicians, trained in both the healing sciences, as well as the business disciplines, would be able to properly balance the conflicting goals of the investors and the patients. Hampers was truly dumbfounded that so few doctors shared his perspective and values, and that so many of his colleagues were openly and vehemently critical of his efforts.

The country has inexorably moved toward a system of healthcare in which third-party payers, both private employers for the working middle class and government for the aged, poor and unemployed, control the quality and supply of services and products available from doctors, hospitals, specialty clinics, dentists, therapists, pharmacies and every other healthcare provider. Patients are directed to a limited choice of caregivers, who are under contract with the HMO and Medicare/Medicaid payers to ration care in accordance with explicit and rigid guidelines. Large employers in a particular city, such as Boeing in Seattle, could conceivably purchase their own hospital, employ their own doctors and dispense drugs through their own pharmacy for all their employees, who would either accept these limited company benefits or go without. Similarly, Medicaid might find it more efficient to purchase a municipal hospital, like Cook County Hospital and direct all the indigent in its service area to its exclusive provider. HMO's are, in fact, a transitional, and quite unnecessary agent or "middle man" which will disappear in the future, as private employers and the government assert increasing control over healthcare rationing.

In Hampers' view, only physicians and other healthcare providers can prevent this Orwellian scenario of centralized healthcare rationing by employers, governments, and their HMO agencies. Individual patients lack the knowledge or power to have significant effect. Unions and other patient/consumer collectives that could provide a counterbalancing force will necessarily act politically, negotiating and trading for services and lobbying for those benefits that serve the majority of their members (such as an extra day's maternity care), largely leaving the individual with a rare, costly and poorly understood condition (like AIDS), unprotected. Physicians, organized in strong associations, unions and their own healthcare corporations, represent the only means to properly ration scarce healthcare resources. Rather than face the reality that rationing of healthcare is happening and taking the responsibility for controlling the delivery of healthcare, physicians have denied scarcity, blamed HMO's for filling the accountability gap, and demanding that the government burden the system with even more rules and regulations.

In the case of renal dialysis, if the efficient delivery system created by NMC became a chain of "outlet stores" for a particular product manufacturer, a dangerous, new dynamic would be introduced into the healthcare system in the United States. Physician choice over the dialyzers and other products available to his patients would shrink, and doctors, like automobile mechanics, would become employees of a manufacturer's dealership, offering only its brand products to the consumer. With captive doctors and patients, the manufacturers would lack the incentive to improve their products and reduce costs. From there it would be a short step to a system in which large medical supply companies, like Abbott Labs, and drug manufacturers, such as Merck, could create joint ventures to purchase and operate hospitals, cancer care centers, and dentists offices. Purchasing healthcare would be like buying a refrigerator; the patient would decide, without the advice of an independent physician (but likely influenced by TV, radio and magazine ads), what kind of product he wanted and then go to the appropriate franchise where the doctor would "service and install" the chemotherapy, prosthesis, or heart pacemaker. If this scenario appears far fetched, consider the evolution of optometry over the past two decades from independent profession to competing Pearle Vision and For Eyes mall outlets, as well as the direct marketing of prescription drugs during prime time television.

In an odd twist, Dr. Hampers had in fact planted the seeds of interest to acquire NMC from Grace in the minds of both Fresenius and Baxter executives. During 1993 and 1994 when Hampers and J.P. Bolduc were operating harmoniously at Grace, before the events that began in November 1994 with the Bolduc-Peter Grace fight, he and Bolduc were promoting deals with both these manufacturing giants. They gave Baxter and Fresenius all the data they needed about NMC to enable these manufacturers to analyze the value of such a combination, whetting their appetites for a merger. Hampers had also had similar, but less intense, discussions with Gambro during the same period. The discussions had stalled over the precise parameters of the deal, the structure of the resulting combination, tax implications, and, most importantly, control issues. After his bid to become CEO of Grace had failed in the spring of 1995, and knowing that Grace was under intense pressure from its large investors to profitably dispose of NMC, Hampers felt he had to act fast with his own offer to buy NMC and to make it clear to Baxter, Fresenius and any other potential buyer that his services and goodwill would not be included, if these manufacturers made a competing bid. Mr. Costello and the other Grace executives would not have the same sensitivities to the need to have medical doctors in charge of any resulting entity, and, in fact, they perceived their responsibility to their shareholders, not to the dialysis patients and their physicians.

The story that emerged in the financial press, however, was

that of a vengeful, spurned CEO candidate who was pressuring the new Grace CEO into selling him its most profitable subsidiary (in 1994 NMC accounted for 42% of Grace's operating profit). The distortion didn't faze Hampers any more than the many unflattering portraits that the press had published about him in the past, starting 25 years earlier when he, Gene Schupak and Ted Hager had decided to raise capital from the investing public in order to start a chain of dialysis clinics across the country. For all the business acumen he'd acquired during the ensuing quarter century, Dr. Hampers had not learned how to cooperate with the press or project a positive image of himself. In fact, as a result of his innate diffidence, he appeared aloof and cold. "Dr. Hampers has a reputation as being short tempered and uncommunicative with analysts and investors," The Wall Street Journal proclaimed. In the May 8, 1995 New York Times article prepared by Kenneth N. Gilpin, Hampers was described by unnamed sources as "Machiavellian," "not a team player," and a "raider." The Wall Street Journal on May 5, 1995 described the $3.5 billion offer as a "bold gambit" [and]... "the latest twist in the tumultuous corporate drama..."and noted that Hampers' timing, a few days prior to the annual stockholders meeting, "is certain to add more turmoil to next Wednesday's annual meeting." And in its "Who's News" column of May 8th, the Journal portrayed Hampers as "urbane, sometimes imperious," and characterized his $3.5 billion offer as an "audacious bid [that] has raised eyebrows on Wall Street."

These articles also raised questions about the bona fides of Hampers' offer, since it was subject to financing. But the offer was deemed credible by the stock market, as reflected in the one day increase in the price of Grace common stock of $4.875, or about 9%. Over the weekend prior to the Grace annual meeting, Hampers publicly revealed that a group of investors assembled by former Grace vice chairman, Terry Daniels', firm, Quad-C Inc., had committed to approximately $800 million of equity, and that they had secured bank financing from Bankers Trust New York Corp. of another $2.2 billion. On Monday, May 8, 1995 the price of Grace shares rose another $2.75 to close at $61.25 per share, a 52-week high on the strength of this news. As they headed for the Boca Raton annual meeting, analysts and substantial Grace investors, whose Grace portfolios had increased in value by 15% in less than a week, were pressing Costello to accept the Hampers' offer or come up with a better one.

Costello didn't disappoint the Grace shareholders. "The die is sort of cast already," the new CEO stated at the time, referring to the likely divestiture of NMC, converting Julius Caesar's bold assertion of inevitability into a passive prediction of impotence. In meetings with leading investors and analysts in New York two days before the official stockholder gathering, the new Grace CEO assured them that Grace would either spin NMC off to its share-holders to be operated as a separate company, or sell it to the highest bidder. These meetings were reported to the public in advance of the annual meeting, resulting in a surprisingly tame and uneventful stockholders meeting, as predicted in The Wall Street Journal's headline that day (May 10, 1995): "Clouds Over Grace Dissipate in Time For Its Meeting." The meeting at the Marriott hotel across the road from Grace headquarters in Boca Raton was packed, but instead of a rancorous debate about the future of the company, the participants respectfully watched a video tribute to the late Peter Grace. No one mentioned the name of Mr. Grace's successor and nemesis, but J.P. Bolduc's wife was among the attendees, according to the report in the next day's New York Times. As he sat through the meeting with the rest of the Grace directors, Hampers was already planning for the day in the not-too-distant future when he and NMC would be independent of the Grace bureaucracy and the tumultuous, time consuming and unproductive events of the past several months.

On June 14, 1995, just six weeks after receiving Hampers' purchase offer, the Grace board unanimously endorsed CEO Costello's recommendation to reject Hampers' bid and to spin National Medical Care off to the Grace shareholders in a tax free divestiture. In a spin off stockholders end up owning stock in two corporations instead of one, combined company, and they can individually decide whether to hold onto their shares in both, sell both or sell one and keep the other. By most calculations, if Grace had simply sold NMC to the investment group headed by Gus Hampers, Grace would have faced capital gains taxes in the range of $850 million to one billion dollars, taxes avoided by a spin off procedure. The spin off plan would shift the potential capital gains taxes from the corporation onto the individual stockholders. Each stockholder would pay taxes on the difference between the price he paid for Grace stock and the amount he received, if and when he sold the shares of either the "new" NMC or the "reconstituted" Grace. While Grace wouldn't receive the cash that Hampers' purchase would have offered, Grace would receive the same benefits of a cash infusion to the extent that NMC assumed part of the Grace indebtedness (as permitted by Grace's lenders), thus unburdening the Grace balance sheet.

The decision to spin off a subsidiary is only a decision to make many further, detailed decisions, however. The Grace management would have to decide how much its NMC subsidiary was "worth," which assets would be retained by Grace and which would be handed over to the new, independent NMC, how much of the Grace debt NMC could carry, and whether there would be any long term contractual agreements between the two corporations that would survive the spin off. It was assumed and widely reported that Hampers would continue to operate the new NMC after the spin off by Grace which was expected sometime in the final calendar quarter of 1995. However, Hampers knew that his leverage in securing the best terms for the new NMC and its management team required him to hold back on any final commitment to operate NMC. Hampers understood that running a corporation weighed down with heavy debt and other costly expenses inherited from Grace and without a potentially lucrative incentive program for the managers and top employees could be impossible. Independence was important, but not at any price. While Grace executives, especially Mr. Costello, set about cleaning up the disarray that had accumulated during the first six months of 1995, Hampers' mind was fixed on his goal of springing NMC loose from Grace with as little debt, with as many assets and with the best prospects for growth and profitability as possible. His task was the obverse of the job of 1984 when he was selling NMC to Grace. Hampers properly put himself in the role of buyer of the new NMC and negotiated the best terms by down playing the value of the company. In this endeavor, as NMC's chief executive negotiating with a new CEO who had already announced the spin off publicly before perfecting the terms, Hampers held the upper hand.

Wall Street analysts roughly estimated that NMC was worth half of Grace, and applying this estimate to the $62 price of Grace common stock, derived a value of $30-35 per share of Grace common stock. Hampers had a much lower value in mind in the summer of 1995. In a July 25, 1995 letter to Costello, Hampers presented his case for a less valuable NMC. While emphasizing that by accepting 70% of Grace's debt, NMC would be burdened with a highly leveraged balance sheet, Hampers argued that NMC's "goodwill" account was overstated by at least $100 million, because during the decade it had owned NMC Grace had taken an aggressive position with respect to amortizing goodwill over the longest possible period of time. Hampers' position was that Grace had increased its reported earnings over the past ten years by stretching the acquisition costs of NMC clinics over too long a period. Similarly, Hampers contended that the Health Care Financing Administration (the bureau of the Department of Health and Human Services that administers Medicare, including the ESRD Program) had altered an ESRD-Program reimbursement interpretation on July 1, 1995 that put NMC at risk to repay $100 million to various non-Medicare, third-party insurers, and that another recent (May 31, 1995) policy change in covering parenteral nutrition services for dialysis patients might require NMC to reduce its receivables for these services by as much as $65 million. Along with other "minor" adjustments, Hampers was negotiating to reduce the initial net worth of NMC by nearly $300 million (or about 10% of the price Hampers' had offered to pay for NMC in May).

Hampers and Costello were also at odds over how much, and how quickly, ownership in the new NMC should be granted to company management. In the structure of his original deal to acquire NMC, Hampers planned to reserve 10% to 15% of NMC's equity for company executives in order to provide the necessary financial incentives for success. Gus Hampers had learned that the company and its shareholders, whether these were thousands of public shareholders, or one parent shareholder, made out much better under a system that paid executives low base salaries and rewarded them with an ownership interest in the enterprise.

Costello, on the other hand, saw a fiduciary obligation to Grace shareholders not to dilute their ownership in the new NMC by granting an inordinately large piece of the action to NMC managers. Costello set a ceiling of 6.6% of NMC ownership to be granted to NMC management, and wanted no more than 60% of that management share to be granted at the outset of the spin off. Hampers insisted on 7.5% for management with 90% of that share immediately available.

It would later surprise Wall Street analysts that the initial value of NMC would be under $20 per (Grace common) share, or 50% less than they had estimated when the spin off was first announced, based on a thirteen multiple of a much-reduced estimate of 1996 earnings for NMC (13 x $1.50 = $19.50). These reduced, prospective earnings reflected the large debt burden that NMC was expected to shoulder, and the other "subsequent events" that Hampers had described in his July 25th letter. The difference between the value prior to the spin off of the combined companies ($61.25 on May 8, 1995) and the negotiated initial value of NMC at the start of the spin off (say, $19.50) would presumably be the price of the reconstituted W.R. Grace & Co. (or $41.75). Obviously, Costello and Hampers were engaged in a major "reverse tug-of-war," with each trying to establish the lowest baseline for his post-spin off company against which his future performance would be compared. If the stock market didn't agree on the negotiated division of net worth, there would be an immediate adjustment in these prices on the stock exchange, and a resulting "windfall" and loss to the respective management groups of the two companies. A lot of money rode on the outcome of these negotiations and how well Costello could sell the resulting, relative revaluation of Grace and NMC to the market.

During the five weeks between the May 10th annual meeting and the June 14th divestiture decision, only one alternative was publicly disclosed concerning another way for Grace to dispose of its profitable NMC subsidiary. The offer came from VIVRA, Inc., a rival of NMC in providing incenter dialysis services, and with approximately $300 million in revenues (compared to NMC's $2 billion), the second largest dialysis service company in the U.S. VIVRA itself was created in 1989, when it was spun off as a separate corporation by its parent, Community Psychiatric Centers, Inc. The June 1995 proposal involved the merger of Grace and VIVRA with a simultaneous, "reverse" spin off of the non-NMC part of Grace, leaving NMC and VIVRA combined. This corporate somersault was required to avoid the capital gain tax problem. Under the plan Grace shareholders would have received stock in a reconstituted Grace corporation and stock in the combined NMC-VIVRA company. It was a complex proposal that was given short shrift by Grace management. Faced with an uncooperative response from NMC and Dr. Hampers, VIVRA officials themselves down played their chances of success a day after the proposal was disclosed in the press. To be sure, the transaction may have raised anti-trust concerns, but Kent Thiry, the CEO of VIVRA complained that Hampers was "stonewalling," making it impossible to be specific and unequivocal with an firm offer. In an interesting twist, VIVRA and its principal investment advisor, Bain Capital, scheduled a conference call with major Grace stockholders to explain their proposal, thus going around both NMC and Grace management. On the same day as the conference call with investors, June 14th, the Grace board decided to spin NMC off and rejected both Hampers' purchase bid and the VIVRA combination offer. However, the complex technique first proposed by VIVRA would be dusted off and used by Grace management in divesting itself of NMC a year later.

The summer and early fall of 1995 was an exciting and busy time for Gus Hampers. He was engaged in creating the "fourth iteration" of National Medical Care, negotiating with the lending banks, Grace management, and his prospective investors, as well as his own management at NMC to ensure their continued fealty and services for the ensuing five-year period. Hampers was once again putting the essential elements of capital, labor and management together to remake NMC for the next decade, burdened with huge indebtedness, but unfettered by a centralized bureaucracy and corporate politics. He lured some top Grace personnel to leave their employer and join NMC. He recruited former NMC affiliates to join the new board and staff and become re-engaged as medical directors of the NMC clinics. With the help of Terry Daniels and others, Hampers put together an impressive scenario to sell to the lenders and to potential investors and staff. Hampers had no trouble convincing those who had been through any of the earlier incarnations of NMC to trust him again. Under Hampers' direction National Medical Care had made a lot of money for its owners - the small group of insurance companies and other investors in the initial venture, the public shareholders in the 1971-1984 phase, and W.R. Grace & Co. and the leveraged buy-out group in the third (1985-1995) stage.

One loyal lieutenant who was not willing to take another ride on the Hampers juggernaut was Ed Lowrie. Since his introduction to Hampers as a renal fellow at the Brigham Hospital before NMC was even founded, through the early days at the Normandy House and the Babcock centers and for the ensuing twenty-five years, Ed Lowrie had been a trusted associate. Smart, energetic and personable, Doctor Lowrie was regularly assigned the tasks that Hampers despised, like attending medical conferences, analyzing and critiquing complex, bureaucratic initiatives from the federal government, testifying before Congress, and representing the executive suite at employee gatherings. Those departments and divisions that were uninteresting or distasteful to Hampers - human resources, home care services, the laboratory and product divisions - he delegated to Lowrie without clear mandates or instructions. Predictably, when these enterprises failed, Lowrie took the heat, not just from Hampers, but increasingly from Grace managers and directors, as well. During the tense times of 1993 and 1994, when J.P. Bolduc was consolidating his power and centralizing corporate functions under his command at Grace, it was Lowrie who had the pitched battles with Bolduc's associates, making himself persona non grata among the Grace hierarchy. At the end of 1994 Lowrie found himself increasingly squeezed. In his war with the Grace executives Lowrie found Hampers generally ignoring his calls for help, or taking sides with the corporate bureaucrats against Lowrie. On the other side, NMC employees with whom he worked daily were looking for leadership and not finding it from Gus Hampers. Lowrie began meeting with these disgruntled and frustrated NMC officers and conspiring with them to force Hampers' hand in their ongoing disputes with Grace. If Hampers refused, Lowrie would lead a walkout to form a new dialysis services company. At about the same time that Hampers had decided to take Bolduc and his Grace executives on, he learned of Lowrie's plans, which Hampers considered mutinous.

By June of 1995, Lowrie was worn out. His wife, Ernie, who had worked with Hampers since shortly after he first arrived at the Brigham Hospital, had left NMC a few months before. Once Hampers' attempt to become CEO of Grace missed the mark, Lowrie saw his role as the same, thankless (but nonetheless financially rewarding) supporting part he had been playing to Hampers' leading role for nearly thirty years. The final coup came when Hampers announced that, following the spin off, there would not be a spot on the board of directors of the new NMC for Dr. Lowrie. Following Lowrie's "sedition" in contemplating a competitive venture, Hampers did not want Ed Lowrie on the new NMC board. Hampers would be the only NMC executive to join a small group of trusted outside directors like Terry Daniels, Ted Hager and Paul Paganucci on the board. Despite the promise of potential millions of dollars in incentive compensation and stock ownership appreciation, Lowrie submitted his resignation in the summer of 1995, to be effective at the end of the year, following the spin off.

19

Alienation

On October 18, 1995 Gus Hampers was in Chinju, South Korea on a stop over between Kuala Lumpur and Alaska, when he received a frantic call from JoEllen Ojeda, an attorney at NMC, who was responsible for managing the company's litigation, including its frequent, and increasingly hostile, disputes with the federal government. Ojeda and her colleagues in the NMC and Grace law departments, as well as dozens of outside lawyers, were accustomed to fending off attacks from various federal agencies, including the Office of the Inspector General (OIG) of the Department of Health and Human Services, the Food and Drug Administration and U.S. attorneys from around the country. In securing the dominant position in the dialysis services industry, NMC had made a lot of enemies among former employees, patient advocates, critical physicians and healthcare competitors, many of whom were more than eager to complain to federal officials about the manner in which NMC conducted its business and try to initiate so called qui tam lawsuits. These are lawsuits in which the complainant shares in any recovery the government might be successful in securing from the defendant. Handling these inquiries and lawsuits was Ojeda's job, and after a decade of defending the company, she wasn't usually fazed by any one of these filings. However, Ms. Ojeda did recognize the series of subpoenas she received on behalf of NMC on Tuesday, October 17th as unusual, serious, and potentially devastating, definitely demanding an immediate telephone call to Hampers in east Asia, where it was already Wednesday, the 18th.

National Medical Care had been served with a series of seven subpoenas from the OIG of the U.S. Department of Health and Human Services, requesting truckloads of information on a variety of subjects related to the manner in which NMC had conducted its business over a long period of time. What made this legal process unusual was that it was a coordinated attack from several different law enforcement agencies that generally do not cooperate, much less coordinate their activities, including the Justice Department, several U.S. attorneys, and the Health and Human Services Department's OIG. Also, the government took the unusual procedure of sending an FBI agent to Ojeda's office in Waltham to personally deliver the seven subpoenas. Additionally, the service of the October 17th subpoenas was serious, because of the breadth of the legal demands and the mind boggling amount of information that was sought. Finally, the subpoenas had to be viewed as potentially devastating, because of the timing of the process. The spin off of NMC was proceeding, and was expected within a few short weeks. Dr. Hampers flew all night, crossing the international dateline, and arrived at NMC's Waltham office on October 18th to direct the response to the government and to the investment community.

Because service of these subpoenas on NMC constituted a material fact that could reasonably be expected to affect the decision to buy, sell or hold Grace stock, Grace released the news on October 18th, and the market responded immediately by depressing the price of Grace common stock from $65.125 to $56.625 per share, a 13% drop. Investors and analysts foresaw problems with the proposed spin off of NMC and adjusted the value of Grace shares accordingly. Investors and their advisors were worried about both the substance of the government's claims and their effect on company's prospects, as well as the impact the subpoenas would have on the timing of the spin off. With thousands of other, attractive, and less risky places to invest capital, these investors were not interested in sticking with Grace and NMC in a pursuit of justice. Delaying the spin off was as upsetting as terminating the transaction, and few stockholders were willing to wait it out.

The seven subpoenas focused on the general operations of NMC and its corporate structure, as well as on six areas of concern or potential problems regarding the relationship between NMC and Medicare. It took only a cursory review of the subpoenas for Ojeda and the other attorneys helping her to determine that the government was probing the operating and billing practices of the company in six distinct areas, none of which surprised the lawyers or company officials, as these were subjects that had been in dispute for a long time between NMC and the intermediary insurance companies that administered Medicare in some of the states in which NMC operated its facilities. The government was not raising new areas of inquiry, but it had escalated, focused and formalized its process of investigation. It became clear quite quickly that these issues would not be resolved with a few telephone calls and meetings between company officials and law enforcement agents. By issuing the subpoenas en masse the government was serving notice on Grace and NMC that resolution of these disputes over operations and billing practices was going to occur only after a lengthy, exhaustive and very expensive legal process that could take months, if not years, to complete.

The timing was disastrous and very curious. All six of the subject areas had been raised before, and NMC had attempted to cooperate with the Medicare officials to resolve these issues. Why then, was the government dumping all these issues into one concentrated assault on NMC just weeks before it was to be cut loose from Grace as a separate company? Hampers and other company officials knew that even if NMC ultimately prevailed on all six issues, the legal process instituted on October 17, 1995 would raise such serious questions of risk for the lending banks and the Grace stockholders and potential investors that the spin off would be impossible to perfect.

One area of concern had dogged NMC from its earliest days, long before Grace had invested in the company, and that was NMC's practice of offering its dialysis clinic directors a share in the earnings of the clinic, through a variety of mechanisms. These relationships were plainly described and disclosed in the company's public reports, opinions relating to their legality under all relevant laws had been sought from a number of law firms, the relationships were well known to government regulators, and these arrangements were widely copied by competitors in the dialysis industry as well as in other healthcare areas. NMC's goal was to offer the best dialysis service at the lowest cost. Quality was attained by hiring the very best doctors to run the clinics, and efficiency was achieved by compensating these medical directors as if they were partners or joint-owners of the clinics. In Hampers' view doctors who had a financial interest in the clinic's earnings were the best enforcers of top quality and low costs. The NMC model attempted to replicate the quality, care, efficiency, and freedom of the old fashioned physician's office. Conflicts between cost and quality could only be resolved by the patient's physician as these conflicts had always been thus resolved for hundreds of years, despite the fact that the resolution would also affect the doctor's income. Only the doctor, guided by his moral responsibility to his patients and bound by his ethical duty to his profession, could balance the underutilization of services that might endanger a patient's health and the overutilization that would bankrupt the system. Although applied in less dramatic contexts, the same ethical dilemma is present for all professionals, including accountants, lawyers and therapists, since by determining the level of service needed by their clients these professionals set the level of their own incomes.

Medicare was illogically hostile toward these arrangements. If a doctor owned his own dialysis center, as if it were simply an extension of his private practice office, no one questioned his right to all the profits (or losses) generated by the center. If three nephrologists had a partnership practice that included a dialysis service, they were logically entitled to a one-third share of its earnings. However, if NMC compensated its clinic directors with a portion (say, 25%) of the clinic's net income, Medicare viewed this arrangement as more akin to "referral fees" - payments to a physician for referring his patients to a hospital or other healthcare service like a dialysis center, which had always been unethical and illegal. Over the course of its history NMC had altered the arrangement to comply with changes mandated by various Medicare amendments, including legislation named after Congressman Fortney "Pete" Stark of California. The Stark Acts required disclosure, and later banned, some forms of practice where doctors referred their patients to healthcare providers in which they had an ownership or profit sharing interest. NMC was mindful of these changes and modified its arrangements accordingly. Nonetheless, the government in one of its 1995 subpoenas was clearly seeking information about these practices to determine whether NMC had violated these self-referral prohibitions.

The dangers potentially posed by the practice of self-referral, which the Stark Acts attempted to eliminate, were overutilization and fraud. However, the End-Stage Renal Disease Program itself largely avoided these dangers. First, with respect to the decision to dialyze, no doctor had ever been suspected of putting patients on dialysis who didn't need this heroic and unpleasant therapy. Moreover, the ESRD Program set monopsonistic standards for hemodialysis; facilities couldn't earn more by dialyzing their patients too often. The buyer, Medicare, set the price and the terms.

One way a facility and its owner-physicians could inflate income by "cheating" was by cutting corners and saving money by delivering substandard care. With dialysis this was easily monitored. The blood tests of poorly dialyzed patients would indict any potentially larcenous doctor. The only other way of "cheating" was to overprescribe ancillary services that might be deemed discretionary. Nerve conductivity studies, bone density assays, and certain laboratory tests might be ordered by a doctor when these weren't necessary. To monitor these ancillaries NMC compared its record with that of non-NMC facilities, both for-profit and not-for-profit. It discovered that NMC doctors prescribed dialysis ancillaries considerably less (about 25% less) than the national average and that the volume of ancillary charges was not related to the incidence of physician ownership. In other words, NMC medical directors who shared in the profits of their clinics did not order more ancillaries, and in fact, as a group, these facilities charged less than the non-NMC clinics.

Another peculiar area of concern was the manner in which NMC treated discrepancies in the amounts it had properly billed Medicare for ESRD services and the amount it received from the Medicare intermediary payers. Over the course of time and literally millions of dialysis treatments and other ancillary services provided to Medicare beneficiaries by NMC clinics, these discrepancies, usually insignificant in individual cases, grew to substantial aggregate amounts, even though minuscule in relation to the billions of dollars billed during the relevant period. Mistakes such as these are predictably made, but there was no way to correct them. Thus, if the proper charge for a particular patient for a dialysis treatment on a particular day at a particular NMC clinic was $126.25, and the Medicare clerk transposed the last two digits and sent NMC $126.52, the resulting 27-cent discrepancy was very hard to pinpoint, since the intermediary would send the clinic one large check for hundreds of treatments for scores of patient-beneficiaries the clinic treated that month, and was impossible to return. Over the course of several years and millions of dialysis procedures, these 27-cent discrepancies, and other small errors, some as small as a penny, accumulated into hundreds of thousands of dollars.

NMC tried to return these to the intermediaries, but they had no means to accept returns. NMC tried to use these positive discrepancies to offset similar negative discrepancies in under-payments from Medicare that also occurred. And for a long time NMC never "booked" the income, that is, while it deposited the checks and had the cash in its bank accounts, NMC established a reserve or "payable" to offset the discrepancy, just as though these amounts represented a debt or liability it had someday to pay Medicare. That "someday" never came, and by 1985 after NMC had been acquired by W.R. Grace, the so called "unreconciled payment" reserve account was significant and needed to be resolved. NMC went through an elaborate and expensive procedure under the supervision of its independent auditing firm to analyze the millions of entries that comprised the unreconciled payment account, categorize these entries by type, notify the Medicare intermediaries of their right to reclaim these amounts and had several meetings with Medicare officials to find a resolution. As a result, a significant amount of money was returned, but, finally, that amount not claimed by Medicare was "booked," i.e., the reserve and the underlying liability was wiped off the company's books. One of the October 1995 subpoenas sought information about these practices which were universally acknowledged as "old news."

The other matters that underlay the issuance of the subpoenas were just as stale as the physician compensation issue and the unreconciled payments matter. Three subpoenas concerned the company's billing practices and whether NMC and its dialysis clinics and home care service providers were charging Medicare too much for certain services - disputes that normally arise in the course of doing business in today's healthcare market, and are generally resolved through negotiations. These included a dispute over the fees charged by clinics for administering parenteral nutrition solutions to dialysis patients who were undergoing dialysis. Another involved whether certain ancillary services and drugs which NMC clinics delivered to its patients were separately billable and payable or were included in the dialysis fee. The third area of billing concerns focused on the practices of Lifechem, the NMC subsidiary that provided laboratory services, mainly performing certain blood tests, despite the fact that prior to the October 1995 subpoenas, NMC had itself performed a thorough review of Lifechem billings and in the summer of 1995 had voluntarily returned $4.5 million to Medicare that arose from these clerical errors.

The final inquiry concerned whether the company and its subsidiaries were paying the insurance premiums for its indigent patients so they could qualify for Medicare and also for other third-party insurance programs. Some government agents viewed such practices as fraudulent. Others saw them as beneficial and charitable. Despite the fact that these practices and procedures were disclosed, routine, and had been adopted and practiced for several years, the government chose to land on NMC with both feet at precisely the worst possible time. With these subpoenas hanging over the company's future, the spin off would be delayed at best, and very likely deferred.

At the very least, complying with the government's seven subpoenas, which sought immense volumes of documents and data, would cost NMC and Grace millions of dollars in legal fees. Experts had to be retained by NMC in the substantive areas of Medicare law, litigators had to begin working on defensive strategies, criminal defense counsel had to be retained, and legions of junior attorneys and paralegal professionals, who could comb NMC's records to find the documents demanded by the government, had to be engaged. In addition, the Grace executives viewed

Hampers and the rest of NMC's management team and its phalanx of attorneys as arm's length adversaries in setting a price and terms for the spin off of NMC. Consequently, Grace retained its own team of lawyers to shadow the NMC lawyers' efforts. The process would consume the next three years.

What the public, including Grace stockholders, knew on October 18, 1995, while limited, was enough to cause a splurge of selling and the 13% one day drop in the price of Grace common stock. The next day, The New York Times reported, "[T]he announcement stunned investors," and noted that the OIG spokesperson claimed the subpoenas, issued "in pursuit of a potential criminal and civil matter," started a process that could take from six months to five years. In the same article, however, CEO Costello announced that "Grace plans to continue with the spin off of NMC." Those plans were quickly abandoned, as it became clear that the resolution of these issues raised by the government would not meet Grace's timetable for disposing of its NMC subsidiary. On November 1 Grace announced that the NMC spin off would be delayed from late 1995 to "early next year."

Grace started to look for potential purchasers for NMC who would understand the issues raised by the government and be able to assess and evaluate the resulting risk. On December 1, 1995, The Wall Street Journal reported that in the wake of the government's investigations, Dr. Hampers was no longer able to raise the financing necessary for the spin off of NMC. Given the breadth and amorphous nature of the government's probe, the effect it would have on the value of NMC and its ability to assume a large amount of debt was impossible for the bankers to assess. Would it mean $10 million, $100 million, or more, and over what period of time? Hampers was convinced that the deal could have gone ahead if Grace had been willing to stand behind the transaction and guarantee part of the NMC debt, but Costello insisted that Grace had to walk away without any continuing risk. The universe of potential buyers was a small one, and it consisted entirely of dialysis product manufacturers. NMC was once again "in play," and Hampers was hard pressed to maintain control.

In a revealing exchange of letters with Chairman Costello in November, 1995, Hampers expressed his concerns about selling

NMC to the highest bidder, which would undoubtedly be one of the three major artificial kidney manufacturers - Baxter International, Inc. (U.S.), Fresenius AG (Germany), or Gambro AB (Sweden). In a letter dated November 21, 1995 Mr. Costello put Hampers on notice that Hampers was to cooperate and direct his NMC staff to cooperate with Grace, as it attempted to sell NMC, and that "a failure on your part or the part of others at NMC or your advisors to [cooperate] will be viewed as a breach of [your employment] contract." Costello noted that he was in an "uneasy position," since he was relying on Hampers to supply the data necessary to meet the reasonable requests of the potential buyers and that Hampers' interest in orchestrating a spin off or his own purchase of NMC put him in conflict with the goal of "consummating a transaction in the best interests of the shareholders of Grace."

Hampers' November 30th response was equally unambiguous: "Grace will have my continued full support and cooperation in a transaction which is in the best interests of the three principal constituencies of National Medical Care, namely NMC's patients, the stockholders of Grace and NMC's employees. My principal concern is to assure that any acquirer of NMC would continue to provide first class treatment to NMC's patients." Hampers made it perfectly clear that he, not Grace, would decide whether any proposed transaction met those criteria. Hampers went on to say "...you should not be uneasy if I insist on my right to provide you with...information and advice...," and further put Costello and Grace on notice that pursuant to the terms of his employment agreement, Hampers would end his fulltime employment status on March 31, 1996 and exercise his contractual right to assume the role of consultant (at a handsome retainer) thereafter. This provoked an agitated reaction from Costello by letter dated December 4, 1995, in which he reiterated his position that he and the Grace board, and not Hampers, would decide what was in the best interests of Grace stockholders. Costello went on in his rebuttal to warn Hampers "not...to spend your time putting together a management proposal which may conflict with what I am attempting to accomplish with others."

Other passages in these letters made it clear that Costello and Grace executives were not sharing the details of their conversations with potential buyers with Hampers. Costello even noted in the December 4th epistle that "other parties...may insist on limiting the dissemination of their proposals..." In other words, these buyers saw Hampers as the major stumbling block and they didn't want him to know what they were proposing. Hampers and his NMC colleagues were being shut out of the negotiations. As long as the acquirers were willing to buy NMC and manage it without Hampers at the helm, he had lost his leverage. At about this time, a group of top managers at NMC offered to confront Grace with a mass mutiny, if Hampers would lead them. The continued services and goodwill of these managers was a major piece of the investment and a threatened walkout would surely impede the sale and regain leverage for Hampers and the NMC group. But Hampers rejected the scheme as futile. Without $3.5 billion in capital and loan commitments, there was simply no way for Hampers and the NMC managers and the clinic directors to stop Grace's determination to divest NMC and get out of the healthcare business.

On December 1, 1995 The Wall Street Journal reported that Baxter was negotiating with Grace to purchase NMC, and specifically that the misgivings held by Baxter Chairman Vernon R. Loucks, Jr. about acquiring healthcare service providers, which competed with other Baxter customers, had been set aside. In 1992 Baxter had spun off its Caremark International, Inc. subsidiary, a provider of home healthcare services, for that very reason. A few days later the Journal reported that the spin off of NMC had been placed on hold and that Grace was also talking with Fresenius and Gambro about a possible acquisition of NMC. On December 5th, the CEO of Gambro, Berthold Lindqvist, denied that report with respect to the Swedish manufacturer. Grace was clearly a "motivated seller," given the recent squeeze by the federal government on NMC. Unlike Dr. Hampers, Mr. Costello hadn't experienced the methods of government investigators and couldn't share Hampers' more sanguine and long term outlook on NMC's future. Nor did Costello understand or share Hampers' concern for the welfare of NMC's patients, should the firm be acquired by a product manufacturer. Costello had been elected CEO on a simple promise of increasing shareholder value and had courted the favor of Grace's major investors with an assurance that Grace would divest NMC. Hampers felt Costello was panicked and selling NMC short.

What Grace executives were selling was the untapped, added value of combining NMC and its 625 dialysis clinics with a strong dialysis product manufacturer. What these executives didn't appreciate was the importance of having the resulting combination controlled by the service providers, and not the manufacturer. Hampers' projections for the business and the potential "unlocked" value of such a combination were used to entice the three largest manufacturers into a deal. How the delicate symbiosis would be nurtured and controlled after the transaction was not Grace's concern, as it was for Hampers, who would have had a large personal financial stake and a major professional interest in seeing that the symbiosis was successful. Using NMC's 625 centers as captive outlets for the products of its manufacturing partner could not work, in Hampers' view, unless the physicians were in control.

Amid this turmoil and adding to it, on December 4, 5, and 6, 1995, The New York Times published a series of front page articles by Kurt Eichenwald about National Medical Care and the End-Stage Renal Disease Program, basically rehashing the old familiar charges that had plagued the company since its founding. The articles focused on NMC's size and alleged monopolistic practices, the dialyzer reuse issue, the high cost of the ESRD Program, the company's former FDA problems which had been resolved, and, of course, the series of subpoenas issued in mid-October by the OIG of Health and Human Services. Given the prominent placement, unprecedented length, and accumulation of charges against NMC, some of which were over a decade old, the Times expose painted a grim picture of NMC and its management. The timing of this publication, six weeks after the government's subpoenas and during Hampers' last ditch effort to preserve the spin off and forestall an ill considered sale of NMC to one of the manufacturers, was disastrous. The critical impact of the articles was internal, as they strengthened Costello's resolve to dispose of NMC at any price and diluted Hampers' standing with the Grace board. Needless to say, the series further depressed the morale of the employees of NMC.

The major stumbling block for Grace in finding a buyer for

NMC at a price that was near the $3.5 to $4 billion that Wall Street expected was the pending legal process brought by the OIG. There were two possible approaches. Either the buyer and seller could attempt to agree on the magnitude of the risk and appropriately adjust the price downward to accommodate these uncertainties in value, or Grace as the seller could stand behind the price and guarantee any civil penalties, damages and expenses that resulted from the lawsuits. Baxter proposed a straight forward, "garden variety" acquisition which suited its corporate culture and past acquisition experience. Baxter offered to buy NMC and its 550 U.S. clinics and 75 foreign clinics for $3.8 billion, comprised of $1.28 billion in cash, plus the assumption of $425 million of NMC's debt, $1.8 billion in Baxter stock and another $300 million in the form of a note from Baxter. Baxter would assume up to $100 million in costs, fees and fines that might result from the government's action against NMC, but anything beyond that first $100 million would have to be guaranteed by Grace. Grace balked. It wanted to walk away from the transaction with no continuing risk. Feeling rebuffed by Grace management, Baxter went public with its proposal on February 1, 1996. The next day, a Friday, the news boosted the price of Grace common stock by $7.38, or 12%.

Confronted with the pressure applied by Baxter's public announcement, Grace completed its negotiations for the sale of NMC with Fresenius, and the announcement of the terms was published on Monday, February 5th. Fresenius, which controlled 13% of the worldwide dialysis product market (compared to Baxter's 42% share, and Gambro's 32% share), and Grace would create an entity which would be controlled by Fresenius holding 55% of its stock. The remaining 45% of the stock of the new entity would be held by Grace stockholders. The transaction would result in a cash payment to Grace of $2.3 billion, tax free, and would be implemented as a reverse spin off, in a model that copied the proposal of the VIVRA group proposed in June of 1995. In negotiating the necessary financing with the lending banks, Fresenius agreed to guarantee the loans, putting the German manufacturer on the line for any financial disaster that might occur as a result of the government's lawsuits against NMC. Essentially, Grace transferred both the capital gain tax liability and the legal exposure to Grace shareholders. In gross terms, the transaction valued NMC at $4.17 billion, with Fresenius paying $2.3 billion for a 55% share and the remaining $1.87 billion value (45%) being spun off to Grace shareholders. Wall Street analyzed the deal as better than the Baxter offer by "about $1.50 to $2.00 a [Grace common] share." Grace management accomplished its objectives: no corporate taxes, no continuing risk, and lots of cash.

In its February 5th announcement Grace noted that Dr. Hampers would continue as CEO of National Medical Care after the transaction, but in fact Hampers had not come to any agreement at that time with Fresenius and his continuing tenure as NMC's chief was not a condition of the transaction. The large stockholders of Grace liked the deal with Fresenius, and Hampers was quoted in a February 6, 1996 Wall Street Journal article, criticizing Baxter's plan to convert many NMC patients to Baxter's peritoneal dialysis therapy: "Our philosophy has been you should let the physician decide what is best for the patient." Finally, on February 23, 1996 Baxter announced that it was withdrawing its bid to purchase NMC, thus clearing the way for the transaction with Fresenius.

The transaction was naturally conditioned on financing, and the principals - Grace executives, Fresenius management, their lawyers, Hampers and his NMC staff - set about the task of convincing the banks that the deal would work, that the future earnings of NMC, now in combination with its German manufacturing parent, would be sufficient to retire the large debt, and that the government's pending lawsuits against NMC would not impair the company's ability to pay its loans and operate its business in the expected manner. Hampers knew that a key element in the success of the venture entailed sufficient incentives for management to make sure the plan was attained, and he didn't see a commitment from Fresenius to provide that level of incentives for NMC's management, which was infected at that time with very low morale. Many managers were already talking about bailing out, and employees at all levels, unsure of their futures with Fresenius, were updating their resumes. In addition to convincing the bankers to lend the new entity two and one-half billion dollars, the principal players had to present the transaction in a formal way to Grace stockholders for their collective approval. While it was a foregone conclusion that Grace stockholders would approve the deal and accept shares in the new entity, subsequent lawsuits could and would arise if any of the statements, assumptions and forecasts in the proxy statement, on which these Grace stockholders relied in approving the spin off, were later proved false or misleading.

Hampers was not sanguine about these operational and financial predictions, not because he didn't believe that NMC under his direction could attain them, but because, he wasn't sure Fresenius would either give him the incentive and control necessary to achieve them or, alternatively, without Hampers, Fresenius could find other executives who could motivate the staff and drive the organization sufficiently to achieve these tough goals. As a result, after considerable anguish, Hampers decided he could not "sign off" on these financial predictions and representations, and he consequently decided to resign as CEO of NMC and not continue to run the operation for Fresenius and the public shareholders. Hampers announced his resignation on June 15, 1996, his 63rd birthday, and 28 years after the incorporation of National Medical Care. In consideration for $7 million Dr. Hampers agreed not to compete with the company and to provide consulting services to Fresenius on request for the following two years.

The Fresenius transaction was approved in due course by the lending banks and by Grace shareholders, and became effective September 30, 1996.

The alienation of National Medical Care was effected on three levels. The company had come under the control of foreign investors, and was quite literally an "alien" corporation. It had also become subject to the direction of its parent, a manufacturing company expecting to increase its product sales. And thirdly, the former NMC was no longer managed by physicians. Whether and how these differences in the culture, experience, mission and orientation of the company's top executives would affect the quality and efficiency of the healthcare services provided to its patients remained uncertain. By engaging the genius and efficacy of the free enterprise system to deliver healthcare and by inviting capitalists to invest in the enterprise, National Medical Care, Inc. accepted the burdens of the bargain as well as the benefits. In making their individual investment decisions, the owners of capital accept, shift and alienate the control of enterprises, regardless of their underlying purpose and effect. Through twenty-eight years Dr. Hampers had been able to control, and accepted responsibility for, the outcomes, managing not only the operations of the company, but also the expectations of its investors, whether these were a small group of venture capitalists and insurance companies, thousands of public stockholders, or a multinational, conglomerate parent corporation.

At a farewell gathering in Waltham on July 8, 1996, Gus Hampers seemed embarrassed to accept the plaudits and recollections of many long time NMC employees and associates. Self-effacing of his own contributions and repeating his well worn maxim that "it's better to be lucky than smart," Dr. Hampers urged the company employees to continue their mission to provide the best patient care and not to be deterred by critics. "The value of what we have done together at National Medical Care in terms of saving and improving the lives of thousands of patients can never be measured and will always be questioned. But none of us should have any regrets for having succeeded," Hampers noted in conclusion and quietly and quickly stepped down.

20

Epilogue

On January 23, 2000 President Clinton used his regular Saturday radio broadcast to the nation to heap praise on his Justice Department for securing the largest settlement in history from a healthcare provider accused of defrauding Medicare. He went on to condemn Medicare fraud and abuse and to propose a new federal program in his fiscal year 2001 budget for a team of Medicare fraud fighters to ferret out additional fraud, abuse and waste in the $285 billion annual federal Medicare program. The settlement to which Clinton referred was a stunning $486.3 million to be paid by Fresenius Medical Care AG, the successor to National Medical Care, and exceeded the previous record in Medicare fraud cases ($379 million paid by National Medical Enterprises) by over $100 million.

Fresenius announced the definitive settlement on January 19, 2000, but the general outline of its terms of surrender to the government had been forecast in its November 23, 1999 press release announcing its third quarter earnings. In order to settle the government's claims against National Medical Care, Fresenius agreed to pay $385 million in civil reimbursements to Medicare and $101 million in criminal penalties to the government. In addition, the three NMC subsidiaries that pleaded guilty to criminal allegations - NMC Medical Products, Lifechem laboratory, and NMC Homecare - were disqualified from further participation in the Medicare program. In a separate, but related, agreement HHS agreed to pay Fresenius $59.2 million to settle disputed claims the company had regarding reimbursement for intradialytic parenteral nutrition therapy delivered to dialysis patients prior to December 31, 1999. It was reported that about $65.8 million of these penalties would be paid to several "whistle blowers" who had filed qui tam proceedings against Fresenius. The whistle blowers were competitors and former employees of the company, three of whom themselves participated in the activities that led to the allegations of fraud.

As these reports clearly indicate, the story of National Medical Care did not end in July of 1996 when Dr. Hampers left his role as chief executive officer at the age of 63. In order to continue his ties to the company, and more importantly, to prevent him from starting a competing entity, Fresenius management retained Hampers as a consultant for a term of two years, commencing on April 1, 1996. Not only was it critical to ensure Hampers' loyalty to the corporation he had co-founded and for which Fresenius was paying approximately $4.4 billion, but his assistance in defending the company against the claims instituted by the government was viewed by the purchasers in the spring of 1996 as essential in protecting their investment.

Since the federal government initiated litigation against NMC on October 17, 1995 with the issuance of seven broad subpoenas in a legal process that coordinated the offices of the U.S. Attorneys and the HHS Inspector General, an enormous cloud hung over the company's prospects and even threatened several individuals with criminal penalties. The immediate effect in the fall of 1995 was to frustrate Hampers' attempt to perfect the spin off of NMC from W.R. Grace & Co., which Grace had announced the previous June. The spin off would have reestablished NMC as an independent (albeit heavily burdened with debt) company with Hampers as its CEO.

Fresenius agreed to acquire NMC from Grace in a complicated, tax free (to Grace) merger followed by a "reverse spin off" for consideration valued at the time at $4.2 billion. Fresenius managers, assisted by competent legal counsel, carefully examined the government's case against NMC and, unlike its rival Baxter, assessed the risk as assumable. The terms of the deal required the German parent corporation to own 55% of the new company (with Grace shareholders owning the remaining 45%) and to guarantee the terms of the loan and the other obligations of the new company. These obligations and contingencies included civil or criminal liabilities NMC might have to the U.S. government as a result of the legal proceedings. Fresenius had access to the information then available, and performed their diligence before signing the definitive merger agreement. During the period between late February and September 30, 1996, when the Fresenius purchase of NMC was perfected, the buyer had plenty of time to consider, plan and begin to facilitate its strategy of defense to the government's legal attack. Moreover, had facts come to light during that seven month period that materially and adversely affected the terms of the deal, Fresenius would have been able to back out of its commitment.

Obviously, Fresenius had put some value on this legal contingency, and decided that the cost of defending the company, or conversely the cost of settling the proceedings, was within an acceptable and assumable range. No one would have argued in 1996 or more recently that the range came close to the $486 million settlement finally reached in late 1999, which represents over 11% of the acquisition package of $4.4 billion. Does the explanation lie in the strength of the government's case that was so badly misjudged by cadres of lawyers working for NMC, Grace, and Fresenius and their respective bankers? Or was the 1999 settlement the product of a radical shift in strategy by Fresenius management that essentially decided to "throw in the towel" and blame the previous owners and managers, irrespective of the half billion dollar price tag?

Dr. Hampers easily concluded that management decided to abandon the company's defense in order to help the government lawyers and bureaucrats score big at the expense of Hampers and other former NMC managers and of the current Fresenius investors. "Most of the government's allegations are completely off base and defensible," Hampers stated. "And giving the feds the benefit of every doubt still leaves me way short of $250 million, let alone $486 million. Fresenius management completely caved in, and the long term consequences are more harmful than just the payment of half a billion dollars of investors' money," he emphasized.

After four years of investigation and millions of dollars in legal fees, the facts underlying the allegations of criminal and civil liability were essentially unchanged from the facts known in October of 1995. The government had focused its investigation and legal attack in five areas, all of which either involved the anti-kickback statutes [these laws make it illegal to pay for patient referrals] or the False Claims Act.

The first, broad based assault involved what Hampers described as an "old chestnut," since the issue had been around since NMC's founding, and hit at the essence of NMC's desire to include its medical directors as part owners or financial partners of their individual clinics. Prior to its listing on the New York Stock Exchange, NMC offered its medical directors a minority interest consisting of shares of stock, typically five or ten percent of the total shares in the corporation that held title to the individual clinic. The company had an option to repurchase these minority shares and the doctor had a corresponding put to sell his shares back to the company at a price based on a formula that tied the price to the earnings of the clinic over a specified period of time, usually five years. When National Medical Care applied for listing on the NYSE in 1973 [it was first listed on May 8, 1974], the Exchange found this ownership structure confusing and an impediment to listing. By then NMC had over a dozen subsidiaries, each operating a clinic or hospital and each with a physician held minority interest subject to these complementary puts and calls. Consequently, NMC abandoned the earlier structure and simply granted the medical directors direct profit sharing agreements, typically for five-year terms, at the end of which the doctor would receive a lump sum payment equal to a multiple of the profits his clinic had generated. These profit shares were substantial and could range from 20 to 40% of the five-year after tax earnings of the clinics. The object was to hold the directors' loyalty and services for the full five-year term and to motivate the directors to (a) build the patient base and (b) cut expenses and operate efficiently.

Effective January 1, 1995 federal legislation known as "Stark II" [named after its Congressional author, Fortney "Pete" Stark of California] banned such arrangements by prohibiting doctors from referring patients to any healthcare provider (such as a dialysis clinic) in which they held a financial interest. NMC dutifully complied with Stark II by eliminating the profit sharing agreements and constructing individually negotiated contracts with each of its clinic directors.

The pre-Stark profit sharing arrangements were often criticized by opponents of proprietary medicine, but far from hiding these arrangements, NMC was open about their existence and promoted them as essential to its success and efficient operation. Not only lawyers for the company, but lawyers for its medical directors, W.R. Grace & Co., and for NMC's underwriters all examined these arrangements, specifically to determine whether they violated the federal anti-kickback precepts. Other dialysis operators copied the NMC system. HCFA itself was well aware of the profit sharing system and expressed no reservations about these prior to 1995. The law prohibited payments for referrals, not profit shares. There was no direct correlation between the number of patients referred to a clinic by a particular medical director and the amount of his profit share. There were three factors that could influence the amount of the profit share paid to a clinic director. One was the number of his patients he referred to the clinic. Another was the number of patients other physicians referred to the clinic, and the third was how well he operated the clinic in terms of cutting expenses and improving its efficiency. In many, if not a majority of cases, patients were referred to outpatient clinics for care by an independent committee of hospital based physicians over which the individual clinic director had no control.

In its 1995-1999 investigation of NMC, the federal government was attempting to apply Stark II retroactively. This obviously raised the issue of why Stark II was necessary, if HCFA and the Justice Department already considered profit shares illegal. Secondly, the government was avoiding the issue of its own knowledge and acceptance of these profit sharing arrangements for over twenty years. In addition, in the area of chronic maintenance dialysis, the referral to a clinic in which the physician had a financial interest could only hurt another dialysis clinic, not Medicare. In other words, if Mrs. Jones didn't go to her doctor's NMC clinic, but instead went to Saint Mary's dialysis clinic for care, Medicare would end up paying the same amount (or more) for her care.

There were two ways in which the doctor's financial interest in a dialysis clinic could theoretically affect his medical prescriptions and hence impact the patient's health or Medicare's finances. First, an unscrupulous profit sharing doctor (or a doctor that owned his own clinic and there were many of these outside the NMC system who were not indicted) could inflate his profit-share by cutting services. This would not hurt Medicare directly, but it might hurt the patient. This issue, however, was not the gravamen of the government's complaint. The government lawyers were looking for waste and fraud on Medicare's finances, not the effect on patient health. In the case of chronic dialysis patients, under-service (e.g., inadequate or short dialysis, failing to administer necessary medications, or employing inadequately trained staff) was policed by state health departments under contract with Medicare to insure that minimum standards were met. These were health and safety issues, not issues of Medicare fraud.

The one area where doctors could conceivably defraud Medicare through these profit sharing arrangements was by over-prescribing therapies, mainly drugs and lab tests, that were not necessary and that were separately reimbursed by Medicare. The government focused on the laboratory (Lifechem) and products divisions of NMC. To the extent that doctors purchased products and services from these inhouse suppliers, their profit-shares were increased by a so called "add back," which essentially allowed the medical directors to share in the profits of these affiliated suppliers. The laboratory "add back" was eliminated effective January 1, 1992 in response to legislation known as "Stark I." The company reasonably felt that the efficiencies derived from a central laboratory service and supply business should be shared with the medical directors. The government's theory was not that the medical directors were getting paid for referring patients to the clinics, but that they were getting referral fees, by way of these "add backs" from the laboratory and product subsidiaries. The theory however had to be proved, and the facts were on the side of the company. Following the October 17, 1995 attack, NMC commissioned a broad study of the use of these ancillary services and products, comparing NMC clinics with those of non-NMC clinics, most of which were operated by non-profit entities. The study found that NMC underutilized available ancillary products and services compared to the industry average. If the government was asserting that the profit sharing system, which included these "add backs," violated the pre-Stark II anti-kickback laws, they had a very tough row to hoe.

The government was also asserting that even the post-Stark II compensation arrangements between NMC and the medical directors, which did not involve profit shares, were illegal, because Stark II prohibits compensation that exceeds "the fair market value" for the services provided by these directors. That theory was untested, and would have required the government to convince a jury of the fair value of the services of a medical director, and that the company knowingly paid more than this fair value in order to induce patient referrals.

The second front in the government's legal case against NMC involved the manner in which NMC accounted for and reported discrepancies between the amounts it billed the Medicare intermediaries (the insurance companies in each state that process Medicare claims under contract with HCFA) and the amounts it received. Over the course of years of submitting millions of claims for payment, discrepancies would occur between the amounts due and the amounts paid. Many of these individual discrepancies amounted to less than ten cents each. Where payments exceeded the amounts properly due, NMC created a credit balance that it called "unreconciled payments." By the mid-1980's this account grew to a very large number and the company's independent auditors required the company to undertake an aggressive program to return these overpayments to Medicare. The account essentially consisted of cash that had been received but could not properly be included in the income account because it wasn't "earned." The Medicare intermediaries had no way to take these funds back.

NMC undertook an extensive account-by-account analysis and did end up returning some of these funds. Under the procedure adopted by NMC and approved by its auditors, if after four years, the Medicare intermediaries continued to refuse these returns after notice, the company transferred the amounts to its income accounts. Partly due to NMC's incessant attempts to return these mistakenly paid funds to Medicare, HCFA finally issued a regulation in 1992 that required providers to report every calendar quarter the amount of these credit balances. The first report due June 30, 1992 was to report credit balances that had accumulated up to that point in time. The amounts reported by NMC on its June 30, 1992 report did not include amounts that had been "reversed" (i.e., taken into income) in years prior to the immediate four years before 1992.

The government alleged that NMC intentionally understated the credit balance, thus violating the regulation and the False Claims Act. The well documented history however would support the company's defense that starting as early as 1983 NMC had tried everything that it and its auditors and lawyers could think of to return these funds to the Medicare intermediaries. Moreover, there was the defense of selective enforcement available to NMC, since thousands of other Medicare providers had retained these overpayments without any attempt to return them to the government. At worse, this matter could be resolved by returning the overpayments to the government. The government would have had an impossible task in trying to convince a jury that NMC had intentionally defrauded the government on this count, given the documented attempts by the company for over a decade to deal with this problem directly.

The government's third complaint against NMC concerned the payment by NMC of premiums for supplemental insurance to cover healthcare costs for NMC's indigent patients. Dialysis services are covered under Part B of the Medicare program. Part B requires the insured beneficiary to pay a monthly premium. Indigent patients who could not afford to pay this monthly premium were technically not covered by Medicare for their dialysis care and would become Medicaid beneficiaries. It was in the company's interest, as well as the interest of the patient and his other healthcare providers like his doctors, to have the patient covered under Part B of Medicare. Consequently, the company would pay these premiums on behalf of the patients. There is no strict prohibition against this procedure of helping the patients pay their insurance premiums, and it certainly assisted the patients and all their healthcare providers. The government never advanced a convincing theory as to why this practice was illegal or how it harmed the Medicare system. Ironically, in the mid-1990's Congress and the

President created a special program to help the indigent pay their Part B premiums to ensure their coverage under Medicare. It asked the states to implement this premium paying system, and the states largely failed in these efforts. The government was attempting to punish NMC for doing exactly what it was trying to have the states do under another government program.

As with the issue of medical director compensation and the issue of credit balances, the issue of paying these premiums for patients was open and "above board" on the part of NMC, and well known by the bureaucrats who were administering the dialysis program. There were no factual disputes in these matters, and the government attorneys were interpreting the facts differently from the interpretation of government bureaucrats charged with operating the program for several years in order to reach a conclusion of criminality.

Similarly, the fourth area that concerned the government, NMC Homecare division's method of billing for parenteral nutrition services, which it provided to dialysis patients, had been a matter that NMC and Medicare officials had been trying for years to solve. The essence of the problem was an omission in the regulations, and the attempts by NMC and Medicare bureaucrats to extemporize a workable solution became the crux of the government's case against NMC in 1995-1999. Parenteral nutrition services (basically intravenous feeding) are required for patients who have no ability to eat or absorb nutrients through their digestive system. Without "total parenteral nutrition," or TPN, these patients starve and will eventually die. Once TPN services could be provided outside the hospital, generally in the patient's home, Medicare Part B covered the costs for Medicare patients at a fraction of the in hospital expense. Regulations were prepared to cover documentation of the need for TPN and the amount that Medicare would pay for the feeding solutions, which were subject to prescription, the necessary equipment (poles and pumps), and the services of a professional to administer the treatment. Basically, these regulations were drafted to cover the large majority of patients and contemplated daily TPN treatments in the patient's home or in a nursing facility.

There was, however, a subset of TPN patients for whom the

Medicare regulations did not apply, and these were dialysis patients, who had not only lost kidney function, but so called "gut function," or the ability to digest food, as well. In reviewing masses of data that NMC collected on thousands of patients, Dr. Lowrie and his assistant Nancy Lew queried whether there were any laboratory test data that might predict patient mortality or morbidity. In turned out that dialysis patients with low serum albumins (3.5 mm per 100ml) had a significantly higher probability (4 to 5 times the average) of death within a year. They theorized that these low levels of albumin indicated that the patients were starving. This starvation syndrome may have been caused by the difficulty dialysis patients experience in eating as a result of frequent nausea, or it could have been caused by a systemic problem of malabsorbtion of nutrients, or both. In any event, to reduce the risk of morbidity and mortality, doctors began ordering TPN for their patients. Using TPN to counteract the starvation syndrome for these patients was driven by serious patient care concerns, i.e., without it they would die. Reimbursement was not the motivating factor.

This small group of very sick patients presented a distinct problem for their physicians and for Medicare. If they received TPN services everyday, as contemplated by the Medicare regulations, they would suffer from fluid overload since their kidneys did not function. If they were denied TPN services, they would starve. Physicians for these patients saw an opportunity to administer TPN services at the dialysis clinics at the same time the patients were being dialyzed, or so called intradialytic parenteral nutrition ("IDPN"). Patients on this IDPN therapy improved as they were simultaneously "cleaned out and filled-up." In truth the regulations had not made provision for these patients, because prior to the mid-1980's most of them expired very quickly.

Medicare began covering IDPN in 1984, and NMC led the way, as it was able to combine its expertise in dialysis and homecare services. It was an uphill struggle that involved Dr. Hampers and even Terry Daniels from W.R. Grace & Co. to convince the Medicare intermediary to cover IDPN. Despite initial refusals from the intermediary, NMC continued to provide these services for its patients without any reasonable idea that it would be paid. Four basic billing problems arose over IDPN services.

First, finding coverage for 12 or 13 infusions per month, rather than daily infusions presented a conundrum for Medicare, since the fee was paid on a monthly, rather than a per treatment basis. NMC brought this to their attention and was told to bill for the full monthly amount, because for any given month the patient was "on" TPN, even though he might have received 13, rather than 30 actual treatments. Second, the regulations, contemplating home care, reimbursed each patient for an individual IV pole and a separate infusion pump, whereas in a dialysis clinic this equipment could be interchanged and used for more than one patient. Thirdly, the regulations paid for a healthcare worker (like a visiting nurse) to administer the treatment. At a dialysis center this was not necessary as dialysis personnel could administer the treatments, although this duty did put extra responsibility on the clinic. As a result, NMC Homecare (which billed for these treatments) paid the dialysis clinic a "hanging fee," or a service fee for the administration of the therapy. Finally, the basic coverage requirement under the Medicare regulations involved criteria that the patient suffered from malabsorbtion and needed TPN everyday, and while this was true for some of these patients in a general sense, in fact, because of their ESRD, they could not accept TPN daily, like other TPN patients. For other IDPN patients, malabsobtion might not have been demonstrated, but they were still starving as evidenced by their low albumins. In other words, but for their kidney failure, these patients would have required TPN daily, but because they suffered from ESRD, daily infusions would have killed them.

In its investigation, the government lawyers tried to "nail" NMC on all counts relating to IDPN, interpreting the same facts which were not essentially in dispute into a conclusion of fraud. Thus, giving 13 treatments and billing for 30 was alleged to be fraudulent. Similarly billing for individual IV poles and pumps, when these were not used in the centers was deemed to be fraud by the OIG and Justice Department. Paying the dialysis clinics a "hanging fee" was looked at as kickback to the center by the Homecare company. And finally, certifying patients as requiring daily TPN services and then infusing them only during their thrice weekly dialysis treatments was asserted to be fraudulent.

The government lawyers were taking the exact opposite position from the Medicare regulators on which NMC had relied. The "flexibility" that NMC had finally persuaded Medicare bureaucrats to accept in order to cover IDPN was being seen as "fraud." In its public relations zeal the OIG even cited one instance where an IDPN patient had been certified for this service on the basis of weight loss only to discover that his weight loss was partially due to a leg amputation. Whether the amputated patient was also suffering from loss of gut function and loss of kidney function did not occur to these lawyers-turned-pundits. Unfortunately, in the world of diabetic, ESRD, starving, elderly patients, complications that involve more than one diagnosis often do arise, and cases are not so easily categorized as black and white choices. The larger message this ex post facto analysis sends to physicians, healthcare facility operators, and Medicare bureaucrats, who want to make the necessary exceptions and adjustments in order to fit the patients within the broader coverage picture, is that these attempts to extemporize and build flexibility into Medicare will not only be unrewarded, but will be severely punished.

Princeton University Professor Uwe E. Reinhardt noted this phenomenon in a Wall Street Journal column on January 21, 2000. "So spooked are the executives of the health industry that they have taken to billing government programs less than they legitimately could...As added precaution, the health industry pays huge fees to outside compliance consultants, whose only job is to help facilities understand impenetrable Medicare rules," he wrote in commenting on the NMC case.

For his part, Dr. Hampers was eager to take this case to a jury. "The everyday requirement was okay for people with gastrointestinal problems alone, but not for individuals who could not handle excess fluid loads," he argued. "I consider it a very winnable issue if it were to be tried."

The fifth and final area of government concern involved business and billing practices at Lifechem, NMC's laboratory business. One practice alleged by the government, if true, was clearly illegal, and was recognized as illegal by everyone in the industry. The government alleged that the vice president of sales for NMC's medical products division (MPD) arranged for kickbacks, rebates and entertainment perquisites to clinic operators in order to induce them to refer laboratory and product sales business to MPD. The individual, David Weber, pleaded guilty in December 1998, and by the date of the January 2000 settlement, had not been sentenced. Obviously the government would try to secure Weber's cooperation against the company. The government alleged that these business practices were common and known by other employees at NMC and constituted a conspiracy to violate the anti-kickback statutes. To the extent that the facts alleged could be proved, there would be no defense, but whether proof of the facts asserted existed at all is conjectural.

The second asserted Lifechem transgression involved over-billing Medicare for services performed by the laboratory. Not only did the company acknowledge these errors, but NMC voluntarily disclosed these mistakes which arose from rapid growth and inadequate computer systems to support it. In September 1995 and again in mid-1996 and finally in 1999, in three separate disclosures, the company voluntarily tendered repayment along with interest which the government deposited, but the government had not accepted Lifechem's explanation and continued to assert a conspiracy to over bill and defraud Medicare.

The final issue concerning Lifechem was the company's practice in packaging lab tests which the government alleged had the effect of forcing doctors to order unnecessary tests for which Lifechem then billed the government. In addition to NMC, the government indicted three Lifechem and MPD employees, one of whom pleaded guilty in June 1999 to a charge of defrauding Medicare, but had not been sentenced as of the date of the Fresenius settlement. One of the indicted employees was the president of MPD during the relevant time period, and all counts against him were eventually dropped, except for one misdemeanor count. The facts are largely undisputed and pathetically anemic. Lifechem offered physicians a panel of hepatitis tests that the doctors could order for their patients, combining in one line for the doctors to check, a test that was routinely made every month to detect the patients antigen for hepatitis B, along with a test for hepatitis B antibodies to determine the degree of infectiousness, and finally a test for hepatitis C. The same bundling of these three tests was effected on paper forms and on Lifechem's electronic order form.

The government alleged that the bundling constituted a practice designed to force or trick doctors into ordering the hepatitis C test, which, in the government lawyers' view, was unnecessary, and comprised a conspiracy to defraud the government. In order to prove its allegation the government would have to prove that doctors were inadvertently ordering the hepatitis C test, and secondly that the test was unnecessary. For the second assertion, the government relied on the opinion of the Centers for Disease Control (CDC) to the effect that periodic hepatitis C testing among the general population was not required. Dr. Hampers noted that this would be an extremely difficult case for the government to prove. "The CDC advice did not concentrate on the testing of dialysis patients specifically," Hampers argued. "And CDC advice is not binding on individual doctors caring for individual patients in any case. A doctor has an obligation to order those blood tests that he considers necessary to treat his patients. The CDC opinion was not universally accepted."

In Hampers' estimation the doctors knew what tests they were ordering, or should have, and the alignment of these three tests was done as a time saver for the doctors, not a subterfuge. "I'm absolutely convinced that an overwhelming majority of doctors, both those at NMC clinics and those outside the NMC system, would dispute the government's argument that they were unconscious of which tests they were ordering."

What's most curious about the U.S. government's case against NMC was not that NMC charged for, and was paid for, services that NMC failed to provide. The government's case was that NMC provided too many services, and that these weren't necessary. The doctors and their patients received quality services and products from NMC's dialysis, homecare, products and laboratory divisions. NMC and its doctors, they asserted, were doing more laboratory and ancillary services than were absolutely necessary. None of the services, tests or products was provided by NMC, moreover, without a physician's order. In the two areas of greatest concern for the government, namely, Lifechem hepatitis testing and IDPN billings, NMC was fulfilling the orders of the patients' physicians. The government's contention was that NMC either tricked or coerced or bribed the physicians into prescribing these tests and therapies or, in the case of IDPN, that the doctors and NMC had conspired to infuse nutrients intravenously into dialysis patients who didn't really need these treatments. Whether the government could have come close to proving these allegations became moot once Fresenius decided to settle the case. Particularly in the case of IDPN, NMC and the doctors were pre-scribing and providing this service openly and after protracted negotiations with Medicare bureaucrats.

These sorts of disputes, essentially over "coverage," are com-mon place between healthcare providers and insurance compa-nies, Medicare and Medicaid, and HMO's. Physicians, hospitals and other providers are accustomed to contests over coverage, particularly in high tech and emerging fields of care, such as IDPN. Very often the providers lose these contests and when they do lose, they can't "retrieve" their healthcare services and medical products. What was unusual and chilling about the government's case against NMC/Fresenius was that the Justice Department criminalized the dispute. Thus, the government raised the stakes considerably; the provider not only risked millions of dollars for services and products already provided which could not be recouped, but it and some of its employees risked criminal penal-ties as well.

By raising the stakes in this manner, the government stifles any risk taking. With respect to IDPN services, for example, Hampers and NMC knew when they initiated this service for starv-ing dialysis patients in the mid-1980's that there were consider-able risks involved. The therapy was beneficial and necessary to lessen the risk of death for these patients in the opinion of NMC officials and the attending physicians. Whether or not Medicare would pay for these services was problematic, since the service could not meet Medicare's rigid requirement that the TPN service be required by demonstrated malabsobtion syndrome and that it be administered on a daily basis. Drs. Hampers, Lowrie and other officials personally made the case for IDPN to the Medicare inter-mediary and disclosed exactly what they were doing and how they would bill. While they waited for the Medicare intermediary to finally consent, NMC continued to provide this service adding years of life to hundreds of patients, but always knowing that they might never be paid for these services. Years later their admitted "creativity" in flexing the TPN requirements in order to cover dialysis patients was alleged to be criminal behavior.

The entire ethos and culture of NMC, which included reasonable risk taking in order to help patients, expand or create new coverage categories and assume the role of unpopularity, if it meant keeping patients alive, were driving Hampers and NMC towards this show down with the government. Had Hampers remained in control of NMC he would not have backed down. "I am thoroughly certain that the IDPN services were necessary and helped these patients, and that Medicare could have, and should have, paid for them," Hampers later argued. "What we did was not criminal or fraudulent in any way, and no jury would have found differently in my opinion." Of the $486.3 million settlement, nearly 63%, or $303 million, involved these disputed IDPN claims.

The Lifechem billing matters comprised about $149 million of the eventual settlement. Some of these matters were problematic for the company, since two former employees had agreed to plead guilty and would have been expected to testify against the company in exchange for reduced sentences and fines. However, on the issue of tricking doctors into ordering unnecessary tests, the government would have had a serious burden of proof, since it would be difficult to find doctors who had been tricked or who would have admitted that that might have been tricked.

Fresenius clearly lacked the motivation that Hampers had to fight the government on these matters. Certainly saving $486.3 million, or even a portion of that incredible settlement figure, provided considerable motivation for Fresenius management and investors. However, none of the decision makers had the level of personal financial stake in retaining those assets that Hampers would have had as the largest stakeholder in a new, independent NMC following a Grace spin off. Moreover, the events and actions that provoked the government into filing these complaints did not happen during the tenure of the Fresenius managers. The decisions and practices that were being labeled fraudulent and criminal by the government occurred during Hampers' watch. His integrity and judgment were at stake, as well as a king's ransom in fines and damages. In addition, for Hampers there was a matter of principle, forming the underlying ethos of NMC since its very beginning, that was worth the fight. NMC existed because he and his early colleagues refused to accept government bureaucrats and lawyers overriding physicians' decisions about patient care. Initiating a patient on dialysis, testing him for hepatitis C, or ordering IDPN should the patient develop starvation syndrome were all physician decisions, in Hampers' view. Even if he had no financial stake in the outcome or even if he had not been part of the management at the time, Hampers believed the company should respect its attending physicians and not cave into the government's demands.

During the 38-month period between September 1996 when Fresenius acquired NMC and the settlement of November 1999, Fresenius management had time to build its reserves to cushion a large multimillion dollar settlement, and to precondition Wall Street for the blow. As the new managers of NMC, they could curry favor with the government by not fighting but by being as cooperative as possible, and hoping that they could charm their way into a smaller settlement. There were early signs that Fresenius would not fight the government in court. They systematically purged the company of executive and midlevel managers who were part of the Hampers' regime, thereby contending that they had "cleaned house." One of the first to go was Hampers himself. Although he was still bound by a consulting and non-competition agreement with Fresenius until April 1998, Fresenius cut him loose and paid him off at the end of 1996. He and his personal staff were persona non grata at the company offices. In addition, Fresenius lawyers treated the investigation and imminent criminal trial as a negotiation, and not a particularly "arm's length" negotiation, either. They worked with the government's lawyers, compiling every iota of evidence, analyzing it, offering up summaries and essentially helping the government do its investigation without spending any effort on building its own defenses.

In putting up such a dispirited defense and cooperating with the U.S. attorneys, Fresenius gave slight encouragement to the five employees that were individually named as criminal defendants by the government. Their lawyers experienced less cooperation from the company attorneys than the prosecutors did. It was no wonder that two of these employees pled guilty and threw in the towel. In the end Fresenius gave up without a day of trial, handing the government lawyers the biggest Medicare anti-fraud settlement in the history of Medicare up to that time. Fresenius took the financial loss to be sure, but it was preparing for the hit for many months. Beyond that, the company could claim the role of the "good guys" that cleaned up the mess that was created by the former executives and managers.

In the words of Ben Lipps, the chief executive officer of Fresenius, "From the day of the merger, our objective has been to achieve a reasonable settlement that would allow us to continue to provide high quality patient care while maintaining our leadership in the industry and preserving the company's financial strength." As if there was any doubt, Lipps continued, "We have worked long and hard with the government to achieve this settlement."

Fresenius paid a lot of money for NMC and it was fully entitled to settle the matter, as it did, or fight the assertions. Beyond the issues and merits of the NMC investigation, however, anyone concerned about patient care and the significance of the doctor-patient relationship should feel uncomfortable about the Fresenius decision. One can only conclude that the government will be emboldened by its success in this case to use these tactics of intimidation in the future whenever a healthcare provider disagrees with the coverage decisions of Medicare or its intermediaries or HMO subcontractors. On the other side, doctors and other providers will have serious concerns about prescribing any tests or therapies outside those pre-approved by Medicare. When open, honest differences about coverage and payment between Medicare/Medicaid are transformed into criminal procedures and when assertions by doctors that they know what is best for their patients are characterized as fraud, everyone in the system is affected. This is the point that Professor Uwe E. Reinhardt made in his published opinion piece a few days after the Fresenius settlement was announced. Professor Reinhardt wrote, "Given the tangled web of Medicare legislation, more fraud investigations are inevitable. Rather than engaging in a long, protracted fight to set the record straight...a healthcare company's best bet may simply be to hand over the fines and get on with business."

From a strictly economic basis Reinhardt is probably correct and that's the way Lipps and the Fresenius team played the NMC matter. Hampers would have decided differently, forcing the government into court and making their lawyers prove to a jury that each and every physician prescription and order was wrong and that the company should have known that it was wrong. In the end, the stockholders and executives will survive, the bureaucrats and lawyers will retain their livelihoods and the players will adapt to the new rules of engagement. The patients will pay the real price, however. A dialysis patient presenting symptoms of starvation will not receive IDPN, for example, as quickly as his counterpart at NMC clinics in the late 1980's, and he will die sooner. All third party insurance systems, whether private or Medicare-funded, anticipate disagreements and expect the physicians to fight for coverage for their patients. Nearly every American has experienced this phenomenon with his or her doctor spending a lot of time and energy trying to secure coverage for his patient's care. The government's tactics and the Fresenius decision in the NMC matter makes that phenomenon less likely.

It's highly unlikely that President Clinton knew any of the facts lying behind and supporting the $486.3 million settlement when he cited it approvingly in January 2000. If told that a doctor prescribed a life saving therapy for a very sick and starving dialysis patient and the patient's insurer refused to pay, and moreover, years later accused the doctor of criminal fraud, one suspects the topic of his discourse to the nation that day would have been on the importance of getting insurance companies and HMO's out of the doctorpatient relationship.

21

Prescriptions

The founders of National Medical Care confronted, challenged, and changed a healthcare system that was unresponsive to an inhumane system of rationing dialysis resources among kidney patients who had reached "end-stage." Without any business, financial, organizational or public relations experience among them, these kidney specialists, tutored in a school and tradition of risk taking to save lives, stepped out of the cocoon of the academy and began a corporation to deliver dialysis in a new way, with little expectation of government assistance or financial reward. The radical approach of empowering physicians by making them responsible for their individual clinics financed with private capital met fierce resistance.

Nearly thirty-five years later the healthcare system in the United States itself has reached an "end-stage" crisis. Healthcare economists and other experts in Congress, the federal bureaucracy, state and municipal governments, insurance companies, Wall Street, universities, and healthcare providers, all of whom are studying and promoting various solutions, comprise a substantial subindustry by themselves. The cost of healthcare escalates. The public, for the first time in recent American history, is increasingly suspicious of the quality of healthcare they can expect from their doctors and other providers. Despite revolutionary improvements in transportation and communications systems, access to healthcare services is more uneven than in the 1960's, due largely to financial rather than geographical or demographic reasons. The charity hospitals operated by religious organizations and municipal governments are dead or dying with most desperately seeking partners in the private sector. The physician, once the captain of medicine, and the model of the sole, professional entrepreneur has become a salaried worker, and his or her role as decision maker has been filled by insurance executives. Barrels of ink have been devoted to editorials in medical journals and the popular press on the subject without altering the basic scenario.

The experience of NMC, its history, structure, successes, and failures provide a singular model from which to extrapolate and distill solutions to the general crisis of healthcare delivery in the United States for the future.

In order to change the inadequate, expensive, and moribund system of providing renal dialysis to an enormous and largely undetected population of kidney patients in the 1960's and 1970's, Doctors Hampers, Hager and Schupak, and the colleagues they recruited to manage the individual dialysis clinics, had to initially change themselves. In essence, this personal change was fundamental - a sine qua non for systemic improvement. They were successful, because they changed the paradigm from one focused on an individual patient with renal failure to one focused on an audience of thousands of current and future kidney patients. Their field of responsibility enlarged almost overnight from providing the best possible care to the patient at hand to delivering a system that could, with the help of their many similarly minded colleagues across the country, render life saving, quality care efficiently anywhere in the world. NMC would not have been successful, and indeed it would not have been created, unless and until this personal transformation in terms of responsibility and vision had taken place.

Similarly, for the kind of change to occur in the American healthcare system today, the NMC experience suggests strongly that the first and fundamental step is the transformation of the American physician. Today's typical doctor bears little resemblance to the doctors of his father's generation. Thirty-five years ago few patients had medical insurance and none was an HMO subscriber. Patients went to the doctor, he treated them or referred them to specialists or admitted them to an appropriate hospital. He billed the patient and the patient paid the bill, sometimes with help from an insurer, and sometimes under a long-term arrangement with his physician. Few physicians requested or accepted assignments of benefits, preferring to have little or no contact with the patient's insurer. It was a simple two party system with the doctor delivering medical care and the patient paying for the service. People went to the doctor knowing it would cost money and they went only in times of acute need. For working class people seeking medical care was akin to a luxury, and for poor people it was impossible.

Once organized labor bargained for and won healthcare benefits from American employers, similar coverage for non-unionized workers at nearly all rungs of the corporate hierarchy was readily granted by employers in order to compete for labor. The federal government allowed employees to exclude these benefits (both the premiums and the actual amounts paid to healthcare providers) from their tax base, while simultaneously permitting the employers to deduct the cost from their tax bases, thus subsidizing the benefit. In addition, the legislation permitting these substantial tax benefits also prescribed basic coverage criteria in order to eliminate discrimination in coverage, thus limiting the choices for employers and their employees in the type of plans that could be offered. In essence, the health package for the single, 18-year-old high school drop out in the mailroom had to be the same as for the 25-year veteran secretary with four kids and a spouse with his own employer sponsored healthcare plan, and as for the 60-year old chief executive. Over time, in a competitive market the health benefit package became richer and more comprehensive for the skilled worker, and this "benefit inflation" enriched the entry level and unskilled labor force as well, because of the federal mandates of uniformity. The phenomenon transformed American healthcare within a decade, greatly benefiting all working Americans, and the public health system in the United States. The transformation was additionally accelerated with the enactment of Medicare for the aged and disabled and Medicaid for the indigent in 1965. These developments ended the way doctors had previously practiced medicine.

While bringing enormous demand for services and thus increasing physician income, the new third-party payer system introduced an interloping observer into the examination room as well. This invisible, but powerful, third party began to alter the relationship between the physician and the patient simply by its presence in the medical suite. Previously, the goals of the doctor and patient were aligned: fixing the medical problem at the lowest possible cost to the patient. Now the doctor didn't have to worry about the cost to the patient, since his employer's insurer or the government was paying, and similarly, the patient wanted the best care, not just the standard or merely adequate. Meanwhile the third-party had conflicting goals, riding herd on both the doctor and the patient not to overuse the benefit and run up costs. For awhile the doctors and patients were too powerful to observe the dictates of the insurers, and the insurance companies simply passed the higher costs along to the employers and the taxpayers. But by the 1980's overuse of healthcare benefits and the resulting escalation of healthcare costs in the United States became too enormous to ignore. Taxpayers and employers demanded an end to cost inflation and service overuse.

In simple, stark terms, the essential function of rationing medical services was transferred from the patient and his physician to employers and their insurance and HMO agents.

In the last decade, first employers and now increasingly the federal and local governments have empowered the insurance companies and HMO's to dictate the terms of the health benefit and to ration care, rather than simply pass higher costs of care onto the employers and the taxpayers. Consequently, the third party payers have dictated prices, rationed the amount and level of service, required preapproval of all higher levels of care, and denied patients the choice of physician. Their actions have been denounced in the media and have been challenged by enterprising trial lawyers seeking ways to hold them financially responsible for limiting coverage. There have been feeble and patchy state and federal legislative attempts to force insurers to cover certain benefits that have wide appeal, such as longer hospital stays for uncomplicated births.

All the players are unhappy with the system and attempts to "reform" the system quickly parse down to titan struggles over costs, with insurers arguing that improving choice for some will raise costs for all and force many out of the system all together. And there is some evidence on their side, since these increasing costs have been a factor in stemming the gradual, but constant, decline of uninsured people that began in the 1950's. Now, the number of uninsured Americans, both workers and the unemployed, is rising and could reach 50 million within the next few years. The reform dilemma that has been set up for the public and policy makers is a trade off between more choice and less interference from the insurance companies versus higher costs and fewer enrollees. Sadly, everyone has accepted this paradigm.

Only the physicians, individually and collectively can change the terms of this dilemma, and create a system that reduces costs, while increasing access and simultaneously expanding patient choice. Individually, the doctor needs to remove the uninvited observer from the exam room, attend the patient in the "old fashioned way," and extract himself from the battle between the insurer and the patient. In order to accomplish this the physician may have to refuse accepting benefit assignments, end affiliations with HMO's, and essentially stop "playing the insurance game." On an individual level, such actions by a doctor would mean financial suicide. Consequently, these individual actions must be reinforced by collective action that offers patients, their employers and the government an alternative to a system that is controlled by insurance companies. Such an alternative cannot be a return to the "Norman Rockwell" era of the sole practitioner who accepts a dozen eggs from his farming patients and an oil change from his auto mechanic patient in exchange for his medical services.

Physicians need to recognize that the practice of medicine has become and will continue to be corporately organized, that the days of private practice are in most of America, over, and that governments and charities are no longer willing or able to subsidize the costs of medical services. The choice for physicians is whether they move to control the corporate system of delivering care or stay controlled by the system. The essential first step is acceptance of the environment in which doctors practice today and embracing a desire and a commitment to change those circumstances.

As corroborated by Richard Rettig and others, Medicare's ESRD Program ably met the initial (1973) challenge of ending rationing of transplantation and dialysis services. The Program has also scored high marks in terms of access across economic, racial and geographic strata. Most, but not all, commentators rate the Program well in terms of economics, since the standard dialysis treatment costs less than a third of the 1973 cost, in constant dollars. Judgments about quality of care are more varied, but given universal access and an ever increasingly sick and aged population of ESRD patients, kidney patients across-the-board are in better health in the United States than in any other country. Moreover, there is no question that the United States led the world community in the 1970's and 1980's in expanding dialysis and transplantation options for ESRD patients. However, since the ESRD Program is universal and has no U.S. "rivals," it's impossible to say whether patients are better off than they should be, or than they would have been, had the ESRD Program never been enacted or had been enacted or administered differently.

From the government's point of view the Program is, in the aggregate, much larger than it "ought" to be, i.e., 0.5% of the overall Medicare population consumes about 6% ($13 billion out of $212 billion per year) of Medicare expenditures (whatever that "factoid" means). From the patient's and physician's viewpoints, Medicare's single minded pursuit of containing aggregate costs by limiting reimbursement for chronic dialysis and routine physician services has pushed providers to reduce quality, or at least not to pursue better outcomes.

HCFA has pursued a "penny wise, pound foolish" strategy, fed in large part by its prejudice towards and ignorance about, proprietary dialysis providers. As long as NMC and others were making profits, HCFA saw its mandate as squeezing the unit profit lower and lower. The government's incessant and illogical counter argument to complaints about lowering reimbursement (or bundling more services for the same price) was that new, additional dialysis centers were opening everyday. Dr. Hampers recalled that the Administrator of the Health Care Financing Agency (Medicare and Medicaid) told him as much in a face-to-face meeting in her office. "Dr. Lowrie and I met with Carolyn Davis in her office and she told us that she couldn't accept our argument that the Medicare rate was too low as long as NMC continued to open new centers." As a result, not only did these policies force less efficient providers out of business (arguably a "good" result), but they discouraged quality enhancement efforts, and most importantly, they missed the big picture.

HCFA has been largely unable and/or unwilling to do the "big" jobs of: (a) shifting non-kidney related costs back onto the private sector; (b) containing the escalating hospitalization costs of kidney patients; (c) controlling the increasing incidence of kidney failure resulting from dietary and other life style factors, public health ignorance, and poor medical management of diabetic and hypertensive patients; (d) increasing the low rate of kidney transplant donations; and most significantly, (e) eliminating an inefficient monopsonistic (one buyer) system by decentralizing the system and encouraging experiments and demonstration projects. Sadly, the patient organizations fell into the same rut of casting profit-makers as villains rather than friends, and ignoring the forest while they scrutinized the trees. In addition to HCFA and patient organization leaders, the media, always on the alert for black-and-white melodramas with identifiable scapegoats, and the medical ethicists such as the editors of The New England Journal of Medicine, who see immorality in making money, but not in rationing care, piled on. Consequently, the ESRD Program became, and remains, the poster child of "bad healthcare policy."

The providers, both proprietary and not-for-profit, were not clamoring for change either. They had invested in delivery systems and business methods that accommodated to the reality of HCFA's policy of reducing unit costs, without trying to change that reality. In a sense they "enabled" HCFA to pursue its bad policies (and vice versa). Dialysis providers, for instance, didn't see it in their best interests to increase transplantation rates, or reduce the incidence of kidney failure by more aggressive screening and care of hypertensive patients.

After twenty-eight years, it's time for a shift in the ESRD Program away from the government provider "game" of micromanaging dialysis costs to a broader, macroanalysis that looks to control Program costs by containing the ESRD population, not by denying access or rationing as in the pre-1973 days, but by improving quality, decreasing morbidity, and increasing transplantation. HCFA should stop second guessing the providers and start doing its larger job.

The ESRD Program pays for all the Medicare covered health-care costs of kidney patients who are Medicare beneficiaries by virtue of their ESRD disability. This "comprehensive" feature of the Program results in huge expenditures totally unrelated to the patient's primary disease and puts ESRD patients in a special and unique category. As a result, it relieves the contracted burden of private insurers to cover these expenses. By eliminating those costs from the ESRD Program, they would be shifted back onto the private sector which would have paid for these expenses but for the ESRD Program. Why shouldn't Blue Cross pay for emergency room services of a kidney patient who has a car accident? Why shouldn't Kaiser Permanente cover the costs of an MRI and physician services for diagnosing a ruptured disc? Why shouldn't the patient himself be responsible for paying for his own eyeglasses?

This is not to deny coverage to aged, disabled or indigent people, but to fairly shift their non-renal care expenses from the ESRD Program back to the appropriate Medicare or Medicaid program. With respect to patients covered by private insurance plans or HMO's, this policy change simply realigns the costs back to their primary carrier.

Over the past decade, Congress and successive Republican and Democratic Administrations have shifted ESRD costs by extending the "MSP" interval, i.e., the amount of time (currently 30 months) that Medicare acts as a secondary payer, requiring the primary, private insurer, or HMO, to cover the ESRD costs. This proposal of confining ESRD Program costs to those directly related to kidney failure essentially does the same thing with respect to non-renal expenses for an indeterminate time.

Critics of this approach will offer the compelling "holistic" argument that kidney failure accounts for systemic changes that manifest in all sorts of medical problems, and that a patient and his physicians and providers shouldn't be "bounced around" between the private insurer and Medicare. Recovering these non-renal costs from the primary insurer shouldn't be the patient's or the doctor's responsibility. The primary insurer should pay the provider or physician directly and then seek contribution/subrogation from Medicare. The primary carriers and Medicare can negotiate from time to time over the limits of responsibility, and what is and is not "renal related."

When enacted, the ESRD Program was seen as a forerunner to a larger, universal government health insurance program. The government never intended in 1972 to have kidney patients treated so uniquely. Lawmakers assumed there would be a universal program within a year or two, and that allowing kidney patients to expire while waiting for coverage would be unconscionable. Twenty-eight years later, with no national healthcare program on the horizon, it's long past time to shift non-renal costs back onto the private sector wherever possible.

Except for regular Medicare patients (those over 65 or otherwise disabled under standard Medicare definitions), this proposal envisions a capitation fee, or voucher, that Medicare would pay to a private insurer or HMO to underwrite the renal care of the beneficiary. In other words, after the initial 30-month MSP period expires, the private insurer/HMO would continue to be responsible for covering the patient's expenses, and would receive a monthly or yearly stipend/contribution/subsidy from Medicare to cover the patient's care. Medicare would no longer have any relationship with the patient's doctor or provider. It wouldn't set dialysis reimbursement rates, or decide which services and drugs should be bundled. The patient would chose his own physicians and providers under an indemnity plan or chose from an HMO-prescribed list of providers, just as patients with coronary disease, AIDS, Parkinson's disease, or any other chronic illness, would. The providers and doctors would similarly be free to contract with these private plans or not, as they do now with respect to other medical services. The market would replace the monopsony.

The challenge for such a radical "devolution" from a central, uniform system to a market system is that the private plans not drop or "cap out" the renal patients. Part of this could be done by law or regulation but in large part, the government contribution would have to be close to actual costs of providing coverage, in order to ensure continued coverage. The government has data and experience on which to draw from both the current ESRD system, as well as from the Veteran's Administration system and the various federal employee insurance and HMO systems.

The advantage would be to create several, competing, or at least comparable, systems administered by health insurance professionals that would over time offer comparisons. One plan might favor peritoneal dialysis in its reimbursement policies, while another may provide strong incentives for transplantation. Some may determine that paying doctors higher fees in exchange for more frequent and intense care saves money in the long term by reducing in hospital stays.

Patients will predictably resist this approach at first. The ESRD Program has adopted the "first, do no harm" mantra, largely at the behest of patient groups, who fear a loss of political control over the program once it is carved into smaller pieces managed by healthcare professionals. They need to see their long term welfare enhanced by breaking down this monopsony that tends toward stasis, no change, little experimentation, and no breakthroughs. In large part, kidney dialysis patients have the same unhappy lives today that their parents had twenty years ago, and without change, the same one their children will have in 2020.

While the federal government should not discriminate among Americans who suffer from end-stage renal disease on the basis of age, other illnesses, race, economic status or region, there is no compelling reason to segregate these patients from the larger patient communities and healthcare systems. An argument can also be advanced that by ending such "special" treatment and segregation, these patients will be more likely to rehabilitate and integrate into the normal, working regimen of their families and neighbors.

If the myriad arrangements among various private insurance plans and HMO's currently work for the first 30 months of renal care, why not extend it indefinitely with the federal government picking up part or all of the tab after the initial 30 months?

Nearly fifty percent of all ESRD Program dollars are paid to hospitals for services other than routine dialysis. The explanation is complicated and varied, but in its simplest terms, it's because dialysis patients are often very sick and require intensive care in a hospital setting. The followup question is whether anything can be done about this, and the surprising answer is that we don't really know. HCFA has not explored this question with the vigor that one would expect, given the fact that it involves billions of dollars every year. Moreover, it indicates, perhaps, that kidney patients are receiving less than optimal care, which may, in part, result from a static, universal, penurious and short sighted reimbursement policy.

Two significant examples illustrate the challenge for HCFA. The two principal causes for hospital stays by chronic dialysis patients are problems with the access site and cardiovascular complications. When a patient develops access problems that result in negative changes in the flow of blood out of his circulatory system and into the artificial kidney, he often has to go into the hospital for surgical repairs. Earlier detection and routine maintenance of the access site would save millions of dollars annually, but HCFA has refused to approve additional reimbursement for a device that can detect early changes in the flow of blood through the access site using Doppler effect measurements. Similarly, there are devices available that allow precise measurement of fluids in the patient's blood that could prevent fluid overload and the resulting stress on the patient's cardiovascular system that results from untimely and imprecise adjustments to the complementary flows of blood and dialysate in the artificial kidney during dialysis. Use of such devices would permit the doctor or nurse to reduce the stress, which is another major cause of cardiac failure and hospitalization for dialysis patients. So far HCFA has not seen the wisdom of paying the dialysis facility more if it uses these devices in order to pay the hospitals much less to correct the problems that these devices could prevent.

Given the funding involved, HCFA should adopt a more aggressive role in promoting new drugs, devices, and procedures that could improve quality and reduce hospital stays, rather than continuing to play the adversarial role of holding down short term costs.

HCFA needs to research this morbidity problem not just for the obvious welfare of its patient-beneficiaries, but in order to save a lot of money. One suggested experiment would be to devise and implement a system that paid higher rates for better outcomes. There are a lot of data linking measurable outcomes and morbidity and mortality statistics. If, for instance, patients with lower blood urea over long periods of time tend to avoid costly hospital-

izations, then why not pay more for better urea clearance outcomes? Perhaps one measure is simplistic and a combination of
goals could be used to increase reimbursement. This is especially
helpful if better outcomes result from longer dialysis treatments,
which naturally increase costs. Perhaps it would reduce hospitalizations if more frequent and more comprehensive blood tests
were authorized, allowing doctors and nurses to foresee and forestall problems before they required hospital care. Similarly, drugs
and nutritional supplements might be worth the expense if they
retarded hospitalizations. The use of EPO to avert anemia in dialysis patients, which was accepted and paid for by HCFA starting
in the mid-1980's, offers a salutary example. Not only did this
genetically engineered drug replace an enzyme normally produced
by healthy kidneys, thus improving patient health, but it ended
the need for periodic and expensive blood transfusions for kidney
patients that were common in the 1960's and 1970's.

The frequency and intensity of direct physician patient contact
should be studied in the context of reducing hospitalizations.
Perhaps patients would be in the hospital less if they saw their
doctors more frequently and for longer periods of time at the dialysis clinics. To get that result means paying the doctors more gen-
erously, or returning, at least in part, to a fee-for-service or fee-
for-visit basis, rather than the monthly capitation system currently in use for dialysis patients. Along the lines of paying
providers like dialysis facilities more for better outcomes, perhaps
a system could be tried that paid the doctor more for better outcomes as well. Why not give the nephrologist a bonus for keeping
his patients healthy and out of the hospital for a year? Imagine an
experimental program where the physician describes an aggressive patient care plan with measurable improvements in blood
chemistries and other indicators and by achieving the goals the
physician is appropriately rewarded. Could we start a revolution
in healthcare by paying doctors for improving health and preventing disease, rather than just for curing problems after they occur?

The notion of paying a physician as a case manager rather
than as a service provider should also be understood and studied.
Paying a physician who takes on the additional responsibility, not
just of providing medical services, but also of managing his

patient's other services and product providers might be advantageous and economical.

These are radical suggestions, but the idea of studying the suggestions shouldn't be radical when billions of dollars might be at stake, not to mention patients' health and welfare.

In 1973 at the beginning of the ESRD Program, there were approximately 10,000 ESRD patients in the United States. Today, the number is close to 350,000 with the costs for their care approaching $20 billion per year. Partly, this expanding pool of patients is attributable to the Program's success - patients are living longer, healthier lives. Partly, the increase is a natural part of the expanding population. In addition, it's clear that the original, 10,000 patient estimate missed thousands of unidentified patients. Nonetheless, the significant fact is that the patient population is growing largely because the incidence, i.e., the number of new patients with ESRD, is increasing every year. Original estimates of Program growth assumed a constant incidence rate of 50 new cases per million population (roughly 12,500 new cases annually). In fact, that rate was not constant, but has increased, and is at about 315 new cases per million population today (88,000 new cases every year). Among African Americans the incidence rate is 830 per million.

In addition, the primary cause of kidney failure has changed over the past twenty-eight years. Nearly 60% of kidney failure today results from diabetes or hypertension. One obvious way to reduce future Program costs would be to slow down this rate of growth wherever possible, yet the federal government and its state and local counterparts have spent very little time and money attempting to prevent end-stage renal failure through public health initiatives, education, screenings, early interventions and other prevention techniques. Nor do we see any pressure from patient groups in this regard. One percent of the ESRD Program budget would fund millions of dollars of serious experiments in preventing or delaying the progression to irreversible kidney failure.

In the same vein, while willing to spend billions on repetitive, chronic care, the federal government's research priorities do not include kidney disease, presumably because it affects relatively few people and because there is a chronic, maintenance program.

Basic scientific research to better understand the structure and function of the human kidney, the possibilities of regenerating damaged cells, the early detection and cure of kidney cancers, the development of implantable artificial organs, the use of xenographs from other mammals to replace human kidneys, techniques to save one kidney after its twin has shut down, as well as looking at advances in dialysis, separation membranes and technologies, and drug therapies to alter and absorb impurities and waste in the blood could improve health, prolong the function of failing kidneys, save lives and cut dialysis and transplantation costs, all to the advantage of thousands of patients, their families and the American taxpayer. In addition, epidemiological studies could point to cofactors and early indicators of ESRD, allowing physicians to intervene sooner and perhaps retard the progression to end-stage, as well as suggest public health measures that might reduce ESRD incidence.

Our body of knowledge about kidney disease, its causes and possible cures, short of replacing the kidney with an artificial kidney or transplantation, needs to expand, and given the annual investment in keeping ESRD patients alive, the federal government has every reason to divert some of that investment into more research initiatives.

Every advance in the past twenty-eight years in the care and treatment of end-stage renal disease patients in terms of dialysis and transplantation has been developed by the private sector. Many came from research sponsored by universities, medical schools, and medical foundations, but the vast majority came from profit making corporations that manufacture drugs, artificial kidneys and other devices, and clinic operators. Not only have patients benefited, but so have HCFA, and the other private and public agencies that pay for ESRD care. None of the funding for these research efforts came from HCFA, even though it was the single most affected entity. Moreover, HCFA has not even convened panels of experts to advise it and the research community on directions and goals for applied and clinical research in those areas that would improve patient health, encourage transplantation, save money and reduce the incidence of kidney failure and mortality rates among the ESRD population. HCFA should do more than pay for the system that exists. It should be striving to improve the system in all directions through research and pilot projects.

The overwhelming failure of the ESRD Program has been its inexplicably passive, uncreative and excessively cautious approach toward kidney transplantation and organ donation. Although the clearly preferable treatment for irreversible kidney failure, transplantation rates have fallen behind demand. The demand for human kidneys has always exceeded the supply, and the gap has widened, yet the federal government, patient and physician groups, healthcare experts and the general public lack strategies to solve the problem. As a result, every year we inter thousands of patients who die for lack of kidney transplants and a few feet away, often in the same cemeteries, bury thousands of functioning human kidneys.

First of all, transplantation results in a better and longer life, than the various dialysis alternatives, for the vast majority of end-stage renal disease patients. A study led by Dr. Robert Wolfe of the University of Michigan and published in the December 2, 1999 edition of The New England Journal of Medicine found that patients who receive kidney transplants live ten years longer on average than ESRD patients of comparable age, sex, race and severity and cause of disease, who stay on dialysis. Among patients in the 20 to 39 year old category, the difference was a startling seventeen years. The major danger to transplant patients has been complications resulting from suppressing the body's immune system, which would otherwise reject the graft. In the early days, these drugs which had to be continued for the rest of the patient's life, left the patient susceptible to all sorts of infections. With the advent of cyclosporine in the early 1980's, the immune response was moderated to prevent rejection, while allowing the immune system to combat threatening infectious agents. As a result, over 90% of patients who receive a transplanted kidney are still using the kidney a year later, with the percentage higher for living related donor transplants than for cadaver transplants. Approximately 50% of transplant patients have functioning transplants ten years after the procedure. Approximately 23% of patients on hemodialysis die each year compared to 3% of patients with kidneys from living related donors, although this statistic does not account for the fact that the larger pool of patients on dialysis are sicker and older than their transplanted counterparts.

The FDA has approved additional new drugs such as Rapamune and Zenapax that may improve these survival rates for transplant patients. In addition, there have been some promising developments in adapting the phenomenon known as "chimerism" to organ transplantation. Led by Dr. Thomas Starzl of the University of Pittsburgh Medical School and Dr. Benedict Cosimi at the Massachusetts General Hospital in Boston, these studies involve double transplants to alter and adapt the immune system itself into accepting the new kidney (or other organ). In the MGH study the patient received a bone marrow transplant from a biologically close sister followed by a kidney transplant from the same sister. After 73 days the patient stopped the use of immune suppressant therapy and a year later the transplanted kidney was functioning fine.

Life with a kidney transplant is far preferable to life sustained by thrice weekly trips to a dialysis center or hospital. Not only are the dialysis treatments themselves uncomfortable, time consuming, and over time somewhat risky, but the rest of the patient's life revolves around his disease and the dialysis procedures, curtailing his diet, activities, work habits, procreative functions, energy levels, ability to travel and generally to enjoy life like every one else with healthy kidneys.

Life for the living related (or in some, rare cases unrelated) kidney donor is not affected adversely. Aside from the inconvenience and relatively low risk of the actual surgery itself, the living donor leaves the hospital and resumes his or her normal life. Studies of living donors have found no increase in morbidity or mortality linked to the loss of one kidney, and human beings seem equally adept at surviving and functioning with one kidney as with two. Dr. John Najarian and others at the University of Minnesota reported in The Lancet (October 3, 1992) that a study of 78 kidney donors found no significant health differences between these donors and their siblings who had two kidneys over a twenty-year period. In fact, insurance companies, which know how to evaluate risk, do not increase their healthcare premiums for kidney donors, treating them the same as individuals of like age and health risks with both kidneys intact. Still the number of living kidney donations is relatively small with 4,038 reported in the U. S. for 1998. Of these, 163, or about 4%, were from individuals not related to the recipient.

It's not particularly difficult to understand why an individual would be willing to overcome his or her fear to donate a kidney to a close relative, say, a child, a parent or a sibling. What's more challenging, and therefore more interesting, is understanding the motivation for an individual to donate a kidney to an unrelated patient. Some of these cases have received public attention, none more so than the case of Marian Neal, a 40-year old woman who donated one of her kidneys to a young boy, Terrance Varner. As reported in The New York Times (September 6, 1999), Neal knew the boy's family and helped them take him for his dialysis treatments. When none of the boy's relatives had a kidney that matched, Neal decided to donate one of hers. Her story came to light when she was forced out of public housing and subsequently received a subsidized unit from HUD upon the intervention of HUD Secretary Andrew Cuomo. In defending his eviction of Neal from a public housing apartment, where she had lived with a friend in violation of the lease, the agency head stated the essential question: "There are 60 people on the waiting list ahead of her. Some of them are homeless. Would it be right to put her ahead because she is a kidney donor?" Secretary Cuomo, on the other hand, described Neal as a "heroine who should be treated decently." Although Neal donated her kidney with no expectation of personal benefit, was it wrong for the federal government to subsequently reward her for her generosity?

In February 1999 The Washington Post reported the story of Loretta Kaczorowski, a 41-year old woman who freely donated one of her kidneys to her best friend, Marian Calhoun, after Marian's siblings refused, belying the adage that blood is thicker than water. D.C. Superior Court Chief Judge Eugene N. Hamilton, for whom the two women worked, characterized the donation as "a truly wonderful and beautiful act of unselfish sacrifice." Even more astounding was the case of a middle aged woman in suburban Washington, D.C. who read about the shortage of kidneys and decided to offer one of hers to the neediest and most compatible recipient, who turned out to be a man from southern California. The donor and recipient met a few hours before the successful surgery at the University of Maryland Medical Center.

While the value of a kidney transplant to the patient is convincing, standing on its own, the value to the healthcare system and Medicare and the taxpayers who support Medicare is also compelling. Although the cost of transplant surgery is high (nearly $100,000 for the first year after surgery), these costs are recouped very quickly. According to a study at the University of Maryland, the transplantation option starts to save money for the system after just two and a half years after the surgery. These transplantation costs are decreasing as well as post-operative hospital stays have decreased from ten to seven days on average, and as less expensive oral drugs to suppress the immune response have replaced injections. Since the average cost of caring for an ESRD patient on dialysis is $54,000 per year (1999), the advantage is obvious. In the first five years after transplant surgery this study found the savings averaged about $47,000. If the forty thousand ESRD patients waiting for kidney transplants could receive organs tomorrow, the system would save $1.9 billion in the next five years.

In addition to the cost savings for medical care, the financial rewards from transplantation for the patient and his or her family are incalculable. Dialysis patients, their spouses and other family members sacrifice enormous numbers of hours to their medical needs, and these hours translate into lost opportunities and lost value. In addition, while many dialysis patients pursue their careers and earn substantial wages, most do not. With a successful kidney transplant, however, patients can retain a normal life in its economic as well as its social context. At the extreme is the case of Sean Elliot, a 31-year old star basketball player for the San Antonio Spurs who received a kidney donated by his brother without which he would have had to begin dialysis and terminate his professional career. With the transplant his life as a talented and highly paid basketball player can resume. Not all kidney patients will be able to play professional sports after receiving a kidney transplant, but, like Elliot, they will have no medical obstacle blocking a productive and rewarding life.

Kidney transplantation is the preferred and recommended therapy for the majority of ESRD patients from all points of view, yet the number of people on the waiting list continues to grow every year. The same is true of other organs, such as livers and hearts. As reported in The Washington Post on May 17, 1999, the number of organ transplants increased from 1990 to 1998 by 35% from 15,462 to 20,926. However, during the same nine-year period the waiting list grew from 21,914 to 64,423, an increase of about 194%. For many, the wait means death; in 1998 approximately 5,000 patients died waiting for transplants (mostly liver).

The potential supply of kidneys from living donors is virtually limitless, since everyone has "a spare." The actual supply is meager because of a number of factors, and the first step in solving the problem would be for HCFA or other appropriate agency to study why people do or don't donate kidneys. Is it simple ignorance, or does it involve religious beliefs, economic factors, social pressures, and other influences? With these data in hand, appropriate mechanisms to effect change can be rationally debated. The potential supply of kidneys from deceased individuals is another matter, since the harvesting of kidneys must be effected quickly and under ideal conditions. Most people don't expire in hospitals where their kidneys and other organs can be harvested, and most that do die in such circumstances have not expressed their intent to donate their organs.

Traditionally kidneys are harvested from individuals declared brain dead prior to cessation of the heartbeat. In some foreign countries and among many cultures (such as Orthodox Judaism), death is not recognized before the heart stops beating, and this consequently reduces the number of viable cadaver transplants. However, there is evidence that using kidneys from cadavers with no heartbeats can increase the number of transplants without altering successful outcome rates. One study from UCLA and reported in The New England Journal of Medicine found the comparable success rates as 83% for those transplants using a kidney where the heart had stopped beating versus an 89% success rate for those with beating hearts. The expansion of the supply of transplantable cadaver kidneys from this source needs to be explored and HCFA would be well advised to encourage more research in this area.

Another possible, future source of supply that is being explored is the use of xenografts, or organs from other mammals, most particularly pigs. No pig-to-human organ transplants have been tried (to our knowledge) or approved. However, patients have been exposed to pig organs via the injection of pancreas cells from pigs into humans with diabetes, and via pig skin grafts on burn patients. In addition, some patients without liver spleen function have had their blood filtered extracorporeally through the spleen of pigs. The concern is infection with retroviruses (porcine endogenous retrovirus or "perv") from the pig cells that are benign in pigs but may be dangerous once in the human body. Studies of patients who have been exposed to these pig cells and perv have not found any infections yet, but the studies are inconclusive and may take years to perfect. For the foreseeable future relying on pigs as a source of supply for kidneys is not realistic. More fundamentally, why not spend the resources that would be required to perfect the science of xenotransplants on means of increasing the supply of human kidneys available for transplantation?

The government's response to this acute and ever increasing shortage of organs for transplantation is to create a new and potentially risky system of rationing the scarce organs. Like re-arranging the chairs on the Titanic, the U.S. Department of Health and Human Services spent hundreds of staff years and millions of dollars to scrap the former regionalized system to require a national system. While compelling from a fairness perspective, it aggravates the shortage problem, and does absolutely nothing to increase the supply of organ donations. Critics fear that donations may decrease if people can't be sure the organs will benefit someone in their region. While this parochialism is not worth defending, the new regional system may well suppress the efforts of states and regions to increase the organ donations through creative, experimental programs. Why should Arizona spend tax dollars on a public education campaign or a computerized registry of those who consent to donate their kidneys in order to promote a greater supply of organs, when the federal government will allocate these organs throughout the country based on greatest need.

In fact, if each state were responsible for its own program, we might see some creative approaches to stimulate the supply.

Some state governments have already tried to counteract the federal government's initiatives by requiring that donated organs be used locally. In May 1999 Texas passed legislation that gives Texans first claim on organs donated in Texas before they can be sent out of state. Whether the HHS is correct or not, and whether we parse the few donated organs into 50 state piles, ten regional piles or one big national pile, these schemes don't address the central problem.

In a world unfettered by legal, ethical and religious proscriptions against the sale of organs, the gap between supply and demand, like any other commodity, would be bridged by commerce in these organs. When a man offered to sell his kidney to the highest bidder via an auction on the Internet, the bids rose to six figures, before the auction site shut the offer down. In October 1998 Italian authorities arrested an American who allegedly offered to sell a kidney via the Internet for $20,000, contending that the arrested man was part of a large scale international ring of kidney brokers. And in a widely publicized 1998 case, two Chinese nationals were arrested in the United States and charged with conspiring to sell kidneys. The case was later dismissed for lack of evidence.

The sale of organs is universally condemned by governments, religious leaders and national and world medical organizations. In the United States the National Organ Transplant Act ("NOTA," P.L. 98-507, 1984) makes the sale of organs a felony, and the law has been interpreted to include the exchange of an organ for any benefit or value. Still there is evidence that in many parts of the world, the power of the market to bridge the gap between supply and demand will ignore and circumvent these proscriptions. Michael Finkel's honest and shocking article "This Little Kidney Went to Market" (New York Times Magazine, May 27, 2001) presents a fascinating account of the black market for kidneys worldwide.

Obviously securing a kidney is not like buying a cache of drugs or other contraband. The exchange can't occur on the street or in a market stall, but has to be executed by highly skilled physicians in a sophisticated medical center. Even in closed societies, these operations are difficult to hide, especially when they require the import of drugs and devices that are specifically geared for transplantation. India has very active transplantation centers in Bombay, Madras and elsewhere, and even though Indian law bans the sale of organs, doctors and patients use wide loopholes to encourage and facilitate the exchange of kidneys to wealthy patients from all over South Asia and the Middle East from unrelated, poor Indians. China attracts transplant recipients from every part of Asia, largely because its government has adopted the practice of harvesting organs from prisoners upon their execution which are carried out in a manner to facilitate the viability of the transplant. Officially, these transplants are explained as having occurred with the consent of the convicted prisoner, but how informed and voluntary that consent could be is seriously questioned. The Chinese system is structured to accommodate the needs of the recipient and his physicians, so that prisoners are executed at places and times that coincide with the recipient's (usually a foreigner) needs. The recipients pay handsomely for the convenience.

Some commentators have begun to question the logic and morality that condemn all organ transactions. If not totally persuasive, their arguments point up some disturbing inconsistencies. A libertarian view would exclude all government interference with the ability of a person to control, sell, barter, or donate any part of his body, unless these actions would have a negative impact on others. What a woman chooses to do with her ova, fertilized or not, and her fetus has been and continues to be a hugely contentious issue in all human societies. At this point in the United States, however, it is clear that there are definite constitutional limits to what the government can compel and condemn in this regard. Moreover, the most persuasive minority view on abortion is based on the argument that the fetus is another independent living person, so that the woman's decision is seen by the anti-abortion advocates as ending the life of another human being. This argument has no relevance in the case of kidney transplants. There is already commerce in the sale and donation of ova as a solution to infertility, and sperm banks are commonplace.

Ova and sperm are not indispensable organs, a traditionalist would argue, and neither is blood, at least in small quantities that can be replaced by the human body. In the early days of blood transfusions, the debate over the morality of selling blood was intense, as well, but it is now a settled practice. Bone marrow is also routinely transplanted, and commerce in its donation may also become a question for society to resolve. In all of these cases, no other human being, including the donor, is harmed or is placed at significant risk. How are human kidneys different? All data and studies suggest that living with one kidney presents no risk to the donor. One could argue that by trading a kidney for money, or other consideration, a person has lost the potential of a later donation of that kidney to a family member that might need it, but that is hardly a compelling reason to limit a person's ability to control his own body.

If society permits the sale and exchange of human kidneys for consideration, the practice will be confined to the poor, many argue. Assuming that argument is valid, the obvious response is that requiring poor people to keep both kidneys does not change their economic and social status. In other words, what does the poor man or woman gain by being prevented from such exchanges? The more salient question is whether a system that permits the sale or barter of human kidneys for transplantation would add more misery to their lives. In fact, if relaxing the strictures on the sale of kidneys for transplantation makes sick people healthy and poor people financially more secure, the proposal does not choose between the lesser of evils, but, in fact, improves the lives of two individuals. In that sense, the prohibition appears immoral.

Moreover, society has already addressed that issue in permitting people - largely poor people - to sell their blood. It's also important to point out the hypocrisy of some who advance this argument. Society exploits the poverty of people every day in every way. Wealthy people don't take back breaking, dangerous, or unhealthy jobs; they are not breathing coal dust in the mines or cotton dust in the textile factories, or second hand cigarette smoke for eight hours every day in a tavern. In the current booming American economy, we rely on poor, largely uneducated immigrants to clean public latrines and pick berries twelve hours a day.

All of these tasks present greater risks to a person's health (and the consequent welfare of his family) than a kidney transplant. Even our state and local governments exploit poor people through the sale of lottery tickets, openly enticing people to gamble. While many wealthy people also play the lottery, participation rates are much higher among the poor, and the relative sacrifice is much greater for low income people.

To point out that society exploits poor people already does not mean society should extend this exploitation into the realm of organ transplants, however. The real point of contention is whether the sale of kidneys is, in fact, exploitative. If a person, rich or poor, decides to donate a kidney to his child, we appropriately label the act benevolent and heroic. If the same person has the same kidney removed and sold so that his same child can use the money for a college education he would not otherwise have, some label the transaction exploitative. The issue is not the morality of organ sales, but the morality of poverty and inequality in general. If our hypothetical, poor, potential kidney donor came to the moralists and said that he would sell a kidney to give his daughter a college education, would these moralists, instead, pay the college tuition? Poor people have vital interests - decent housing, food, education for their children, good healthcare, to name the obvious - that society allows to remain unmet. If a person in those circumstances decides to jeopardize his health by working in a coal mine, or wastes his money gambling in a lottery, or sells his blood for a few dollars, we accept the sacrifice as enterprising, if not noble. The sale of a kidney (or a portion of the liver) is not that different.

What are the logical parameters that should guide a fair and humane policy that accommodate the desperate need for kidneys against the principles of equality, fairness and respect for all human persons, regardless of station in life? First, of course, is medical necessity for the recipient and medical appropriateness for the donor. Competent physicians need to attest to the lack of risk for the donor, and the evaluation must be made by a doctor totally unaffiliated with the recipient and the institution that will perform the transplant. This is true even for living related donors where the motive is altruistic, and in fact, may be more necessary where there is an intense emotional bond between the potential donor and recipient. The donor, in other words, needs his own independent medical advisor. Part of the medical evaluation should include a psychological assessment, so that the patient's competence can be certified. Obviously, comprehensive counseling of the donor, so that he knows the risks and can be certified as giving his or her full and well informed consent.

From the recipient's stand point the system should be fair and not tied to wealth or influence. The significance of wealth in a system of organ donation, whether a system that is rationed by the government or a system that permits some degree of commerce either with currency or other type of consideration, is that wealth should not determine who receives a kidney. Access to kidney transplants in the United States (and elsewhere, but that is hard to control) should not be based on the ability to pay. Thus, under the universal ESRD system now in place in the United States, Medicare would "pay" (or exchange other, non-monetary benefits) the donor for the kidney, and the amount could be determined as fair from time to time. This limits the free market aspects, of course, but it does insure fairness and equal access. It would also insure universality and a fair method of allocation until there was a sufficient supply of kidneys, and a price that made sense vis a vis the cost of dialysis. Of course, wealthy people would be able to travel to foreign countries where the market might be "freer."

Nor would the price be exhorbitant. The potential supply is in the millions and the demand is not like to exceed 50,000 kidneys per year in the United States. Once the public accepted the idea, and the first pioneering donors were seen to lead healthy, risk free lives following transplantation, the supply would increase to meet the demand. The demand for kidneys is a function of the incidence of kidney failure which would be more or less static, and the price would fall to reasonable level.

Some argue that permitting people to receive some form of consideration for donating a kidney will result in ending the current altruistic system. No doubt people waiting for kidneys would say "amen," but there really is no evidence that this would be true. When there is need, people still freely and altruistically donate blood, even though some people may at the same time be selling blood. The fact that all kinds of goods and services are freely exchanged every day does not stop parents from making gifts to their children or from brothers making gifts to their siblings.

There is little doubt that a commercial or barter system for kidney donations is not on the horizon, at least in America. However, having examined the slim rationale that supports the universal prohibition as legislated in "NOTA," policy makers at HHS and at the state level should examine and plan other, pilot programs to stimulate kidney donations, seeking waivers or limited exceptions, if necessary, from NOTA. Year after year, the disparity between supply and demand grows wider, while the risks of transplantation grow smaller. In isolated circumstances we already observe people donating one of their kidneys to unrelated recipients. There are any number of ways the supply might be enhanced without actually paying cash for kidneys. The real problem here is not lack of means to increase the supply, but a lack of will and lack of a strategic plan on the part of the government, patient organizations and physician groups.

One method might be to offer comprehensive lifetime health insurance to the donor and his or her family. The donor's contribution to cutting ESRD Program costs for Medicare by donating a kidney to a dialysis patient would be appropriately rewarded with immediate Medicare enrollment for the donor and his dependents. Other non-cash benefits suggest themselves, as well, such as public housing (we saw how Secretary Cuomo did just that in the case of Marian Neal), or perhaps a pension contribution or a hefty paid-up life insurance policy, where the government actually "wagers" on a long life for the donor.

Some jurisdictions are contemplating and implementing a transplant banking program and this should seriously be studied by HHS. Similar to the traditional "blood bank," people are motivated to donate their kidneys in order to move their loved ones to the top of the transplant list. Thus, if a father was an inappropriate match to donate his own kidney to his son he could donate a kidney to another dialysis patient in exchange for moving his son to the top of the list for a compatible kidney. Such a system worked very well in stimulating free blood donations in the past, it respects the prohibition on selling organs, but still provides a powerful incentive to increase the supply.

The federal government actually has a creative and comprehensive model to examine in its veterans' programs. During time of war our government has enlisted and drafted men and women to fight and put their lives at stake for the nation. Many died and many more came home with disabling injuries. A statistical analysis would conclude that it was much more dangerous to be in combat in Vietnam than it is to donate a kidney. The government has created a whole range of benefits for our veterans from housing subsidies and loans to college education stipends, to free medical care and pensions. These benefits were not intended to encourage young men and women to die for their country, but to honor and partially compensate them for their sacrifices. And, one should note, these benefits do help poor people disproportionately more, and, in fact, are used to recruit enlistees from the lower-income class.

The most benign and least objectionable program to stimulate supply would involve aggressive attempts at changing public attitudes and behavior with a far ranging public education campaign. Combining this education effort, which could involve clergy, sports figures, entertainment celebrities and business, union and community leaders, with a registry of people who have agreed that upon death they would consent to organ donation, would by itself make a major contribution in augmenting the pool of available kidneys. Part of the problem with generic protransplantation campaigns is that people aren't sure how to convert their interest in donating into action. With advanced information systems, the engagement of the healthcare community - doctor's offices, providers, hospitals, clinics, and HMO centers - there should be an easy way to "register."

Politicians, celebrities, and other role models could be encouraged to make a public show of designating their kidneys for transplantation upon their death. Some might even donate a kidney while still alive to an unrelated donor and encourage this kind of altruism. We saw movie stars donating blood in World War II, and sports and military role models like Secretary of State Colin Powell leading efforts to encourage volunteerism, aided by enormous public relations and advertising budgets. Today we see Jesse

Jackson enlisted in taking a public HIV test in order to stimulate positive public health behavior. Compared to these and other efforts, like the many campaigns against smoking, drug use, and unsafe sex, the public relations efforts to stimulate organ donations are paltry at best. The government, again, is not treating the disparity between organ supply and demand as the real public health crisis that it is. If there is a developing free commercial market in kidneys in places like China and India, the western governments are passive participants by failing to address the supply problem in more "moralistic" ways.

Unless a person has perfected his intent to donate his kidneys in writing, the legal presumption is that he does not intend to donate his organs and harvesting his kidneys or any other body part without the consent of the next-of-kin, which is very difficult to secure under stressful circumstances, is illegal. In Spain and Belgium, the reverse presumption has been enacted into law, so that unless a person has specified his intent not to donate his kidneys upon death, the presumption is that he intends for his kidneys to be harvested. Patients who expire in hospital settings where harvesting is possible have thereby donated a surfeit of kidneys in Belgium. There are no waiting lists for kidney transplants in Belgium as a result, and ESRD patients from other parts of Europe regularly travel to Belgium for transplants. Similarly, Spain has the highest rate of cadaver kidney donations in the world for the same reason. One or more states with the support of the federal government could adopt such a reverse presumption to see how it would work in the United States.

A more controversial proposal would be to motivate the family of a potential, recently expired donor to consent to harvesting his kidneys. A cash stipend may appear exploitative, but what of a special healthcare insurance benefit that enrolled the next-of-kin (or perhaps the children or grandchildren of the deceased) in a program that essentially paid for their healthcare for the rest of their lives? A similar proposal could be offered to potential donors while still alive. Why not offer a $100,000 life insurance policy or a ten-year healthcare plan for surviving dependents to any person who agrees to donate his kidneys upon death?

Objections would include the traditional, "protect-the-poor-from-themselves" argument that such a proposal would dispro-portionately motivate poor people, and that wealthy people would be less likely to agree. The responsive counter-arguments would be that increasing the supply of transplantable kidneys would disproportionately help poor patients, since wealthy patients are more likely to secure scarce kidneys under the current system (It's not supposed to work that way, but it does). In addition, how is this different from any number of government programs that attempt to modify behavior by paying or extracting money - they all disproportionately affect poorer people, e.g., taxing cigarettes or clothing. One could even argue that fining people for not wear-ing seat belts disproportionately affects poor drivers. In the end, the most responsive counter argument is "so what?" Kidneys that are interred don't help anyone, so why not motivate people to donate kidneys from their deceased relatives?

As noted above, in China, where the death penalty is liberally applied to several categories of criminal behavior, convicted felons, who would be executed anyway, are executed so that their kidneys and other organs can be harvested and transplanted. Allegations that this program encourages capital punishment, judicial proce-dures that efface civil rights, and a thriving market in the sale of such organs to foreigners in order to secure foreign currency, have obscured the fact that the basic idea of using body parts to save lives is preferable to incinerating or burying them. If one or more American states adopted such a policy, would anyone convincing-ly argue that it would result in more and "easier" convictions and executions under our constitutional system with its rigor for due process of law?

Consider a program that allows commutation of a death penal-ty to one of imprisonment for life, in exchange for one kidney. Is it immoral to permit a prisoner to bargain for his own life by giving a life saving organ that he doesn't need to an ESRD patient? In a moral universe that holds the selfless donation of a kidney by a brother to a sister at the highest order of morally approved behav-ior, why is the offer of an option to a man otherwise condemned to die to make the same donation considered immoral? The public prohibition on such an exchange appears immoral in the sense that it requires that two people die where both could live. The ancient precept that demands a "life for a life" takes on a whole new meaning if the exchange is permitted. Given the relatively few convicted criminals that are executed in the United States each year, however, this exchange program would make only a small dent in the problem. Nonetheless, it's an important symbolic policy on the part of government to value life and redemption over death and retribution.

Other permutations of education, encouragement and motivational programs to get people to donate their kidneys at death (or one of them during life) come to mind, yet after twenty-eight years of paying billions of dollars to keep people alive on artificial kidney machines, the federal and state governments have been surprisingly uncreative and unresponsive (irresponsible?) to the need for more donated kidneys.

The history of administering the ESRD Program has been one of bureaucrats attempting to "outmaneuver" physicians and dialysis clinic operators, lowering reimbursement rates and thereby jeopardizing patient health, while simultaneously missing opportunities to save enormous expenditures by keeping patients healthier, decreasing the incidence of ESRD, increasing the supply of transplantable kidneys, and allowing the market to replace an unresponsive, uniform, monopsonistic and static system.

The failure of the ESRD Program, despite its clear successes in keeping people alive on dialysis, is its lack of a dynamic, strategic plan. Having discovered a means of keeping ESRD patients alive via dialysis, the government has stopped searching for a better solution. Unfortunately, patient organizations and physician groups have been accomplices in this static mind-set. Chronic maintenance dialysis was the solution for ESRD in the 1960's, and thus it remains, forty years later. This temporary prosthetic has become a permanent fixture in solving a deadly condition that affects more and more people every day. Just as the founders of NMC challenged the status quo in the sixties, the leaders in the next generation of nephrologists, as well as patient advocates and government and insurance bureaucrats, need to take some risks and find new and better solutions for ESRD in the 21st century.

While overgeneralization and hyperextension of the anecdotal to the systemic are temptations to be strongly resisted, the NMC experience and the ESRD system of using capitalism to help deliver services suggest definite applications for the national healthcare delivery system. The hallmarks of the system include competition, investor owned providers, government support for indigent patients, sharing the burdens with private insurers, patient choice, and most importantly, physician control.

First, the roles of the investor and the capital markets are essential. The free market economy is not only an efficient system in theory, but, in fact, has overwhelmed every other economic system yet devised in terms of delivering the goods and services that people want and need in the most cost effective manner. For years, healthcare economists and healthcare professionals have argued that healthcare is different. Healthcare is certainly not different because it is so important: air travel, food production, home construction, and pharmaceutical manufacturing are equally life sustaining and important. The NMC story is one sterling example of the advantages of delivering healthcare services in a market economy by investor owned corporations. The early capitalists that invested in the Hampers-Schupak-Hager enterprise were risk-takers, but not financial suicides. They assessed the risks against the potential returns (at a time before the federal government had started its comprehensive ESRD Program), analyzed the competence of the management and the market for dialysis services and saw an opportunity that compared favorably with other, competing uses for their capital.

These venture capitalists and the more cautious generation of NMC stockholders that followed them were largely successful because they were patient and focused on the long term, rather than the day-to-day returns. While NMC's growth in the 1970's and early 1980's was impressive, it was measured and steady, rather than meteoric. The role of the investor in a healthcare system that relies on the free market to deliver services is that of a capitalist with the patience to wait for returns over a three to five year period. The demand of the NMC/Grace investors for immediate change and their lack of trust in Dr. Hampers during the transitional period of 1994-96 resulted in a sale of NMC to a German medical products corporation (Fresenius) that did have a longer-term outlook. In order to attract and retain investors who have the necessary patience and long term focus, the healthcare executives need to maintain excellent investor relations. Gus Hampers and his team largely did not have the necessary positive relations with the public investment community. While they did an excellent job in maintaining good relations with a small group of early investors and bankers and likewise with the W.R. Grace management in the 1984-96 period, the NMC team did not win the trust of the "Wall Street" crowd. Successful management of any corporation requires this skill, and particularly in healthcare where a malpractice threat, a medical or scientific break through or a new government policy can cause an investor stampede.

The system must be open and competitive with as little government control as possible. One of the weaknesses that developed in the ESRD Program during its first decade was the fact that facility growth was stifled by state and federal "determination of need" controls. This highly structured regulatory system blocked the market's ability to allocate resources and resulted in granting monopoly status to existing providers, often inefficiently run hospital-based units, and deprived the patients and physicians from more convenient, lower cost, and better equipped choices. Fortunately the entire "DON" system was largely eliminated in the past decade and the growth of facilities has been unfettered, contributing to the system's efficiency. It's unlikely that the unit cost of dialysis would have dropped so dramatically, thus saving billions of Medicare dollars, if the "DON" system had remained in place.

One area where the ESRD system did not allow the market to function was in adopting a "dual rate" structure that essentially paid higher per treatment fees to hospital based facilities. This has been discussed previously, but it's worth repeating in this context that paying hospitals more for the same service subsidized inefficiency. The hospitals' contention that their patient census was more complicated than the free standing outpatient clinics was never proven. Moreover, that argument requires different reimbursement rates based on patient diagnosis, not on the treatment venue. Similarly, whenever the ESRD payment system differentiated its rate of payment based on treatment modality or delivery system, rather than on patient diagnoses, the optimum market solution (and even the proper medical prescription) was perverted. This happened when Medicare favored peritoneal dialysis and also when Medicare set up different ways to reimburse providers and suppliers for home dialysis patients.

The obvious lesson is to construct a payment system that does not influence the method of delivering care and that is neutral with respect to the variety of prescriptions available to the physician and the patient. In sum, the government may be concerned with regulating quality of care and with helping insure patients, but it should not interfere with the market forces that will naturally determine the most efficient way to allocate resources and produce the services most needed by doctors and patients alike.

From a progressive or "liberal" point of view, the proper role for the government is to insure universal and equal access to all and to support those unable to pay without thereby skewing the market. In this regard the ESRD Program worked very well insofar as it granted patients an entitlement that was universal and not tied to income. However, the government should not be dictating or influencing the manner of care and should be neutral in terms of form of delivery.

Also, the government, particularly the state governments should be much more actively engaged in monitoring the quality of care being delivered by doctors and providers. This quality control should focus on patient outcomes, rather than institutionalizing biases against particular forms of care or certain types of economic arrangements.

In addition, the government should encourage strategic planning among its own bureaucrats, private insurers, clinical care physicians and surgeons, and researchers. Not since the pre-ESRD Program era with the Gottshalk Commission has the federal government regularly convened panels of experts first to understand the trends in end-stage renal disease and the newest forms of care, and second to construct a three-or-five-or-ten year plan that will try to reduce the incidence of ESRD, provide the best and least expensive care possible, encourage transplantation (if that appears to be the best solution), and finally map out a rational research blueprint for government, the academies and private pharmaceutical and other healthcare companies. This recommended application goes well beyond kidney disease and is the most vital role for the federal government in healthcare. Part of the long term, strategic blueprint should also address the public's role and the way to educate the public in terms of prevention, detection, early treatment and continuing care regimens with respect to all diseases and conditions.

The patients and their attending physicians need to be informed consumers. Patients and their family members certainly have a role in this regard, and sadly, the ESRD Program points to a passivity that should be avoided in the future. Both individual patients and patient advocates have too often taken a conservative, "head-in-the-sand" approach to changes in care, new products and methods, and available alternatives. Rather than acting as agents to change the status quo, particularly with respect to the Medicare program itself, patients and patient groups have tended to resist change. The government, the providers and the physicians have an important role to play in erasing this knowledge gap and keeping patients and their advocates better informed.

The private insurers and their employer subscribers need to be creative, open minded and flexible in shifting benefits from one form of care and delivery to more efficient forms. Payments that focus on outcomes have to be explored, for example, and both government insurance programs like Medicare and Medicaid, and private insurance systems have to constantly and aggressively resist the temptation to oppose change and require physicians, providers and suppliers to fit into preexisting forms of treatment. Again, by shifting to an outcome based payment system, rather than a procedures based system, the payors will encourage innovation and cost savings.

Finally the physicians need to reassert a command position in the healthcare delivery system. As described at the beginning of this chapter, the physicians have allowed the third-party payors, whether HMO's, Medicare, or conventional insurance plans, to control the healthcare delivery system in the United States. While complaining loudly, they nonetheless act passively, expecting the government to shift the power equation in their favor. If organized the medical profession could control the system of healthcare delivery in the United States. Why they shrink from this critical role and abdicate their role to insurance executives and bureaucrats is puzzling.

The example set by Drs. Hampers, Schupak and Hager and their colleagues is imperfect in some respects, but is nonetheless of a kind that doctors in all specialties and in general practice need to emulate to regain control of the healthcare system. Better care for individual patients will always improve the collective system, and no one will be able to identify what is "better" than the physician. If patients are dying or remaining ill for lack of equipment, drugs, hands   on care, or any other service or product, then it is absolutely the physician's responsibility to fight for those patients, individually and as a group. The physician needs to be trained, prepared and motivated to attack not only the viruses, cancers and injuries that afflict their patients, but also the political and economic systems that deny these patients the care and the cures they need.

Tim McFeeley